BIOLOGY

THE AUTHOR

Gordon Alexander has been a member of the Department of Biology, University of Colorado, since 1931. He became a full Professor in 1939, and headed the department from 1939 to 1958. In addition to teaching and conducting research, Dr. Alexander is curator of birds, University of Colorado Museum. He has traveled widely and served two years (1928–1930) as Visiting Professor of Biology, Chulalongkorn University, Bangkok, Thailand, under a joint project of the Government of Thailand and the Rockefeller Foundation. In 1957 he returned to Bangkok for a year's appointment as Fulbright Lecturer. At present Dr. Alexander is conducting research on animal distribution in relation to altitude.

Professor Alexander is a member of Sigma Xi, of the Ecological Society of America, of the Entomological Society of America, of the Society for the Study of Evolution, and of several ornithological societies. He was President of the Colorado-Wyoming Academy of Science from 1963–1964, and was Chairman of Local Arrangements for the 1964 national meeting of the American Institute of Biological Sciences.

He is author of *Zoology* (a companion College Outline), *General Biology* (a standard textbook), and numerous articles on the biology of Thailand, on animal distribution in relation to altitude, and other aspects of biology.

COLLEGE OUTLINE SERIES

BIOLOGY

GORDON ALEXANDER

Eighth Edition

BARNES & NOBLE, INC.   NEW YORK

Publishers   •   Booksellers   •   Since 1873

This is an original outline (Number 4) in the original College Outline Series. It was written by a distinguished educator, carefully edited, and manufactured in the United States of America in keeping with the highest standards of publishing.

PREFACE

When the First Edition of this Outline appeared, over twenty-five years ago, no one talked of "molecular biology," and physical scientists were still scornful of biology as a "descriptive science." Biology has so changed since 1935, however, that it has not only won the respect of physical scientists but is now recognized as the science that has the most to offer the scientifically curious investigator.

In the interval since the First Edition of this Outline appeared, many basic discoveries have been made. The chemical nature of viruses has been determined. The processes of respiration and photosynthesis have been analyzed into complex series of reactions. The chemical machinery by which energy is mobilized for use in living cells has been discovered. The structures and functions of minute cell constituents, such as mitochondria, are now known. The structure and role of nucleic acids are being unravelled. And we even have the beginnings of a coherent theory to explain the origin of life on this planet.

These discoveries, properly in the field of molecular biology, have not been the only profitable ones. We now see living nature as part of a large-scale system, energy for its operations being derived by producer organisms from the sun and passed along to those organisms that benefit secondarily. Within natural communities of organisms, populations of species undergo changes; we see evolution involving the genetics of whole populations. The cause of the great variety in nature is still the central problem in biology, but the next few years will undoubtedly be marked by increased understanding of this problem.

Recent discoveries have made no change, of course, in the *purpose* of this Outline. As in previous editions, it is designed for use with many types of General Biology courses. It may be used as a supplement to standard textbooks or, with rather complete lectures, as a syllabus. It should be useful to beginning students in either Botany or Zoology, and to advanced students who wish a rapid review of general biological principles. Students who desire an Outline prepared

specifically for Botany or Zoology should refer to *Botany* by Dr.
Harry J. Fuller or *Zoology* by the present writer.

The sequence of topics in the present Outline follows a common
pattern, but, naturally, this sequence differs from that in some textbooks. To make fullest use of this Outline, therefore, the student
should use the Tabulated Bibliography and the Quick Reference
Table. Note that the Appendix includes a list of References and a
Glossary.

—G. A.

ACKNOWLEDGMENTS

The ideas incorporated in this book have had such a complex history that it is difficult now to trace the influences behind them and to make appropriate acknowledgments. I am indebted to many individuals, particularly to those teachers, colleagues, and students with whom I have been directly associated. My greatest obligation is to my colleagues in the Department of Biology of the University of Colorado, a Department in which my associations extend for more than thirty years. I wish especially to thank Dr. Edna L. Johnson, now Emeritus Professor of Biology in the University of Colorado, for her critical reading of Chapters IV to VIII when in manuscript for the First Edition.

In a few cases, methods of presentation have been original with me. I have been gratified to find these used subsequently in other books. Most of the illustrations were prepared by me particularly for this work. To those who permitted reproduction of copyrighted illustrations I extend my thanks; specific acknowledgment is made in connection with each such figure.

I will appreciate suggestions and criticisms designed to improve the usefulness and accuracy of this Outline, and I will welcome these from students as well as instructors. As implied above, I am indebted to many users of previous editions for contributions of this kind.

—G. A.

ACKNOWLEDGMENTS

TABLE OF CONTENTS

HOW TO STUDY BIOLOGY

Biology is the science of living things. It deals primarily, therefore, with objects about us, not human ideas. Such a science is not and cannot be based on "book learning," and those who study it today use books only to acquire information that was acquired originally by direct observation of nature. The following study suggestions are based therefore on the realization that lectures and textbooks are aids in the study of biology but that a real understanding of the science is acquired only when life is observed directly. The fundamentals of biology are best acquired by the direct process of observation by the student. Laboratory or field work is essential, and the student in a course without organized laboratory work should make up for this deficiency by a conscious effort to apply what he learns in class to the world of living things around him.

Scheduling Your Time. Course programs are set up to require approximately three hours per week of a student's time for every credit hour. Thus, a course that meets three lecture hours and one three-hour laboratory period each week, and that probably gives four credit hours, demands an average of six hours per week in outside study. Use such a figure in determining the time you should schedule for study, and distribute that time over several days. Concentrated study for periods of one or two hours is better than attempting to cram a week's study into one day.

Learning the New Vocabulary. Every science deals with exact expression — the right word, correctly spelled. In the biological sciences a specialized and technical vocabulary is essential for complete comprehension of the subject matter. The new vocabulary is large, but it is not difficult to acquire if each new term is made a part of your vocabulary when it is first introduced: its meaning (and its spelling) should be understood by use, not learned by rote. The best method of learning meaning and spelling together is to analyze the origin of the word. Most biological terms are of Greek or Latin origin, but that does not mean that one must study either language to learn the meanings of the roots of English words. Many commonly recurring roots are not difficult to recognize or to learn, and the derivations of most new terms can be found in a modern unabridged English dictionary. If you acquire the new vocabulary by learning its origins, you will soon find that you already know the roots for various new terms as they appear; acquiring the vocabulary therefore becomes simpler rather than more complex as time goes on.

Getting the Most from Lectures. Textbook assignments are made to correspond to lecture material. Therefore, you should read your assignments before going to class. Good lectures are not simply a rehash of textbook material, but, even if they were, one could get much more out of them after having done some reading on the subject ahead of time.

Useful lecture notes are very important. Record these legibly in permanent form (in ink) during the lecture. You should not have to waste time rewriting your notes afterward; instead, organize the material of the lecture at the time of the lecture. Even if the lecturer does not indicate the principal topics, these should be obvious if you have read the assignment.

Discipline yourself to take down only the important points. If you try to record every statement, you soon become so involved in the mechanics of the process that you listen for words instead of ideas.

Getting the Most out of Textbooks. The major problem in reading, assuming that the ordinary English vocabulary is understood, is concentration. Speed in reading the average textbook in biology is not important. Rapid reading for ideas alone is definitely disastrous. The average assignment in a biology textbook is short in number of pages but full of details that must be mastered. Therefore, you must read for retention of details as well as for an understanding of principles. On the other hand, memorizing facts without understanding them is of no value, so read for comprehension as well as retention.

A good environment during study time is necessary. Have a comfortable chair (but not one best used for lounging), an adequate desk or table, and good light. Distractions (human voices being the most serious) should be eliminated as far as possible. It may be better to study in a library reading room than in a dormitory.

Outlining the textbook is a good idea if your outline is not merely a copy of subdivisions already indicated in the text. Underlining key words and phrases, and using special notations in the margins, may prove as useful as a more formal outline. Nothing is gained by underlining several consecutive lines of type, however; that simply makes the passage more difficult to read.

Getting the Most out of Laboratory Work. Since it is only in the laboratory that you have an opportunity to acquire first-hand information through your own observations, it is essential that you develop good laboratory habits. This means, first of all, the habit of working alone rather than depending upon others. This is good practice in general, of course, but in the laboratory it is essential if an appreciation of the objective point of view and the critical approach of the scientific method are to be acquired.

Use care in examining the materials you study or dissect. This means making observations in the best possible sequence. Since laboratory directions are ordinarily prepared to give the student the best sequence, you should read the directions carefully before beginning the study, and then these directions should be followed in order. Preserved specimens in liquid should be kept moist while being studied. If they are to be used again, store them in appropriate containers, completely submerged in the preservative.

Prepared microscope slides are easily breakable and should be handled with care. They should be cleaned and dried carefully before being put away, care being exercised to avoid any pressure on the cover glass. When you focus a slide under the microscope, bring it into focus under low power and center the objects you wish to study before transferring to high power magnification. Never carry a microscope when it has a loose slide on the stage.

Keep your dissecting instruments sharp. They should be cleaned and dried carefully each time before being put away. The acquisition of skill in their use should be one of your aims. This means using scissors and forceps much more frequently than they are used by most students.

The primary record of observations in the laboratory is made in the form of labeled drawings. These indicate to the instructor that you have made the observations; they help fix the observations in your mind in a way that dissection alone can never do;

and they give you a record to use when you review the work. There is good evidence that prepared outline drawings which a student labels do not serve well for either of the first two purposes. A poor drawing made from your own observations will teach you much more than you can learn from looking at an excellent drawing made by somebody else. And you can learn to draw. The complaint, "But I can't draw," has little validity. You can make biological drawings if you can write your name legibly, if you can use a ruler to measure with and as a guide in drawing a straight line, and if you can observe accurately. Poor drawings in the biology laboratory are usually due to poor observation, for biological drawings are supposed to be, first of all, accurate in proportions. If you measure a series of critical dimensions and transfer these, in proper relations, to the drawing paper, you can usually fill in the details freehand with close approximation to accuracy. Attempting to draw a complete dissection freehand, without taking measurements, usually leads to inaccuracy. For this reason one finds that training in mechanical drawing is usually of more value in the biology laboratory than is the usual course in freehand drawing.

Good drawings require, of course, suitable instruments and appropriate paper. Line drawings in pencil, without any shading, are usually called for. Such drawings should be made with a very sharp, hard pencil (3H or 4H) on paper with a hard, moderately smooth surface. Have a ruler available for taking dimensions and for making faint guide lines to be used in lettering the labels. Printed labels are usually required, and they certainly make for greater legibility and more attractive appearance. The process of lettering, being purely mechanical, can be learned by anyone. The forms of the letters correspond to those on a printed page, so one need not learn special lettering styles unless such are specifically required.

Drawings made from objects under a microscope present special problems. Transfer of such images to the drawing paper becomes relatively simple, however, when you learn to use both eyes at once. Look through the microscope at the focussed object with the left eye but keep the right eye open. Now bring a sheet of drawing paper close to the base of the microscope on the right side. With a little practice you will soon be able to see the drawing paper and the object under the microscope superimposed. The process of drawing then becomes little more than the process of "tracing" the object as seen in the field of the microscope.

Supplementary Study. Much can be gained by examining library sources in addition to standard textbooks. Assuming that the books are on open shelves and under the widely used Dewey Decimal System of library classification, you will find the most useful references under 570 (Biology), 580 (Botany), 590 (Zoology), 612 (Medicine), and 630 (Agriculture). If the Library of Congress System of classification is used, the most valuable references will be under QH (Biology), QK (Botany), QL (Zoology), QP (Physiology), R (Medicine), and S (Agriculture). Subject catalogues may be consulted if one may not browse along the shelves.

Museums, like libraries, are valuable sources of supplementary study. Some university and college museums have special sections devoted to surveys of the plant and animal kingdoms. Such sections are particularly useful in reviewing the characteristics of different groups.

Man's environment is full of living organisms, plants and animals. As a student of biology you can gain a great deal by carrying over into everyday life what you learn of animals or plants in the formal course. There are actually many opportunities to do so — in the parks, in markets, on the farm, or along the beach.

Reviewing the Course. An adequate review of a course in biology involves going over the textbook, lecture notes, and laboratory notes. Recognize the major generalizations of the course but don't forget the details that justify the generalizations. In reviewing the characteristics of different phyla or lower groups of animals or plants, try to follow a definite pattern or outline. Such an outline, applicable to all groups, might be the following: Metabolism, Irritability, Reproduction (each of these headings suggesting both structures and functions), Distribution, Evolutionary Relationships.

Writing the Final Examination. Examinations have several purposes. For students the most important are two: They stimulate review, which makes for better retention. And they test recall of facts and comprehension of principles. In answering the examination take nothing for granted. Assume that you are writing the examination for someone who knows none of the answers. The instructor is not expected to read between the lines. Your answers must therefore be complete and clear.

Planning for an examination should come early. If you keep up with your work throughout the term, an examination should have no terrors. A review of a few hours, scheduled before the last night, should then prove adequate. Cramming may be better than nothing, but it has little to recommend it. Relax the night before an examination and get a good night's sleep.

At the beginning of the examination period look over all questions and plan your method of answering them. This saves time in the long run. In an objective examination answer first those parts that are most familiar; don't spend time trying to recall material that does not come to mind readily until you have answered the "easy" questions. This will give you a feeling of confidence, and it will give you more time in which to recall subconsciously the less familiar material. If properly answered, an essay-type examination, contrary to general opinion, requires mention of numerous details — just as many as in an objective examination. The material must be organized, however, not merely written down in the order in which ideas come to mind. Before starting to answer an essay question, therefore, write or mentally devise an outline to be followed.

Remember, too, that the form in which an examination is handed in is important. It makes a better impression in ink than in pencil, because it is easier to read — especially by artificial light. The writing should be legible, and this legibility is a result not merely of carefully formed letters but of adequate spacing between words and sentences. It is not inconsistent with rapid writing. Finally, the terminology must be exact, the spelling must be perfect, and the grammar must be correct; these are basic requirements.

TABULATED BIBLIOGRAPHY
OF STANDARD TEXTBOOKS

This Outline is keyed to standard textbooks in two ways.

1. If you are studying one of the following textbooks consult the cross references here listed to find which pages of the Outline summarize the appropriate chapter of your text. (Roman numerals refer to textbook chapters, Arabic figures to Outline pages.)

2. If you are using the Outline as your basis for study and need a fuller treatment of a topic, consult the pages of any of the standard textbooks as indicated in the Quick Reference Table on pp. xxii-xxv.

Alexander, *General Biology,* 1962, Crowell.
I (1–3, 214–218) ; II (3–5, 219–220) ; III (9–15) ; IV (16–26) ; V (27, 41–43, 86–88) ; VI (124, 130, 150–152) ; VII (152–153, 157–158) ; VIII (125–127, 131–132, 153–155) ; IX (124–125, 130–131, 155–156) ; X (124, 132, 157) ; XI (134, 157–158) ; XII (122–124, 129–130, 144–149) ; XIII (127, 132–133, 158–160) ; XIV (127, 133–134, 160–161) ; XV (21–24, 136–137) ; XVI (127, 162–163) ; XVII (137–143) ; XVIII (141, 162–163) ; XIX (61–70) ; XX (58, 60–61, 68) ; XXI (57–59, 68) ; XXII (58–60, 70) ; XXIII (21–24, 67–68, 72) ; XXIV (73–78) ; XXV (61–63, 82–85) ; XXVI (63–65, 76, 85) ; XXVII (167–173) ; XXVIII (168–174) ; XXIX (174–177) ; XXX (176, 211–213) ; XXXI (189–191) ; XXXII (27–28, 86–88) ; XXXIII (34–37, 89–92) ; XXXIV (92–94) ; XXXV (94–100) ; XXXVI (101–114) ; XXXVII (115–122) ; XXXVIII (44–48) ; XXXIX (29–31, 48–50, 78–79) ; XL (32–33, 50–51, 79–80) ; XLI (51–52, 80–81) ; XLII (52–56, 81–85) ; XLIII–XLIV (192–200) ; XLV (205–207) ; XLVI (178–184) ; XLVII (184–188) ; XLVIII (184–185, 208–212).

Beaver, *General Biology,* 1962, Mosby.
I (xi-xv, 2–3) ; II (14–15) ; III (214–215) ; IV (16–19) ; V–VI (9–14, 19–21) ; VII (44–48) ; VIII (21–25, 41–43, 75–76) ; IX (29–31, 48–50, 78–79) ; X–XI (32–33, 50–51, 79–80) ; XII (51–52, 80–81) ; XIII (52–54, 81–82) ; XIV (54–56, 82–83) ; XV–XVI (56–72, 83–85) ; XVII (86–87) ; XVIII (21–25, 137–139) ; XIX (34–37) ; XX (89–92) ; XXI (92–93) ; XXII (93–94) ; XXIII (98–100) ; XXIV (95–98) ; XXV (95) ; XXVI (101–114) ; XXVII (115–116) ; XXVIII (115–122) ; XXIX (122–128) ; XXXI (144–163) ; XXXII (25, 27) ; XXXIII (19, 21, 66–68, 71–72) ; XXXIV (74–78, 137–143) ; XXXV (167–176) ; XXXVI (176) ; XXXVII–XXXVIII (172–188) ; XXXIX (184–186) ; XL (192–198) ; XLI (198–200) ; XLIII (28–29, 193–194) ; XLIV (203–207) ; XLV (211–212) ; XLVI (154–155, 203–205) ; XLVII (207).

Berrill, *Biology in Action,* 1966, Dodd, Mead.
I (1–5) ; II (16–19) ; III (10–12) ; IV–V (19–21) ; VI–VII (21–24) ; VIII (167–175) ; IX (137–139) ; XI (29–37) ; XII (32–33, 50–51) ; XIII (48–52) ; XIV (56–61) ; XV (61–65) ; XVI (89–92) ; XVII (92–94) ; XIX (98–100) ; XX (101–114) ; XXI (95–98) ; XXII (94–95, 115–117) ; XXIII (117–122) ; XXIV (122–128) ; XXV–XXVI (144–161) ; XXVII (162–163) ; XXVIII–XXX (129–134) ; XXXII (73–74, 136–137, 197) ; XXXIII–XXXIV (180,187) ; XXXVII–XXXVIII (178–179, 184–185).

Cockrum, McCauley, and Younggren, *Biology,* 1966, Saunders.
I (1–5) ; II (9–12, 16–19) ; III (16–19, 21–24) ; IV (73–78, 136–140) ; V (167–177) ; VI (44–48, 86–87, 189–191) ; VII (28–29, 32, 46) ; VIII (29–

31, 46–50, 78–79) ; IX (34–37) ; X (50–51, 79–80) ; XI (51–52, 80–81) ;
XII (52–65, 81–85) ; XIII (89–93) ; XIV (93–114) ; XV (95, 115–117) ;
XVI (115–122) ; XVII (122–128) ; XVIII (130–132) ; XIX (129–130,
132–134, 144–149) ; XX (67–72) ; XXI (192–194) ; XXIII (195–198) ;
XXIV (194–195, 198–200) ; XXV (144–153, 155–156) ; XXVI (140–143,
153–155, 157, 162–163) ; XXVII (157–161) ; XXVIII (184–185, 205–213) ;
XXIX–XXX (178–188) ; XXXI (214–218).

Dillon, *The Science of Life,* 1964, Macmillan.
I (1–3) ; II (3–4, 9–14) ; III (16–19) ; IV (19–24) ; V (41–43) ; VI
(56–61) ; VII (68–72) ; VIII (61–64, 82–85) ; IX (67–68) ; X (4–5, 44–48,
86) ; XI (189–191, 194–197) ; XII (4–5, 44–48, 86) ; XIII (29–37) ; XIV
(48–51, 89–90) ; XV (90–94, 98–100) ; XVI (95, 101–117) ; XVII (129–
130, 145–149) ; XVIII (132–134, 158–161) ; XIX (134, 153, 157–158) ; XX
(130–131, 150–153, 155–156) ; XXI (131–132, 153–155) ; XXII (145, 157) ;
XXIII (137–140, 162–163) ; XXIV (140–143, 163) ; XXV (192–198) ;
XXVI (198–200) ; XXVII–XXVIII (167–177) ; XXIX–XXX (178–188).

Elliott and Ray, *Biology,* 1965, Appleton-Century-Crofts.
I (1–3, 214–218) ; II (4–5, 9–14) ; III (16–21) ; IV (41–43) ; V (192–198) ;
VI (44–45, 86–87, 189–191) ; VII (29–33, 48–51, 78–80) ; VIII (52–54, 80–
82) ; IX (54–56, 61–65, 82–85) ; X (56–61, 67–72) ; XI (76–78) ; XII (33–
37) ; XIII (89–92) ; XIV (92–94) ; XV (93–94) ; XVI (95–98) ; XVII
(98–101) ; XVIII (101–114) ; XIX (95) ; XX (115–128, 184–186) ; XXI
(144–149) ; XXII (157–161) ; XXIII (150–153) ; XXIV (130–131, 155–
156) ; XXV (131–132, 153–155, 204–205) ; XXVI (132, 157) ; XXVII (137,
142, 162–163) ; XXVIII (140–142, 162–163) ; XXIX (21–24, 137–139) ;
XXX (167–177, 211) ; XXXI (178–184) ; XXXII (185–188).

Hardin, *Biology, Its Principles and Implications,* 1966, Freeman.
I (1–4) ; II (16–24) ; IV (9–14) ; V–VI (28–29, 12, 175) ; VII (74–77,
137–139, 177) ; IX (197, 209–210) ; X–XII (178–188) ; XIII (69–70, 196–
197) ; XIV (189–191, 29–31, 48–50, 78–79, 194–195) ; XV–XVI (32–33,
50–51, 79–80) ; XVII (51–56, 80–82) ; XVIII (56–65, 82–85) ; XIX (64,
195–198) ; XX (34–37, 89–92) ; XXI (92–100) ; XXII (101–114) ; XXIII
(95, 115–128) ; XXIV (145–149) ; XXV (155–156) ; XXVI (150–153) ;
XXVII (153–155) ; XXVIII (157–158) ; XXIX (154–155, 203–205) ; XXX
(158–160) ; XXXI (145, 157, 160–161) ; XXXII (160–161) ; XXXIV
(162–163) ; XXXV–XXXVI (167–176) ; XXXVII (174–175) ; XXXVIII
(170–173) ; XXXIX (140–143) ; XL (211–212).

Johnson, Laubengayer, DeLanney, and Cole, *Biology,* 1966, Holt, Rinehart
& Winston.
I (1–4) ; II (16–19, 41–43) ; III (9–12) ; IV (17–19) ; V (19–21, 69–72) ;
VI (189–191) ; VII (56–61) ; VIII (67–72) ; IX (115–128) ; X (130,
150–153) ; XI (130–131, 155–156) ; XII (131–132, 153–155) ; XIII (132,
157) ; XIV (21–24, 74–76, 137–139) ; XV (137–139, 162) ; XVI (139–143,
162–163) ; XVII (132–133, 158–160) ; XVIII (133–134, 160–161) ; XIX
(129–130, 144–149) ; XX (134, 157–158) ; XXI (28–29, 32) ; XXII (29–
33, 48–51, 78–80) ; XXIII (51–52, 80–81) ; XXIV (52–54, 81–82) ; XXV
(54–56, 61–65, 82–85) ; XXVI (44–48, 76–78) ; XXVII (33–37) ; XXVIII
(89–92) ; XXIX (92–94) ; XXX (95–100) ; XXXI (101–114) ; XXXII
(86–87, 95, 115–116) ; XXXIII–XXXV (167–177) ; XXXVII–XXXIX
(178–188) ; XL (192–198).

Kenoyer, Goddard, and Miller, *General Biology,* 1963, Harper.
I (1–5, 27) ; II (16–21) ; III (21–24) ; IV–V (9–15, 196) ; VI (178–183,
189–191) ; VII (34–37) ; VIII (41–43, 86–88) ; IX (89–92) ; X (92–94) ;
XI (98–100) ; XII (95–98) ; XIII (101–110) ; XIV (110–114) ; XV (95) ;

XVI (115–122); XVII (122–128, 144–164); XVIII (67–72); XIX (44–50, 78–79); XX (28–29, 32–33); XXI (34, 50–51, 79–80); XXII (51–52, 80–81); XXIII (82); XXIV (52–54, 81–82); XXV (55–56, 82–83); XXVI (56–65, 83–85); XXVII (167–177); XXVIII (178–188); XXIX (192–198).

Kimball, *Biology,* 1965, Addison-Wesley.

I (1–5); II (189–191); III (29–37); IV (51–61); V (89–117); VI–VII 9–14); VIII (16–19, 41–43); IX (19–21); X (96, 112, 150–153); XI (70–72, 130–131); XII (60–61, 69–70); XIII (112, 124–125, 155–156); XIV (98–100, 112, 120, 125–126, 153–155); XV (57–60, 68–69); XVI (132, 157); XVII (67–68); XVIII (134, 157–158); XIX (133–134, 160–161); XX (132–133, 158–160); XXI (129–130, 145–149); XXIII (21–24, 73–76, 136–139); XXIV (167–173); XXV–XXVI (174–177); XXVII (76–78, 80–83); XXVIII (137–140, 162–163); XXIX (140–143, 163); XXXI (178–183); XXXII (185–188); XXXIII–XXXIV (4–5, 179, 184–186); XXXV (192–195); XXXVI (195–197); XXXVII (197–198).

Marsland, *Principles of Modern Biology,* 1963, Holt.

I (1–5); II (16–20); III (21–25, 73–79, 136–140); IV (9–15); V (12); VI (19–20); VII (150–157); VIII (71–72, 156); IX (68–72) X (4–5, 32–33); XII (60–65, 80–85); XIII (50–61, 68–72); XIV (67–68); XV (41–43, 139–142); XVI (150–152); XVII (108, 153–155); XVIII (152–153); XIX (120, 155–156); XX (157); XXI (136–140, 162–163); XXII (157–158); XXIII (133–134, 160–161); XXIV (129–130, 145–149); XXV (132–133, 158–160); XXVI (167–177); XXVIII (184–188); XXIX (178–183); XXX (194–196, 203–205); XXXI (44–56, 76–78, 189–191); XXXII (86–127).

Mavor and Manner, *General Biology,* 1966, Macmillan.

I–II (1–5); III (9–14); IV (14–19, 21–24, 43); V (19–21); VI (28–29, 32, 203–205); VII (29–33, 48–51, 78–80); VIII (51–52, 80–81); IX (52–54; 81–82); X (54–56, 61–65, 82–85); XI (56–61); XII (67–72); XIII (33–37); XIV (90–92); XV (92–94); XVI (98–100); XVII (101–114); XVIII (89–92, 94–98, 115); XIX (115–128); XX (129–130, 144–149); XXI (130, 150–153); XXII (130–131, 155–156); XXIII (131–132, 153–155); XXIV (132–133, 158–160); XXV (133–134, 160–161); XXVI (132, 157, 162–163); XXVII (134, 157–158); XXVIII (137–143, 163); XXIX (21–24, 76–78, 137–139); XXX–XXXI (167–177); XXXII (192–198); XXXIII (178–188).

Milne and Milne, *The Biotic World and Man,* 1965, Prentice-Hall.

I–II (1, 87–88); III (27–28, 189–191, 229–231); IV (16–19); V (9–12); VI (42–43, 115–117); VII (130–131, 145, 150–153, 155–156); VIII (131–132, 153–155, 157, 162); IX (129–130, 145–149); X (134, 157–158); XI (132–133, 158–161); XII (95); XIII (95–98); XIV (101–114); XV (98–100); XVI (92–94); XVII (89–92); XVIII (69–72, 152–153); XIX (28–37); XX (48–51, 78–80); XXI (51–52, 80–81); XXII (52–64, 82–85); XXIII (21–24); XXIV (67–68); XXV (136–143); XXVI (73–76, 137–139, 167–177); XXVII–XXVIII (192–200); XXIX–XXX (178–188); XXXI (203–213).

Nason, *Textbook of Modern Biology,* 1965, Wiley.

I (1–3); III (4–5, 179); IV (16–19); V (41–43); VII (10–12); VIII (12–13, 19–21); IX (130, 150–153); X (192–198); XI (174–175); XII (167–173); XIII (174–177, 211); XIV (86–88, 189–191); XV (29–33, 48–51); XVI (51–63, 73–78, 80–85); XVII (67–72); XVIII (34–37, 89–94); XIX (95–114); XX (95, 115–117); XXI (132–133, 158–160); XXII (133–134, 160–161); XXIII (134, 157–158); XXIV (130, 150–152); XXV–XXVI (131–132, 153–155); XXVII (130–131, 155–156); XXVIII (132, 157); XXIX (129–130, 145–149); XXX (136–140, 162–163); XXXI (140–143, 162–163); XXXII (178–183); XXXIII (184–188).

Simpson and Beck, *Life: An Introduction to Biology,* 1965, Harcourt, Brace & World.

I (1–3, 214–217); III (16–25, 41–43); IV (9–12); V (19–21, 68–72); VI–VII (167–177); VIII (137–142); IX (73–78, 136–140); X (71–72, 130–131, 150–153, 155–156); XI (68, 131–132, 153–157); XII (134, 157–158); XIII (132–134, 158–161); XIV (67–68, 132–133, 160); XV (187, 196–197); XVI (184–188); XVIII (189–191); XIX (27–37, 44–51); XX (51–65); XXI (86–95, 98–100); XXII (95–98, 101–127); XXIII–XXIV (192–195); XXV (196–199); XXVI (207); XXVII (194–195); XXVIII (198–199); XXIX (178–179, 219–220); XXXI (184–186); XXXII (214–218).

Speed, *General Biology,* 1966, Chas. E. Merrill.

I (1–4); II (10–11); III (4–5, 16, 41–43); IV (16–19, 37, 41); V (21–24); VI (12–14, 19–21); VII (20–21, 69–72); VIII (137–143, 162–163); IX (145–147); X (147–149); XI (155–156); XII (153–155); XIII–XIV (150–153); XV (157); XVI (157–158); XVII (153–160); XVIII (160–161); XIX (73–74); XX (74–76, 82–85); XXI (56–61, 85); XXII (57–60); XXIII (71–72); XXIV (68–69); XXV (67–68); XXVI (189–191); XXVII (29–37); XXVIII (46–56, 76–83); XXIX (89–128); XXX (178–188); XXXI–XXXII (167–177); XXXIII (192–198).

Stauffer, *General Biology,* 1963, D. Van Nostrand.

I (3–21, 42–43); II (57–61, 68–71); III (131–132); IV (132, 153); V–VI (120, 125–127, 153–155); VIII–IX (20, 69–70); X–XIII (21, 150–153); XIV–XVI (21, 71–72, 130–131, 155–156); XVII (129–130, 145–149); XVIII (145); XIX (132, 157); XX–XXI (134, 157–158); XXII (67–68); XXIII (132–133, 158–160); XXIV (133–134, 160–161); XXVI (21–25, 73–76); XXVII (81–85); XXVIII (56–61); XXIX–XXXI (137–142, 162–163); XXXII–XXXVI (167–177); XXXVII (11–12); XXXVIII (176–177); XL (211–212); XLII (192–195); XLIII–XLIV (195–197); XLVI (197–198); XLVIII–XLIX (207); LII (180); LIII (178–179); LIV (184–185); LV (198–200); LVI (189–191); LVII (89–128); LVIII (48–64); LIX (188); LX (185–187).

Villee, *Biology,* 1962, Saunders.

I (1–3); II (3–5); III (9–14); IV (14–20, 41–43); V (12–14, 20–21, 71–72); VI (27–28, 189, 192–195); VII (67–72); VIII (55–61, 68–69); IX (32); X (29–34, 50–51); XI (51–56); XII (73–85); XIII (34–37, 86–94); XIV (95–114); XV (115–127); XVI (132, 153); XVII (131–132, 153–155); XVIII (130–131, 155–156); XIX (130, 150–152); XX (152–153); XXI (132, 157); XXII (129–130, 145–147); XXIII (129–130, 145–149); XXIV (132–133, 158–160); XXV (133–134, 160–161); XXVI (134, 157–158); XXVII (155, 203–205); XXVIII (136–140, 162–163); XXIX (140–143, 162–163); XXX (21–24, 137–139, 167–170); XXXI (170–176); XXXII (176–177, 211–212); XXXIII (178, 184–188); XXXIV (178–179); XXXV (180–183); XXXVI (184–186); XXXVII (192–194, 195–199); XXXVIII (194–195).

Weisz, *Elements of Biology,* 1965, McGraw-Hill.

I (1–3, 219–221); II (4–5); V (9–12, 16–19, 42–43); VI (189–191, 193–197); VII (192–195); VIII (27–37); IX (44–61); X (86–117); XI (68–71); XII (130, 150–153); XIII–XIV (71–72, 130–131, 155–156); XV (148–149); XVII (67–68); XVIII (131–132, 153–155); XIX (132–134, 158–161); XX (21–24, 74–78, 137–139); XXI (29–37, 78–85); XXII (136–143, 162–163); XXIII (167–177); XXIV–XXV (178–188).

Weisz, *The Science of Biology,* 1963, McGraw-Hill.

I (1–3); III (3–5, 10–12); IV (9–12, 16–20, 28–29); V (41–43); VI (189–190); VII (192–197); VIII (32, 46, 48, 190–191); IX (34–37, 48–

51); X (51–62); XI (89–128); XIII (68–70); XIV (130–132, 150–155); XV (153–156); XVI (71–72, 130–131); XVII (71–72); XIX (67–68, 72); XX (134, 153, 157–158); XXI (131–132, 153–155, 157); XXII (132–134, 158–161); XXIII (21–25, 73–78, 136–139); XXIV (29–37, 78–80); XXV (80–85); XXVI (136–143, 162–163); XXVII (140–142, 163); XXVIII (167–177); XXIX–XXX (178–188).

Whaley, *et al., Principles of Biology,* 1964, Harper.
I (1–4); II (10–12); III (9–19, 41–43); V (57–59, 68); VI (58–60, 70–71, 73–74); VII (60–61, 68); VIII (61–65); IX (71–72); X (69–70); XI (67–68); XII (134, 157–158); XIII (132–133, 158–160); XIV (133–134, 160–161); XV (131–132, 153–155); XVI (130–131, 155–156); XVII (130, 150–153); XVIII (132, 137); XIX (130–131, 145–149); XX (129, 145–149); XXI (162–163); XXII–XXIII (28–37); XXIV (21–24, 75, 137–139); XXV (11–12, 167–176); XXVI (63–65, 85); XXVII (140–142); XXIX (189–191); XXX (44–48); XXXI (29–31, 48–50); XXXII (50–51); XXXIII (51–52); XXXIV (52–54); XXXV (54–56); XXXVI (56–65); XXXVII (86–88, 230–231); XXXVIII (34–37); XXXIX (89–92); XL (92–93); XLI (93–94); XLII (98–100); XLIII (101–114); XLIV (95–98); XLV (95); XLVI (115–116); XLVII–XLVIII (116–128); XLIX (4–5, 178–188); L (192–198); LI (203–205).

Winchester, *Modern Biological Principles,* 1965, D. Van Nostrand.
I (3–4, 28–29); II (1–3); III (189–191); IV (29–33, 44–61); V (34–37, 89–117); VI (178–183); VII–VIII (10–13); IX (16–19); X (19–20); XI (21–24); XIII (20–21, 71–72); XIV (20, 69–70); XVI (68–69, 130–132); XVII (68, 131–132, 153–155); XVIII (129–130, 145–149); XIX (120–122, 126–128, 132–134, 158–161); XX (134, 157–158); XXI (67–68); XXII (73–78, 136–140); XXIII–XXIV (167–177); XXV (140–142); XXVI (192–198); XXVII (203–210).

Winchester, *Biology and Its Relation to Mankind,* 1964, D. Van Nostrand.
I (1–2); II (2–4, 28–29); III–IV (4–5, 9–14); V (16–19, 41–43); VI (21–24); VII (19–20); IX (20, 69–70); X (21, 71–72); XI (189–191); XII (29–31, 48–50, 78–79); XIII (32–33, 50–51, 79–80); XIV (32); XV (203–205); XVI (51–52, 80–81); XVII (52–54, 76–78, 81–82); XVIII (55–56, 61–64, 82–85); XIX (55–61); XX (67–68); XXI (33–37); XXII (42–43, 86–88); XXIII (89–91); XXIV (92–93); XXV (93–94); XXVI (98–100); XXVII (101–109); XXVIII–XXIX (110–114); XXX (95–98); XXXI (95); XXXII (91–92, 94, 101); XXXIII (115–122); XXXIV (117, 122–128); XXXVII (122–124, 145–147); XXXVIII (129–130, 145–149); XXXIX (132–134, 158–161); XL (124–125, 130–131, 155–156); XLI (124, 130, 150–153); XLII (131–132, 153–155); XLIII (124, 132, 157); XLIV (128, 137–140); XLV (134, 157–158); XLVI (140–142); XLVII (137–138, 174–175); XLVIII (167–176); XLIX (192–198); L (198–200); LI (178–183, 187–188); LII (179, 184); LIII (184–185); LIV (214–218).

Chapter in This Book	Topic	Alex-ander	Beaver	Berrill	Cockrum et al.
I	Scope	3	31	5	3
II	Protoplasm	39	67, 500	13, 48, 75	40
III	Cells	59, 316	54, 100, 259, 500	10, 112	13
IV	Unicellular Organisms	85		142, 214	155
p. 29	Algae	669	109	214, 253	166
p. 32	Fungi	688	137	233	156, 207
p. 34	Protozoa	552	266	223	190
V	Multicellular Organisms	88	98, 252		
VI	Morphology of Higher Plants	99, 365	91, 221	250	91, 481
p. 48	Algae and Fungi	669, 688	109, 137	232, 253	
p. 51	Bryophyta	711	168	260	220
p. 52	Tracheophyta (Ferns)	726	180	263	229
p. 54	Tracheophyta (Seed Plants)	365, 732	200	266	239
VII	Physiology of Higher Plants	351	221	272	481
VIII	Reproduction of Higher Plants	427	224, 523	153	73
IX	Morphology of Higher Animals	92	247, 404	326, 369	
p. 89	Porifera	567	283	329	268
p. 90	Coelenterata	570	288	335	271
p. 92	Platyhelminthes & Nematoda	581	298	358	281
p. 95	Echinodermata	610	334	448	340
p. 95	Mollusca	600	324	426	302
p. 98	Annelida	604	316	384	308
p. 101	Arthropoda	616	343	396	315
p. 115	Chordata	641	387	464	348
X	Physiology of Higher Animals	107	404, 418	512	433
XI	Reproduction of Higher Animals	289, 316	262, 527	175	73
XII	Morphology & Physiology of Man	107	428	512	575
	Reproduction of Man	306, 336	485	556	479
XIII	Heredity	465	562	134, 158	95
XIV	Evolution	825	632	681, 754	673
XV	Taxonomy	529			
XVI	Ecology	745	651, 682	673, 732	509, 649
XVII	Economic Biology		695		
p. 203	Medicine	175	697, 714		
p. 205	Organisms of Value	801	695, 702		661
XVIII	Social Significance	520, 868	710	829	663
XIX	History of Biology	14	32	835	715
XX	Philosophy of Biology	882	614		
Appendix B	Abridged Classification	548, 664			
Appendix C	Glossary			845	

See pages xvii-xxi

Dillon	Elliott & Ray	Hardin	Johnson et al.	Kenoyer et al.	Kimball	Marsland
3	3	4	1	1	3	3
12	41	9, 64, 100	38	39	81	6, 64
27	61, 695	15	10, 261	18	118, 413	16
	89				20	55
265	152	247	411	377	22	594
268	161	264, 285	388	391	27	173, 601
290	269	373	494	105	20	625
71	90			125, 138	132	
95	222		485		44, 246	
296	152, 169	247	411	377, 409	22, 30	594
178	183	310	441	427	37	610
190	187	314	447	436	40	612
195	199, 222	315	126, 462	454	43	617
114, 157	242	224, 333	150	363	187, 246	158, 236
95, 138	209, 648	136, 321	471	488	408, 475	57, 203
339	89, 492	391				
335	308	385	514	142	49	629
343	310	387	516	146	50	630
350	326	393	528	156	53	635
390	418	426	585	245	66	660
383	350	400	554	185	58	649
359	364	403	544	170	57	647
369	377	408	560	197	60	654
394	427	429	182, 588	252	68	664
419	501	442	195	307	158, 304	126, 291
575	648, 700	135, 617	278	131, 329	408, 490	271, 380
419	492	442	195	308	163, 308	
575	655	617	278	331	497	
695	688	114, 637	598	508	425	475
752	255, 480	183, 205	678	86, 546	539	538
219	139	245	108	94	11	593
231, 633	105	187, 238	735	577	621	573
				568		
		526	242	613		
		362		399		
		161, 695			665	
	796			614		
	825			633		681
	835	714		643		685

for complete titles

Chapter in This Book	Topic	Mavor & Manner	Milne & Milne	Nason	Simpson & Beck
I	Scope	3	1	3	4
II	Protoplasm	10, 30, 66	22	48, 135	22
III	Cells	11, 40	21, 340	43, 171	64, 149
IV	Unicellular Organisms		246	75	87
p. 29	Algae	105	247	82	513
p. 32	Fungi	80	264	79, 357	510
p. 34	Protozoa	221	252	421	515
V	Multicellular Organisms		43	85	89
VI	Morphology of Higher Plants		298	387	
p. 48	Algae and Fungi	107	276	348	522
p. 51	Bryophyta	131	293	367	530
p. 52	Tracheophyta (Ferns)	144	320	371	531
p. 54	Tracheophyta (Seed Plants)	155	326	378	543
VII	Physiology of Higher Plants	203	224, 298	399	388
VIII	Reproduction of Higher Plants	155	388	382	141, 250
IX	Morphology of Higher Animals	342	52	485	547, 569
p. 89	Porifera	322	212	426	549
p. 90	Coelenterata	242	207	428	550
p. 92	Platyhelminthes & Nematoda	256	201	431	553
p. 95	Echinodermata	336	162	467	559
p. 95	Mollusca	331	167	439	583
p. 98	Annelida	274	195	446	557
p. 101	Arthropoda	288	174	451	590
p. 115	Chordata	340	47	471	597
X	Physiology of Higher Animals	361, 483	52, 215	485	281
XI	Reproduction of Higher Animals	475, 503	94, 367	689	224, 264
XII	Morphology & Physiology of Man	361, 483	52	485	281
	Reproduction of Man	477	94, 120	696	141, 273
XIII	Heredity	539	392	263	162
XIV	Evolution	596	531	733	419, 749
XV	Taxonomy	15	11	337	468
XVI	Ecology	573	431	231	627
XVII	Economic Biology		585		
p. 203	Medicine	92			
p. 205	Organisms of Value				694
XVIII	Social Significance				668
XIX	History of Biology				819
XX	Philosophy of Biology				
Appendix B	Abridged Classification	649	16		837
Appendix C	Glossary	654			

See pages xvii-xxi

Speed	Stauffer	Villee	Weisz Elements	Weisz Science	Whaley et al.	Winchester Principles	Winchester Biology
1, 22	2	1	15	3	1	1	1
37	7	16	48, 68	43, 65	4	2	23
35	11, 202	9, 32, 56	76, 348	83, 556, 572	39, 369	123	43
27			133	169, 178, 198	346	39, 49	137, 219
289		147	135	175, 182	464		
285		131, 153	133	169, 200	349, 487	39	137
290		192	142	193	556	49	219
28		46	83	94	71		49, 233
243	22, 224	96	135, 156	213	103, 459	42	171
293	462	145		82, 200	460		116
307	477	163		214	504		158
309	210, 479	168	153		514		163
311	233, 485	169	156	219	532		171
26, 261	22, 70	96	203, 292	329, 466	113, 139	181, 297	81, 206
225, 316	206	173	347, 373	563, 574	136, 153	312	165
30, 323	48, 89	192	173		550	49	233
325		195		262	565		242
327		197		264	569		246
333		201		267	578		255
344		224		290	629		333
342		222		274	622		324
339		210		279	594		273
345		214		281	601		280
359		228		292	635		347
93	35, 81	249	218, 305	354, 486	167, 219	198	93, 420
52, 79	229	418	347, 387	557, 625	332, 434	312, 366	492, 530
93	48, 89	249	218, 305		219	198	405
85	234	421	385		332	366	492
386	274	452	283, 409	677	391	145, 332	526
369	406, 490	512	425	699	694	67	578
277		83	93, 129	119, 163	453	28	104
419	324, 434	89, 570	96	132	718	384	557
		405			732		
		579					147
	406						
437							
	494						607
		597			462, 554		
441	501		462	757		425	613

for complete titles.

BIOLOGY

Chapter I

INTRODUCTION

Biology is the science of life in all its phases. The term (from *bios* — life and *logos* — discourse) was first used in 1801, being introduced independently by Lamarck and Treviranus. In its broadest sense, general biology includes the study of all facts relating to living organisms; but by some authorities it is limited to include only those principles common to both animals and plants. The former definition is accepted in this Outline.

RELATION OF BIOLOGY TO OTHER SCIENCES

The scope of biology is definite, but a knowledge of it requires a certain familiarity with other sciences as well. Basic to it are mathematics, physics, and chemistry. It contributes to and receives information from geology, sociology, anthropology, and psychology, the last three being in part specialized fields of biology. It is basic to the applied sciences of medicine and agriculture — using the latter term in its broadest sense to include forestry, fish culture, etc. (See Fig. 1.)

SCIENTIFIC METHOD

One of the characteristics of a science is that the knowledge comprising it is acquired by the scientific method. This is the method of applying a critical, unprejudiced analysis to determine causal relations in nature. It may involve *observation* under natural conditions alone, or it may involve observation with control of causal factors by the scientist — i.e., *experiment*. The scientific method is usually applied in a series of steps: *observation* of an unsolved problem, *hypothesis* (formulating an intelligent guess as to the solution of the problem), *testing* by simple observation or experiment (to determine whether the hypothesis is correct), and *conclusion* (if the test demonstrates the correctness of the hypothesis).

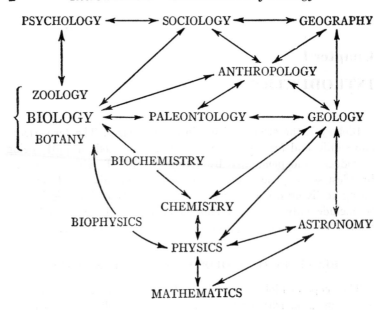

Fig. 1. Relations of biology, including zoology and botany, and other sciences.

SUBDIVISIONS OF THE SCIENCE OF BIOLOGY

Biology is subdivided into subsciences on the basis of either (1) the nature of the organisms studied or (2) the methods of their study.

Subdivisions Based on the Nature of the Organisms. Although there are certain intermediate forms not definitely either plants or animals, in all higher forms of life the distinction between plant and animal is clear. Therefore, one basic division of biology is into two subsciences — the study of plants and the study of animals.

BOTANY. The science of plant life is *botany*. It includes many further subdivisions, examples of a few being *agrostology* (the study of grasses), *bacteriology* (the study of bacteria), *dendrology* (the study of trees), *mycology* (the study of fungi).

ZOOLOGY. The science of animal life is *zoology*. Like botany it has numerous subdivisions, examples of a few being *entomology* (the study of insects), *helminthology* (the study of worms — particularly parasitic worms), *ornithology* (the study of birds), *protozoology* (the study of unicellular animals).

Subdivisions Based on Methods of Study.

ORGANISMS STUDIED AS INDIVIDUALS. There are three subdivisions based upon the study of organisms as individuals.

Morphology. Morphology, the study of the structures of organisms, reflects a static viewpoint. It is further subdivided into (a) *anatomy*, the study of gross structures — e.g., organs; (b) *histology*, the study of tissues (Chap. V); and (c) *cytology*, the study of cells (Chap. III).

Physiology. Because it is the study of function, physiology involves a dynamic or kinetic viewpoint. Organisms and organs are considered from the standpoint of their activities.

Embryology. Embryology is the study of development. It is dynamic in point of view, for it deals with changes in form, but structures are studied at definite points in development as if they were static.

ORGANISMS STUDIED IN GROUP RELATIONS. There are three groups of subdivisions based upon the study of organisms in group relations.

Taxonomy. Taxonomy is the science of animal and plant classification. With hundreds of thousands of different kinds of plants and animals, the biologist must, for convenience, classify them in different groups to indicate different kinds and degrees of similarity or relationship.

Distributional Studies. Ecology is the study of the relations between organism and environment. *Phytogeography* and *zoogeography* are the sciences that deal, respectively, with plant and animal distribution in the larger geographical divisions of the earth.

Genetics and Evolution. Genetics is the study of biological inheritance, the degrees of similarity and difference existing between parents and offspring, and the factors that control the similarities and differences. Organic evolution is the term applied to the progressive development of more complex forms of life from simpler ones. It is to the race what embryology is to the individual. The principles that govern inheritance must, of necessity, also be involved in evolution.

LIFE — ITS CHARACTERISTICS

The quantity of life an organism possesses can not be measured, although the average person distinguishes readily between the living and the nonliving state in familiar organisms, either plants or animals. Life, therefore, can not easily be defined but is described in terms of a series of special attributes, as follows:

Organization. Living matter has a characteristic type of organization occurring in several levels. Living material is called *protoplasm* (Chap. II). This is not a definite chemical compound but a complex mixture varying in different organisms and different parts of the same organism. Protoplasm is aggregated in structural units called *cells* (Chap. III), which in larger organisms are combined to form *organs* (Chap. V). And the whole animal or plant behaves as a unit, an *organism*.

Metabolism. Metabolism is the sum total of all chemical processes going on in living matter. These processes, in part, occur only in living matter and are, therefore, characteristic. Constructive (synthetic) processes constitute *anabolism;* destructive metabolism is *catabolism.*

Growth. An excess of synthetic over destructive processes in metabolism results in an increase in size. This process of growth does not consist of the addition of material on the surface but of an increase in all parts — growth by *intussusception.*

Reproduction. When a cell has grown to a characteristic size, it divides, forming two. In a one-celled organism this is reproduction. In a multicellular organism it is reproduction of cells but only growth of the whole organism. Reproduction in multicellular organisms may take place asexually — only one parent being involved — or sexually — two parents involved. In either case, offspring resembling the parent or parents are produced.

Irritability. Protoplasm responds to a variety of external stimuli. It is capable of conducting the impulse thus set up to other parts of the cell or organism, and it is capable of contracting or responding in some other way to the impulse.

Adaptation. The innate fitness of an organism for the environment in which it lives and thrives is called adaptation. Adaptation develops through various evolutionary mechanisms, and it becomes permanent through inheritance.

THE ORIGIN OF LIFE

There are two theories of the origin of life on our planet that are not based on direct supernatural intervention. One of these is that life in simple form came to the earth from another planet or planetary system. Few scientists accept this theory, however, because, even if a living particle could travel through space, there is doubt that it could survive the extreme cold and the exposure to lethal ultraviolet light.

The alternative theory is that life arose on the earth from non-living matter. This could have happened about two billion years ago, when the cooling planet had reached a stage — warmer than at present, but not too warm for simple living matter — at which time complex chemical compounds could have formed spontaneously. The steps between nonliving and living matter were probably gradual, but must have involved, sooner or later, the formation of enzymes (see Chap. II) and of nucleic acids, which could reproduce themselves.

Evidence for the theory that life arose on the earth from non-living matter comes in part from the fact that every chemical element that occurs in living matter is also a common constituent of nonliving matter. Other evidence comes from the fact that complex compounds do form spontaneously under certain external conditions that undoubtedly were present as our planet cooled. We must remember, however, that theories of the origin of life are still in the realm of speculation.

BASIC CONCEPTS OF BIOLOGY

The most important basic principles of biology are the following:

The Cell Concept (Chap. III).
The Organismal Concept (Chap. V).
The Concept of Organic Evolution (Chap. IV).

Review Questions

1. What is the scientific method?
2. Define biology, botany, zoology. On what basis are the last two subdivided?
3. Name and give the scope of the subdivisions of biology based on methods of study.
4. What are metabolism, anabolism, catabolism?
5. What are the characteristics of life?
6. How may life have originated on this planet?

Part One

LIFE IN ITS SIMPLEST FORMS

Chapter II

PROTOPLASM

All living things are characterized by the presence of a complex mixture called *protoplasm*. Protoplasm is that which is "alive" in animals and plants. It was first recognized as a living substance by the French zoologist Dujardin, in 1835; it was first called "protoplasm" by the Bohemian zoologist Purkinje, in 1839. The term was brought into general use among scientists by the German botanist von Mohl. Protoplasm was called the "physical basis of life" by T. H. Huxley.

Protoplasm is a complex, polyphasic colloid occurring only in living organisms. It is not a definite chemical compound, but consists of water in which are dissolved inorganic and organic compounds and in which are suspended droplets of insoluble liquids and particles of insoluble solids. There are really many different protoplasms, for the composition varies not only in different plants and animals but even in different parts of the same organism.

CHARACTERISTICS OF PROTOPLASM

Living matter exhibits certain physical and chemical properties, but in addition to these it has other properties that are unique. The latter are here referred to as "biological characteristics" because they have no counterparts in the nonliving world.

Physical Characteristics of Protoplasm. Protoplasm is a viscous liquid, capable of changing its state from that of a watery solution to a jellylike semisolid. It is translucent and colorless (but usually appears pale blue-gray). As indicated above, it is a complex polyphasic colloid; i.e., it contains many different insoluble materials in suspension. Early observations with the microscope suggested a structure described as granular, alveolar, fibrillar, or reticular. Present theories are based on colloid chemistry and on direct observation with the electron miscroscope. Protoplasm has marked elasticity as well as fluidity, so colloid chemists (before the invention of the electron miscroscope) considered this good evidence for an ultramicroscopic structure of rodlike particles arranged as in a brush heap. The electron miscroscope reveals a network (reticulum) of strands that are minute, cylindrical membranes.

Chemical Characteristics of Protoplasm. Certain chemical elements occur in protoplasm, certain others do not, but no elements are unique in living matter. The most common elements occur in certain types of compounds which are associated typically with living organisms. It must be remembered, however, that protoplasm averages 75-per-cent water. *Organic chemistry* began as the study of the chemistry of compounds associated with living organisms, but has become the chemistry of carbon compounds. The chemistry of living organisms is now called *biological chemistry* or *biochemistry*.

ELEMENTS. The elements invariably present are oxygen, carbon, hydrogen, nitrogen, phosphorus; sulfur is almost invariably present. Usually present but less abundant are sodium, magnesium, chlorine, potassium, calcium, and iron. Present in special cases are lithium, boron, fluorine, aluminum, silicon, vanadium, manganese, cobalt, copper, zinc, bromine, and iodine.

COMPOUNDS. Several types of compounds occur in protoplasm: carbohydrates, lipins, proteins, various metabolites, nucleic acids, and inorganic constituents. The inorganic constituents occur also in nonliving matter, but the other compounds, which are organic, are typical of living matter.

Carbohydrates. Sugars — and the products of their condensation — are carbohydrates. These are compounds of carbon, hydrogen, and oxygen in which the hydrogen and oxygen are present typically in the proportions of water. (Examples: glucose, $C_6H_{12}O_6$; cane sugar, $C_{12}H_{22}O_{11}$; starch, $(C_6H_{10}O_5)_n$.) Sugars in our food are hexoses (in 6-carbon multiples); but pentoses (5-carbon sugars) occur in nucleotides.

Lipins (*Lipoids*). Three types of lipins commonly occur. (a) The least common, except for food storage, are the *true fats*. These are glyceryl esters of fatty acids; that is, they are compounds of one molecule of glycerol and three molecules of fatty acids (Fig. 2B). They contain only carbon, hydrogen, and oxygen. (Example: olein, $C_{57}H_{104}O_6$.) Closely related to the true fats are the waxes, secreted by living organisms. (b) *Phosphorized fats* (*phosphatides*) are compounds in which one fatty acid has been replaced by a phosphorus-containing group. The best-known compounds in this group are lecithin and cephalin. (Example: lecithin, $C_{42}H_{84}PO_9N$.) Lecithin is abundant in living matter. (c) The *sterols,* or *solid alcohols,* constitute the third type of lipin. Cholesterol ($C_{27}H_{45}OH$) is common in living matter.

Proteins. Proteins invariably contain oxygen, carbon, hydrogen, and nitrogen; they usually contain sulfur. The nitrogen occurs in the amino group ($-NH_2$), which is characteristic of *amino acids.* Only some twenty kinds of amino acids occur in nature. They are the "building stones" of proteins. (Example: hemoglobin, $C_{758}H_{1203}N_{195}S_3FeO_{218}$.) Proteins combine with other compounds to form some of the most important constituents of living matter. These conjugated proteins are in many cases more important than the pure proteins.

Nucleotides and Nucleic Acids. Nucleic acids, highly characteristic of living matter, are made up of units called nucleotides (Figure 3A). Each nucleotide consists of a nitrogen-containing portion (chemically a certain purine or pyrimidine), a 5-carbon sugar (ribose or deoxyribose), and phosphate. Certain modified nucleotides are important in mobilization of chemical energy in cells: ADP (adenosine diphosphate) and ATP (adenosine triphosphate) — the latter transformed from the former by the addition of a high-energy phosphate group. Other nucleotide derivatives are parts of vitamins.

Nucleic Acids. Nucleic acids are complex compounds made up of many nucleotides. When the nucleotides contain ribose, the nucleic acid is RNA (ribose nucleic acid), which is involved in protein synthesis; when the sugar is deoxyribose, the nucleic acid is DNA

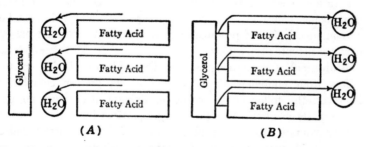

(A)   **(B)**

Fig. 2. Diagrams illustrating the chemical structure of a true fat. (A) Hydrolysis (digestion) of a fat into one molecule of glycerol and three of fatty acid. (B) Dehydration synthesis of a fat from one molecule of glycerol and three molecules of fatty acid, by removal of three molecules of water.

(deoxyribose nucleic acid), which is a major constituent of cell nuclei (Figure 3B) and the basis for biological inheritance.

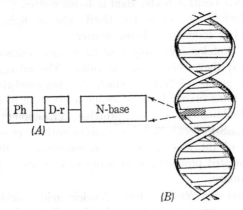

Fig. 3. (A) General structure of a nucleotide in DNA (Ph, phosphate; D–r, deoxyribose; N–base, nitrogenous base—purine or pyrimidine). Its orientation in the DNA molecule corresponds to the cross-hatched portion of (B), which represents part of a DNA molecule. The DNA molecule is a double spiral, its central axis the bonds connecting the N–bases of adjacent nucleotides. The outer ribbons here represent connections between nucleotides in the long axis, these bonds being between the sugar of one and the phosphate of the next.

Inorganic Constituents. Water is the most abundant constituent of protoplasm, and it is essential to it. Inorganic compounds of the various elements previously mentioned occur, the most abundant being chlorides, carbonates, phosphates, and sulfates. For normal functioning of protoplasm certain elements must be present in rather definite proportions.

Biological Characteristics of Protoplasm. Living matter differs from nonliving matter chiefly in its greater complexity. However, the following properties of living matter have no true counterparts in physical or chemical properties of nonliving matter.

METABOLISM. The chemical activities of living matter, collectively called metabolism, include food manufacture, the preparation of food for use, and the steps in the processes by which food is used — either as a source of energy or in the building up of new protoplasm. (Foods are substances that yield energy for living organisms; they are carbohydrates, fats, and proteins.) All metabolic reactions are made possible by special types of proteins called *enzymes*. These cause reactions to occur under conditions (those of living protoplasm) under which they would normally not occur, and they are not used up in the process. They are, therefore, catalysts of living organisms. Certain kinds of organisms can manufacture their own food. These are said to have *autotrophic* nutrition. An organism depending upon other organisms for food, on the other hand, is *heterotrophic*. If we include food manufacturing (limited to autotrophic organisms), metabolism involves four different phases, as follows.

Food Manufacture. Green plants are able to manufacture food from simple inorganic constituents by a process called *photosynthesis*. A few bacteria can manufacture food by *chemosynthesis*. In the former process, light provides energy for the reaction; in the latter, the energy comes from a chemical reaction. The raw materials used in photosynthesis are carbon dioxide and water; carbohydrate is manufactured; and oxygen is given off as a waste product. Photosynthesis is described in more detail in Chapters III and VII.

Assimilation. The use of simple food in the synthesis of reserve food or of new protoplasm constitutes assimilation. It involves the combining of small molecules to form larger ones, the larger molecules thus formed often being different from and more complex than those in which the small molecules formerly occurred. Chemically, the process usually takes place by dehydration, and it is therefore accompanied by the removal of water. Figure 2B shows how the removal of three water molecules takes place in the synthesis of one molecule of fat.

Digestion. Digestion is the process of preparing food, if it is not already in simple enough form, for use. It consists chemically of the hydrolysis of foods and is, therefore, the reverse of the dehydration process taking place during synthesis. This means that, by the addition of water, food molecules are "split" into smaller molecules. This process is illustrated in Figure 2A, in which is demonstrated the addition of three molecules of water for each molecule of fat digested.

Respiration. Food must continually be oxidized in protoplasm to release energy for the various activities of the organism. Respiration is, basically, this oxidation process. The oxidation of simple sugar — the burning of sugar with oxygen — releases carbon dioxide and water (as waste products) and stored energy from the sugar molecule for use by the living organism. The process is very complex, involving numerous steps — including some in which free oxygen is not involved. It will be described in more detail in Chapters III and VII.

GROWTH. Protoplasm grows by intussusception. In other words, increase in the size of a mass of protoplasm is not due to the adding of layers on the outside, but to the addition of new materials throughout its substance. It grows by the addition of new molecules in all parts.

REPRODUCTION. When a unit of protoplasm has attained a certain size, characteristic for a particular organism or part of an organism, it divides, forming two units (cells). The process of division results in two units that are qualitatively as well as quantitatively alike. (See Mitosis, Chap. III.)

IRRITABILITY. The faculty of responding to outside conditions is called irritability. Anything in the outside world capable of causing such a *response* is a *stimulus*. Different common stimuli are: pressure, change in temperature, light waves, sound waves. Protoplasm is capable of conducting an impulse caused by such a stimulus from one part of its mass to another. It is also capable of withdrawing a stimulated portion from an unfavorable stimulus. *Conduction* is ordinarily associated with the nerves of higher animals, and *contraction,* with muscles, but both these evidences of irritability are characteristic of protoplasm itself.

ORGANIZATION. Protoplasm exists only in particular structural units, the cells (Chap. III).

METHODS OF STUDYING PROTOPLASM

Units of protoplasm (cells) are usually quite small, and the various materials suspended in the protoplasm are still smaller; protoplasm is, therefore, best studied under high powers of magnification. For this the compound microscrope is used, with magnifications ordinarily from about one hundred to one thousand diameters. Many characteristics of protoplasm may be studied in living organisms of small size. Permanent preparations of protoplasm, in which it is coagulated and preserved in as nearly the normal condition as possible, involve the following steps:

(1) *Killing.* The protoplasm is killed as quickly as possible, to avoid change. The agents used are selected for great toxicity and power of rapid penetration.

(2) *Fixation.* The protoplasm is coagulated in as nearly the normal condition as possible. Often the same reagent acts both as a killing and fixing agent.

(3) *Dehydration.* Water is removed from the protoplasm, very gradually, and replaced by another liquid. Alcohol is the most commonly used dehydrating agent.

(4) *Clearing.* The protoplasm is rendered transparent, so that it may readily be examined by transmitted light.

(5) *Sectioning.* After being impregnated with and imbedded in paraffin or celloidin, thin sections of the material are cut. The sections are usually from five to twenty microns in thickness. (A micron is $\frac{1}{1000}$ millimeter, or about $\frac{1}{25000}$ inch.)

(6) *Mounting.* The thin sections are freed from paraffin or celloidin and mounted under thin glass slips or coverglasses on microscope slides, in a mounting medium, usually a gum that hardens on standing.

(7) *Staining.* Ordinarily some time during the dehydration process, the protoplasm is treated with one or more dyes of known chemical properties. These give maximum contrast betweeen structures and aid in their examination.

The electron miscroscope magnifies up to 100,000 diameters. Steps in preparation of materials for examination are essentially those just listed, but with greater refinements. (Sections examined may be much thinner even than 0.1 micron.)

Review Questions

1. What are the physical properties of protoplasm?
2. Which chemical elements and compounds are most characteristic of protoplasm?
3. What are the biological characteristics of protoplasm?
4. Distinguish chemically between digestion and synthesis, and illustrate with examples.
5. What is respiration and what is its purpose?
6. What are the steps in the preparation of microscope slide mounts?
7. Define enzyme, autotrophic.

Chapter III

CELLS

Protoplasm exists in the form of masses, usually minute, which are known as *cells*. The term "cell" was first used by Robert Hooke, in 1665, who applied it to the empty chambers which he saw in cork. A typical cell, as recognized today, consists of a central differentiated portion, the nucleus, and a surrounding portion, the cytosome.

THE CELL THEORY, CONCEPT, OR PRINCIPLE

Although Theodor Schwann, a German zoologist publishing in 1839, and Matthias Schleiden, a German botanist publishing in 1838, are generally credited with the first statement that all organisms consist of cells, this concept, the *cell theory* or *cell principle*, was actually stated several years earlier by other biologists, including Lamarck and Dutrochet. During the late 70's and early 80's of the last century, the complex process of cell division was discovered and analyzed (by Strasburger, Flemming, and others). This led to the expansion of the cell theory to furnish the basis for modern interpretations of development and inheritance. Even physiology has become fundamentally the study of the functions of cells. As recognized today, the concept implies that those forms of life in which the protoplasm is continuous are of but one cell, and that other plants and animals consist of many cells and their products.

CELL MORPHOLOGY

The Size of Cells. Cells vary in size from near the lower limit of microscopic visibility (about 0.5 micron) to the size of the yolk of the largest bird's egg.

The Shape of Cells. Cells freely suspended in liquid surroundings are spherical (by the laws of surface tension). In groups, inequalities of pressure from the different sides result in irregularities of form. If all cells in a given mass are of the same size and subject to equal pressure from all sides, they will be flat-

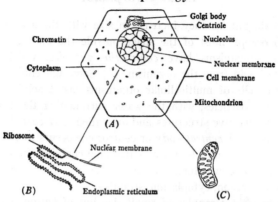

Fig. 4. (A) Section through a typical animal cell under high power (light microscope). (B) The nuclear membrane and cytoplasm adjacent to it (electron microscope). (C) Section through a mitochondrion (electron microscope).

tened against each other, with, according to some suggestions, fourteen faces. Eight of these may be triangular and six of them rectangular, or eight may be hexagonal and six rectangular.

Cell Structures. The major parts of a typical cell are (a) surrounding membrane, (b) cytosome, and (c) nucleus (Fig. 4).

CELL MEMBRANE (AND CELL WALL). The outside boundary of all cells is determined by a thin but definite membrane of live protoplasm. In most plant cells, in addition to the *cell membrane* (or *plasma membrane*), there is present outside it a stiff envelope of nonliving material secreted by the protoplasm lying beneath it. This is the *cell wall*, which consists of cellulose in most cases, sometimes with lignin or waxes added.

CYTOSOME. The cytosome is that part of the cell lying outside the nucleus. It consists of a ground substance, the cytoplasm, in which are suspended various formed bodies.

Cytoplasm. The cytoplasm ordinarily fills most of the space between nucleus and cell membrane. It may, in old plant cells, be but a thin film around a large sap vacuole. In consistency, it varies from fluid to solid, but it typically consists of an inner portion, the granular and fluid *endoplasm,* and an outer region, the clear and rigid *ectoplasm.* Extending throughout it is the *endoplasmic reticulum,* which has associated with it granules of RNA (*ribosomes*). (Fig. 4B.)

Vacuoles. Regions in the cytoplasm occupied by liquid, chiefly water with some compounds in solution, are called vacuoles. Three kinds occur. (a) *Sap vacuoles* (present in plant cells) are spherical when small, but, as they increase in size with the age of the cells, come to occupy most of the space outside the nucleus. (b) Some unicellular organisms have *contractile vacuoles*, which regularly discharge liquid from the organism. (c) Some unicellular organisms and some cells of multicellular organisms ingest solid particles of food. These particles, with the water surrounding them, constitute temporary digestive structures and are called *food vacuoles*.

Centrosome. A *central body* or centrosome occurs in cells of lower plants and most animals. Each centrosome contains one or a pair of granules, *centrioles*, which are division centers from which radiate, during cell division, cytoplasmic strands.

Mitochondria. Granules of small size but of various shapes, suspended in the cytoplasm, are called mitochondria. They are lipoidal in part and are centers of enzyme activity in various phases of cellular metabolism. The electron microscope has revealed their structure as complex series of minute membranes (Fig. 4c).

Golgi Body. The *Golgi apparatus* or Golgi body is a specialized group of granules and rods, or a network, found in animal cells. It appears to be involved in secretion. Its minute structure is similar to that of mitochondria.

Plastids. Especially characteristic of plant cells are certain moderately large bodies of characteristic form and size which function as centers of chemical activity. These are plastids. Products of their activity, either food or pigment, may be deposited as granules in the cytoplasm. The most important plastids, biologically speaking, are the green *chloroplasts* of most plants. These, which contain *chlorophyll*, are the centers of photosynthetic activity.

NUCLEUS. The nucleus is a specialized mass of protoplasm, usually spherical, near the center of the cell. It normally occupies a position in the axis of the cell. In the absense of the nucleus, cell growth and cell reproduction do not take place. In some cells the nucleus is elongated or branched; in others it may be divided into several distinct parts. It is bounded externally by a membrane and contains several types of structures within it.

Nuclear Membrane. The membrane surrounding the nucleus is a protoplasmic membrane of approximately the same constitution as the cell or plasma membrane. Exchanges between nucleus and cytoplasm take place across this membrane. It disappears in most cells during cell division. The nuclear membrane, actually a double layer, is associated structurally with the endoplasmic reticulum (Fig. 4B).

Nucleosome. All structures enclosed by the nuclear membrane constitute the nucleosome. Its continuous substance is the *nucleoplasm* — corresponding to the cytoplasm of the cytosome. Suspended in it is a network of material extending throughout the nucleosome. This network is made up of granular filaments of a material called *chromatin,* which is stained by basic dyes. Chromatin is chiefly nucleoprotein, the nucleic acid involved being deoxyribose nucleic acid (DNA). Ribose nucleic acid (RNA) is also manufactured in the nucleus, where it is concentrated in definite rounded bodies called *nucleoli.* DNA is restricted to the nucleus, while RNA occurs in the cytosome also, having moved out from the nucleus. RNA is involved in protein synthesis. During nuclear division (mitosis) the chromatin becomes condensed in characteristic structures, the *chromosomes,* the numbers and kinds of these being uniform in all cells of a given organism. The chromosomes are believed to retain their individual identities even in a cell that is not undergoing mitosis.

CELL PHYSIOLOGY

Properties of the Cell Membrane. The cell membrane, which is made up chiefly of lipins and proteins, has *differential permeability;* i.e., certain substances in solution are able to penetrate it, others are not. Some substances in solution pass through the membrane by simple *diffusion,* following a concentration gradient; others cannot pass through the living membrane. Movement of solutes is not solely dependent upon diffusion, however; some substances pass through the cell membrane against a concentration gradient. The energy for this activity, *active transport,* comes from the cell.

In addition, the cell membrane may invaginate, or fold inwards, and engulf fluid droplets. The miniature vacuole thus formed is ingested; this is called *pinocytosis.* Similar ingestion of particles is called *phagocytosis.*

Properties of the Cell Wall. The cell wall is nonliving. it is freely permeable to all dissolved substances. Its chief function seems to be the maintenance of *turgor* or rigidity in plant cells. The protoplasm tends to swell with water taken in because of its high osmotic pressure, but the cell wall prevents any actual increase in size. The resulting pressure gives the characteristic rigidity of plant cells, and of plant tissue in general. Another function of the cell wall, evident in certain seeds, is the imbibition of water — resulting in absorbing it and storing it for the plant.

Cell Metabolism. The most important function of all organisms is nutrition — the acquiring and using of food — and this function is evident in every individual cell. Metabolism includes all the chemical processes of nutrition.

FOOD MANUFACTURE. Autotrophic organisms manufacture their own food. The centers of food manufacture are in the cells. The cells of green plants contain chloroplasts the green coloring matter of which is *chlorophyll*. In the presence of sunlight this is able to effect the synthesis of carbohydrate food. The process is *photosynthesis* (literally "synthesis through light"), the light being the source of energy for the reaction. The following equation illustrates in abbreviated form the photosynthesis of a simple sugar in the green plant:

$$6CO_2 + 6H_2O + \text{energy (from sun)} \rightarrow C_6H_{12}O_6 + 6O_2$$

More details of the process, which involves several steps, are given in Chapter VII. Photosynthesis is the basic process by which the oxygen of the earth's atmosphere is conserved for the respiration of all animals and plants, and it is, without doubt, the *most important chemical process* involved in the preservation of conditions suitable for life on earth. It is also the most important process by which energy from the sun is conserved. Although a few bacteria manufacture food by chemosynthesis, most food is manufactured by the cells of green plants.

ASSIMILATION. Simple food molecules like those formed in photosynthesis may be combined (condensed) to form stored food or may be used in the synthesis of protoplasm. Food may be stored as fats of many different kinds, these being synthesized from glycerol and fatty acids. Stored carbohydrate food, condensed from simple sugars, exists as starch (in most plants), as glycogen (in animals and some plants), and as other compounds. The most important compounds in the synthesis of new protoplasm appear to be amino acids, the "building stones" of proteins. The formation of these larger molecules is accompanied by enzyme activity and typically occurs by dehydration. The formation of starch from simple sugar is illustrated by the following equation:

$$nC_6H_{12}O_6 \rightarrow (C_6H_{10}O_5)_n + nH_2O$$

DIGESTION. Complex foods taken into a cell, or stored foods too complex for absorption and use, must undergo digestion — the process by which they are reduced to smaller, more usable molecules. The process involves enzymes that bring about hydrolysis of the foods. The enzymes are quite specific; in other words, a particular enzyme aids in the digestion of only one kind of food. The process, the reverse of dehydration synthesis, is illustrated by the digestion of starch:

$$(C_6H_{10}O_5)_n + nH_2O \rightarrow nC_6H_{12}O_6$$

RESPIRATION. Respiration is the oxidation of food. Its primary value to the organism is in the release of energy stored in the food molecule, this energy being used for all activities of the living organism. While it may require accessory activities in some organisms (for example, breathing, in man), the process is fundamentally an activity of the individual cells. It is extremely complex, occurring in a series of steps and requiring a series of different oxidizing enzymes. Some of the steps do not involve oxygen, and in some organisms, incomplete oxidation of foods takes place in the complete absence of free oxygen. This is *anaerobic respiration,* or *fermentation.* The following equation illustrates, in abbreviated form, the process of *aerobic respiration* in a cell (complete oxidation of the sugar, glucose). Details of the process are given in Chapter VII.

$$C_6H_{12}O_6 + 6O_2 \rightarrow 6CO_2 + 6H_2O + \text{energy}$$

CELL REPRODUCTION

When a typical cell has attained a size that is fairly definite for that particular type, it divides. This process constitutes cell reproduction. Division of a cell (*cytokinesis*) is typically associated with a complicated indirect method of nuclear division (*karyokinesis*). The two processes together constitute *mitosis.*

Mitosis.

DEFINITION. Mitosis is a form of cell division that involves exact division, both quantitative and qualitative, of all essential constituents of the nucleus.

PHASES OR STEPS. Mitosis should be thought of as one continuous process, beginning with a single growing (or "resting") cell, and ending, without a significant pause, only when that cell

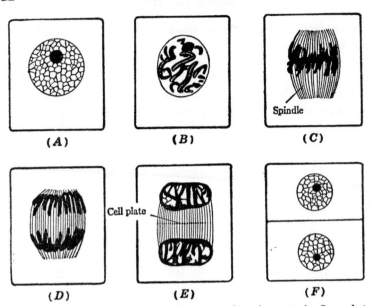

Fig. 5. Mitosis in plant cells, as illustrated in the onion root tip. Somewhat diagrammatic. (A) Growing or "resting" cell. (B) Prophase — formation of the chromosomes. (C) Metaphase — division of the chromosomes on the equator of the spindle. (D) Anaphase — migration of the chromosomes toward the poles. (E) Telophase — organization of the daughter nuclei. The cell plate is beginning to form. (F) The two daughter cells in the growing stage.

has become two independent ones. For convenience in discussing, the process is commonly divided into four steps. These are essentially the same for plants and animals, but vary somewhat among different organisms. As outlined below, the process occurs in most organisms (Figs. 5 and 6). The growing phase may be called *interphase;* during this time the chromatin content doubles.

Prophase. This includes all changes in the cell from the beginning of division to the establishment of the chromosomes on the equator of the spindle (Figs. 5B and 6B). These changes occur in approximately the following sequence. (1) The centrioles separate and move to opposite poles of the nucleus, 90° from the original position. (Centrioles are absent from the cells of higher plants.) At the same time, fibers begin to appear in the cytoplasm, radiating from the centrioles if these are present. (2) The chromatin in the nucleus condenses to form distinct chromosomes, each consisting of two parallel *chromatids.* The number of chromosomes in a cell is characteristic for each species of organism. (3) The nuclear membrane disappears. (In rare cases, the membrane persists and mitosis occurs inside it.) (4) The *spindle* is formed. This is made up of two types of fibers — *continuous fibers*, extending from pole to pole, and *chromosomal fibers*, attached to one particular place, the *centromere*, in each chromosome. (5) The nucleoli disappear. (6) The chromosomes migrate to the equatorial plate of the spindle.

Metaphase. Metaphase is the stage in which the chromosomes are on the equator and during which the separation of the

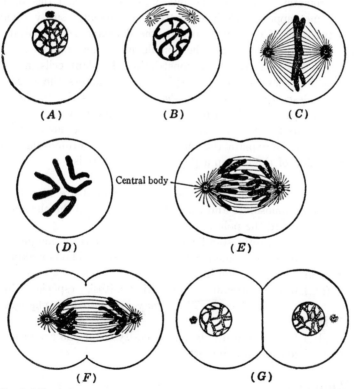

Fig. 6. Mitosis in animal cells, as illustrated in embryo cells of the parasitic worm, *Ascaris*. Somewhat diagrammatic. (A) Growing or "resting" cell. (B) Prophase. (C) End of prophase, beginning of metaphase — chromosomes at equator of spindle. (D) Polar view of chromosomes at equator of spindle. (E) Anaphase. (F) Early telophase. (G) The two daughter cells in the growing stage.

daughter chromatids of each chromosome begins. This phase finds chromosomes in position on the equatorial plate but involves relatively little activity. (Figs. 5c and 6c, D.)

Anaphase. The chromatids of each chromosome separate and migrate to the poles of the spindle — the positions of the new nuclei. They move as if pulled by the contraction of the spindle fibers attached to them. The chromatids are now daughter chromosomes, each of the original chromosomes having divided longitudinally to form two. (Figs. 5D and 6E.)

Telophase. This stage includes the processes of organization of the daughter nuclei. (1) The chromosomes are transformed into the chromatin network of the interphase nucleus, and the nuclear membranes appear. (2) The centriole, if present, usually divides into two. (3) If cytokinesis occurs, the daughter cells separate at this stage. In animal cells the spindle fibers now disappear, and the cells are separated by a constriction. In plant cells, a series of swellings develops on the spindle fibers across the equator; these coalesce to form the *cell plate*, which gives rise to the new cell wall separating the two cells. (Figs. 5E and 6F.)

MECHANISMS OF MITOSIS. Several theories exist, none entirely satisfactory, to explain the movements of the chromosomes and the division of the cell on a physico-chemical basis.

(a) It is obvious that fibers of some kind are attached to the chromosomes and that these seem to pull the chromosomes toward the poles.

(b) The mitotic spindle resembles a polarized magnetic field of force, but evidently is not one — several facts making such an interpretation impossible.

(c) Diffusion streams occur during mitosis, especially in embryonic animal cells. These may be related to changes in surface tension.

(d) Changes in protoplasmic viscosity occur and are probably of considerable importance.

Amitosis.

DEFINITION. Amitosis is nuclear fragmentation. It is usually not followed by division of the cytosome.

OCCURRENCE. Amitosis is a very rare form of cell division, found only in specialized or degenerate cells. It occurs frequently as a means of nuclear subdivision, resulting in an increase in the nuclear surface of a cell, but is only rarely associated with cell reproduction.

DIFFERENCES BETWEEN ANIMAL AND PLANT CELLS

Morphology. The smallest unicellular plant organisms are considerably smaller than the smallest animal cells, whereas the maximum size of animal cells considerably exceeds that of plant cells. Typically, however, plant and animal cells are of about the same size. Plant cells in general possess a rigid cell wall, surrounding the cell membrane. The cell wall is composed principally of cellulose. The cytosome often contains plastids, particularly chloroplasts (involved in photosynthesis), and a large vacuole; and these are absent in animal cells.

Physiology. The cell wall, being rigid, prevents the free expansion of the living cell contained within it. Consequently, the absorption of water, caused by the high osmotic pressure of the protoplasm, results in the development of the characteristic *turgor* of plant cells. Carbohydrates, fats, and proteins can be synthesized by the plant cell from simple inorganic compounds. Specific enzymes are involved in these processes, and the energy for the reactions is derived from sunlight or exothermic chemical reactions.

Reproduction. In the cells of flowering plants, centrosomes are absent. During telophase of mitosis, the daughter cells do not separate by the formation of a constriction, as in animal cells, but by the growth of a structure, the *cell plate*, on the equator of the disintegrating spindle. (Fig. 5.)

THE SIGNIFICANCE OF CELLS

The importance of the cell concept or principle may be seen from the fact that the cell is (1) the unit of structure and (2) the unit of function in all organisms. It is also (3) the unit of development and (4) the unit of heredity; even the processes of organic evolution depend fundamentally on changes in individual cells — the cells from which new individuals develop.

Review Questions

1. What is the cell theory or principle?
2. Distinguish between the cell membrane and cell wall.
3. Draw from memory, and label fully, the parts of a typical cell.
4. Discuss the functions common to all cells.
5. Describe metabolism in cells.
6. Describe mitosis, giving the steps in detail.

Chapter IV

UNICELLULAR ORGANISMS

A unicellular organism is an animal or plant composed of but one cell. The protoplasm is continuous, not being interrupted internally by any cell boundaries. The nucleus in many of these organisms is, however, multiple.

DIFFERENCES BETWEEN PLANTS AND ANIMALS

In the final analysis there are no criteria which enable us to divide all organisms into two clearly defined groups — the plants and the animals. The following differences hold true in most cases:

PLANTS	ANIMALS
(a) Have cellulose cell wall.	Have no cell wall.
(b) Have no powers of locomotion.	Have powers of locomotion.
(c) Are less irritable.	Are more irritable.
(d) Grow throughout life.	Grow to a definite size.
(e) Manufacture own foods.	Require complex foods from outside.

Exceptions to the above differences:

(a) Animals of the group Tunicata produce cellulose. It is doubtful that some of the lower plants have cellulose walls.

(b) Certain plants produce motile cells involved in reproduction. Certain animals are sessile.

(c) The sensitive plant (*Mimosa*) and certain other plants respond to stimuli more quickly than do some animals.

(d) This distinction does not apply to unicellular forms; they grow throughout life, but that simply means to a definite size, for then they reproduce.

(e) Some protozoa, not alone those containing chlorophyll, are able to live on very simple compounds.

INTRODUCTION TO BIOLOGICAL CLASSIFICATION

Major Divisions. In spite of the fact that some forms of life intermediate between plants and animals do exist, organisms are ordinarily first of all classified in either the Plant or the Animal Kingdom. Each Kingdom is divided into several major groups, each group containing organisms related in general structure.

PLANT KINGDOM. The major groups in which plants are classified are called *divisions* by some authorities, *phyla* (sing., *phylum*) by others. The divisions recognized are four in number, but the classification into divisions is somewhat artificial and is being rapidly replaced by a plan which divides the Plant Kingdom into numerous phyla (in this book, twelve). Both schemes of classification are given in this book. For the names and characteristics of both divisions and phyla, see Chapter VI.

ANIMAL KINGDOM. The major groups of animals constitute phyla. The number of phyla recognized varies with different authors, the variation chiefly involving rare, obscure types and being due to differences in criteria used to characterize them. One phylum, Protozoa, is considered in this chapter. The others included in this book are named and characterized in Chapter IX.

Categories of Classification. All organisms that are sufficiently alike to have come from the same kind of parents belong to the same *species*. More satisfactory definitions of species can be suggested later, but this is approximately correct. In other words, a kind of plant or animal is a species. Species of greatest similarity are combined into *genera* (sing., *genus*); genera are combined into *families*, families into *orders*, orders into *classes*, and classes into *divisions* or *phyla*. These groups, of progressively greater size, are called categories of classification. In our consideration of plants and animals we will deal only with types as representatives of the highest categories.

VIRUSES

Of great biological significance are certain agencies on the border line between living organisms and the nonliving world that are capable of producing diseases in plants and animals. These agencies are called *viruses*. They were formerly called *filtrable viruses*, because most of them, unlike bacteria which cause diseases, pass through porcelain filters, and they are too small to be seen by an ordinary microscope. Viruses cause measles, smallpox, poliomyelitis, rabies, yellow fever, and other animal diseases, as well as many plant diseases. One group of viruses, the *bacteriophages*, is parasitic on bacteria.

In 1935, the virus causing the plant disease tobacco mosaic was crystallized by W. M. Stanley. This demonstrated that the virus, unlike known living organisms, is a definite chemical compound — not a complex mixture of compounds. Not all viruses have been crystallized, but those that have prove to be nucleoproteins similar to nuclear constituents of typical cells. Most involve DNA as the nucleic acid, but some, RNA combined with proteins.

In an appropriate living organism a given virus thrives and reproduces (i.e., increases in quantity). A virus can not be grown independently of its host organism, however, and whether it carries on metabolism in the accepted sense is therefore unknown. On the other hand, viruses do undergo evolutionary changes — they show adaptation. In other words, some characteristics of viruses suggest that they are living organisms, while others suggest that they are not; and biologists are not agreed as to whether or not they should be called living organisms. They may be thought of either as intermediate between the living and nonliving or as extremely simple living things. In any case, they do not lend themselves to classification in our conventional schemes.

UNICELLULAR PLANTS — SIMPLE ALGAE AND FUNGI

Two large groups of plants — the Algae and the Fungi — contain unicellular representatives. These are subdivisions of the division Thallophyta. As such, the terms have no significance in classification under the phylum system, but they are useful general terms in any case. The groups differ fundamentally in that the algae contain some kind of pigment involved in photosynthesis, while fungi are colorless, and, with rare exceptions, obtain all their food from the outside.

Algae. The following examples illustrate the principles of morphology, physiology, and reproduction as they occur in unicellular algae.

PROTOCOCCUS (*PLEUROCOCCUS*). This is the genus name of a microscopic plant that forms a green film on the moist bark of trees and the sides of flower pots. It is a member of the phylum Chlorophyta. (Fig. 7A.)

Morphology. Protococcus is spherical, is about 10 microns in

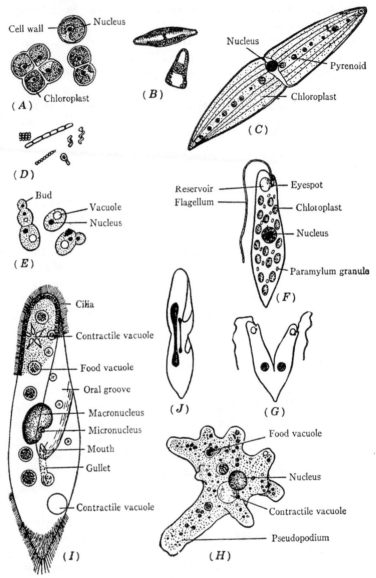

Fig. 7. Unicellular organisms. (A) *Protococcus (Pleurococcus)*. (B) Diatoms. (C) A desmid (*Cloisterium*). (D) Bacteria. (E) Yeast. (F) *Euglena*. (G) *Euglena*, reproduction by longitudinal fission. (H) *Amoeba*. (I) *Paramecium*. Covering of cilia shown at posterior end; internal details, in anterior end. Note formation of food vacuole at end of gullet. (J) *Paramecium*, reproduction by transverse fission.

diameter, and has a small, central nucleus. One large chloroplast occupies most of the cytosome. The cell wall is of cellulose.

Physiology. Water, oxygen, carbon dioxide, and inorganic salts are absorbed through the cell wall and cell membrane. Carbohydrate food is manufactured by photosynthesis, and sugar is oxidized as a source of energy. *Protococcus* synthesizes protoplasm from simple inorganic compounds and the sugar which it manufactures. This type of nutrition, characteristic of all green plants, is autotrophic. (Nutrition involving photosynthesis is also called *holophytic.*)

Reproduction. The method of reproduction is asexual, by simple fission. The parent cell divides into two individuals of approximately equal size. Individual plants may remain attached together in groups, but each cell is independent of the others.

DESMIDS. Desmids are unicellular green algae which, though of angular or otherwise unusual form, are symmetrical. Individual cells in some species occur attached together in filaments or chains. Desmids, like *Protococcus*, are in the phylum Chlorophyta, with *Spirogyra* (Chap. VI). They are common in freshwater ponds. (Fig. 7c.)

Morphology. Two symmetrical halves, the *hemicells*, characterize a desmid. A large chloroplast is in each hemicell, and the chloroplasts contain *pyrenoids*, small glistening bodies associated with starch storage. The nucleus is single, centrally located. There is a cellulose cell wall.

Physiology. Nutrition is autotrophic.

Reproduction. Reproduction may occur asexually, in which case the nucleus divides, each daughter nucleus entering a hemicell; the hemicells then separate and each one regenerates its other half to complete a new individual. Reproduction may also occur sexually, in which case two individuals (exactly alike) fuse to form a *zygote*, from which a new individual arises.

OTHER SIMPLE ALGAE. Unicellular species of both blue-green and green algae (phyla Cyanophyta and Chlorophyta, respectively) are known. One large, economically important group of algae, the *diatoms* (phylum Chrysophyta), consists entirely of unicellular forms. These are minute cells containing a brown pigment, enclosed in a capsulelike cell wall consisting largely of silicon. Diatoms are common both in fresh water and in the sea. They are very important as the ultimate source of food for fishes. (Fig. 7*B*.)

Fungi. The best known unicellular fungi are the bacteria and yeasts. Their characteristics are given below.

BACTERIA. Bacteria constitute the phylum Schizomycophyta. They differ from all other fungi in their small size and in the absence of a distinct nucleus. In the past they have been compared either to nuclei without cytoplasm or to cells in which the nuclear material is scattered throughout, but recent evidence suggests that they do have a nuclear structure. Many bacteria are parasitic in plants and animals, and these may be *pathogenic* (disease-producing). Others are very useful, for example in fixing atmospheric nitrogen or decomposing dead organisms. (Fig. 7D.)

Morphology. The extremely small size (usually less than a micron in diameter), the indefinite nucleus, and the absence of chlorophyll are the most characteristic features. A cell wall of cellulose or some other substance is present, with sometimes a waxy envelope in addition. The form may be rodlike, *bacilli* (sing., *bacillus*); spherical, *cocci* (sing., *coccus*); or spiral or comma-shaped, *spirilla* (sing., *spirillum*). *Flagella*, whiplike locomotor organs, are sometimes present. Some bacteria produce resistant spores, which survive unfavorable environmental conditions.

Physiology. Locomotion sometimes occurs by means of flagella. Nutrition is *saprophytic* in general; i.e., food is absorbed from the outside, not manufactured. This is a form of heterotrophic nutrition. A few bacteria are able to use the energy from the oxidation of simple inorganic compounds in the synthesis of carbohydrates and proteins. This is *chemosynthesis.* Many specialized types of metabolism occur among bacteria. Of special importance are the fixation of atmospheric nitrogen and the oxidation of ammonia to nitrites and of nitrites to nitrates.

Reproduction. Reproduction occurs asexually, by fission; individual bacteria may remain attached together in chains or masses. Sexual reproduction also takes place in bacteria.

YEASTS. These are simple, unicellular fungi of the phylum Eumycophyta, in which the nucleus is distinct. (Fig. 7E.)

Morphology. Yeast cells are ovoid, somewhat larger than bacteria. They have a cellulose cell wall and a simple, definite nucleus. Vacuoles and oil globules occur in the cytoplasm.

Physiology. Nutrition is saprophytic. Yeasts are *facultative anaerobes;* i.e., they do not normally live in the absence of oxygen but are capable of doing so. In the absence of oxygen, yeasts are able to obtain energy for metabolism by the fermentation of sugar. A special group of enzymes, collectively called *zymase*, is involved. The end products of this fermentation are ethyl alcohol and carbon dioxide. The former, in the presence of oxygen, may be oxidized to yield additional energy. The following equation represents, briefly, alcoholic fermentation of sugar by yeast:

$$C_6H_{12}O_6 \rightarrow 2C_2H_5OH + 2CO_2 + energy$$

Reproduction. This occurs asexually, by *budding*. A small swelling forms on the yeast cell. As it enlarges, the nucleus divides, half going into the swelling — the bud. A new cell wall is formed between the two cells. Budding may result in a chain, single or branched, of yeast cells.

ORGANISMS INTERMEDIATE BETWEEN PLANTS AND ANIMALS

Certain simple organisms possess both plant and animal characteristics. These may be considered plants by botanists, animals by zoologists; there is no real significance in either classification.

Euglena. *Euglena* is the genus name of certain green (chlorophyll-bearing) flagellated organisms. *Euglena* may be considered an alga (of the phylum Euglenophyta) or a protozoan (see next pages). It occurs in ponds, often forming an extensive green surface scum or "bloom." (Fig. 7F, G.)

MORPHOLOGY. *Euglena* is usually spindle-shaped, but is variable in different species. The species vary from 25 to more than 100 microns in length. A single flagellum, at the anterior end, extends from a "gullet." Opening into the latter is a reservoir, into which empty several small contractile vacuoles. A red *stigma*, or "eyespot," is in the anterior portion, near the reservoir. Chloroplasts are usually numerous. Granules of *paramylum* (a carbohydrate storage product similar to starch) occur in the cytoplasm. The nucleus is single, the chromatin concentrated in its center. (Fig. 7F.)

PHYSIOLOGY. Nutrition is either autotrophic or saprophytic, a euglena being able to maintain itself in the absence of light if dissolved food occurs around it. In the dark, with saprophytic nutrition, a euglena loses its green color. *Euglena* does not ingest solid food; the "gullet" is misnamed. Locomotion is accomplished by the flagellum. A form of rhythmic contraction ("euglenoid movement") occurs occasionally; it is not a method of locomotion. *Euglena* forms *cysts*, in which individuals may survive drying and other unfavorable conditions.

REPRODUCTION. This occurs asexually, by longitudinal fission, division beginning at the anterior end. (Fig. 7G.)

Other Forms Intermediate Between Plants and Animals.

GREEN FLAGELLATES. In varying degrees, green flagellates other than *Euglena* combine animal and plant characteristics.

SLIME MOLDS. These are relatively large masses of protoplasm, living on or in rotten wood, damp soil, or dung. They are considered by some biologists animals of the order Mycetozoa (class Rhizopoda of the phylum Protozoa), but by others are thought to be highly specialized plants constituting the class Myxomycetes (division Thallophyta) or the phylum Myxomycophyta. They have the structure of large, multinucleate amoebae (see p. 35), a *plasmodium*, but develop fruiting bodies like those of typical fungi, producing flagellate *spores*. These spores fuse in pairs to form new plasmodia; this is sexual reproduction, the fused spores constituting zygotes.

UNICELLULAR ANIMALS — PROTOZOA

The Phylum Protozoa includes all one-celled animals and only these. It is divided into four classes.

The Classes of Protozoa. These are most easily separated on the basis of organs of locomotion.

(1) MASTIGOPHORA (or FLAGELLATA). Locomotion by flagella, one to many elongated whiplike structures which function as propellers. Free-living and parasitic.

(2) SARCODINA (or RHIZOPODA). Locomotion by *pseudopodia* ("false feet"), projections of flowing protoplasm. Free-living and parasitic.

(3) SPOROZOA. Usually passive in movement. All parasitic.

(4) INFUSORIA (or CILIATA). Locomotion by *cilia*, numerous minute hairlike processes which function as oars. Free-living and parasitic.

Examples of Protozoa. The most frequently studied protozoa in the biology laboratory are *Amoeba*, *Paramecium*, and, if we consider it an animal, *Euglena*. These belong, respectively, to the classes Sarcodina, Infusoria, and Mastigophora. The best known representative of the class Sporozoa is the organism which causes malaria.

EUGLENA (see p. 33).

AMOEBA. This is a genus of naked protozoa of irregular, changing body form. (Fig. 7*H*.)

Morphology. An amoeba is approximately 200 to 300 microns in diameter; its external form is asymmetrical, continuously changing during locomotion. The cytoplasm is divided into an external clearer region, the *ectoplasm*, and an inner, more opaque region, the *endoplasm*. A single, definite, spherical nucleus is present, and there is typically one contractile vacuole. Numerous food vacuoles occur.

Physiology. Locomotion takes place by flowing extensions of protoplasm, the pseudopodia. Solid food is ingested (*holozoic* nutrition) by pseudopodia. Digestion takes place within the cyto-

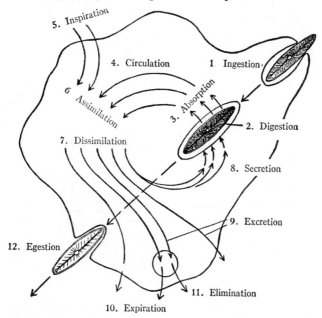

Fig. 8. Diagram showing the steps in metabolism as they occur in an amoeba feeding upon a diatom. (Reprinted by permission from *Animal Biology* by R. H. Wolcott, copyright, 1946, by the McGraw-Hill Book Company.)

plasm. There is no definite place at which undigested material is egested. The contractile vacuole excretes water, chiefly, maintaining the high osmotic pressure. (Fig. 8.)

Reproduction. This takes place asexually, by fission. A form of sporulation (multiple fission) has also been observed.

OTHER SARCODINA. Two amoeboid forms with shells, which occur commonly in fresh water, are *Arcella* and *Difflugia.* Other representatives of the order are parasitic, one being the cause of a serious form of dysentery.

PLASMODIUM. This is the genus name of the causative organism of malaria, a representative of the class Sporozoa. It is parasitic

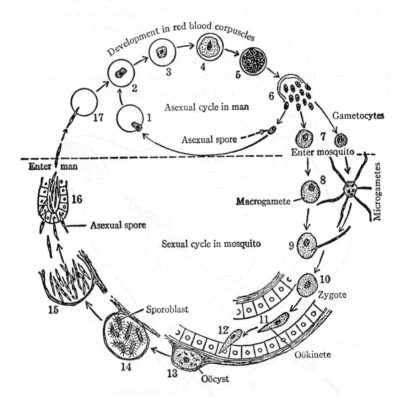

Fig. 9. Diagram of the life cycle of the malarial parasite, showing the asexual cycle in man (1–6, 17) and the sexual cycle in a mosquito of the genus *Anopheles* (in stomach 8–12, cyst on stomach wall 13–15, in salivary gland 16). (Reprinted by permission from *Animal Biology* by R. H. Wolcott, copyright, 1946, by the McGraw-Hill Book Company.)

in insects and the blood of vertebrates. For details of its relation to man and the mosquito (its life history), see Figure 9.

PARAMECIUM. *Paramecium* is a genus of rather large, spindle- or cigar-shaped protozoa, which move by means of cilia. (Fig. 7*I, J*.)

Morphology. This protozoan is about 250 microns long, asymmetrically cigar-shaped. A spiral oral groove leads from the anterior end to the *gullet*, about halfway back. The ectoplasm is thin, containing numerous *trichocysts*, structures which (presumably in defense) are exuded and hardened as threads. One large *macronucleus* is present and one or two small *micronuclei*. Typically, there are two contractile vacuoles and numerous food vacuoles. (Fig. 7*I*.)

Physiology. Nutrition is holozoic, bacteria and other small food particles being ingested through the gullet and formed into food vacuoles. These follow a definite course through the cytosome during the process of digestion and the undigested portion is egested at a definite region on one side, the *anus*. Contractile vacuoles regulate osmotic pressure.

Reproduction. This may be asexual, by transverse fission, the macronucleus dividing amitotically and the micronucleus or -nuclei, mitotically within the nuclear membrane. (Fig. 7*J*.) Sexual reproduction takes place by *conjugation*, in which nuclear exchange occurs between two individuals which then separate and rapidly divide into, in each case, four small individuals. A nuclear reorganization comparable to this process but involving only a single individual also takes place in *Paramecium*. This process is *endomixis*.

OTHER INFUSORIA. In an infusion of hay in pond water there soon appear many kinds of ciliates. Other forms besides paramecia which may be common are *Vorticella, Stentor, Stylonychia.*

Review Questions

1. What are the principal differences between plants and animals? Are these differences universally valid?
2. How are organisms classified?
3. What is a virus?
4. Discuss morphology, physiology, and methods of reproduction of unicellular algae and fungi, giving specific examples.
5. Describe *Euglena* and discuss its biological position.
6. Compare *Amoeba* and *Paramecium* with reference to morphology, physiology, and methods of reproduction.

Part Two

MULTICELLULAR ORGANISMS

Chapter V

THE MULTICELLULAR ORGANISM

An organism may exist as a separate individual or as one of an aggregation or group. The organisms in such a group may be unicellular or multicellular. In either case, organisms of the same kind may occur together, in which case they form a *colony*. A multicellular organism is an individual, however, not a colony of independent cells. A colony of unicellular organisms is comparable to a colony of multicellular ones, not to a single multicellular organism. An illustration of such a colonial unicellular form is provided by *Volvox*. *Volvox* occurs as a colony of green flagellates. The colony is a spherical mass, the flagella of the individuals all directed outward. Specialized reproductive individuals are present. The presence of such individuals suggests a division of labor in the colony analogous with that in multicellular individuals, but a colony of *Volvox* or any other unicellular form is not comparable with a single multicellular organism.

THE ORGANISMAL CONCEPT

Either as a single cell or as a group of cells, the individual organism behaves as a unit. It has organization: the parts are subordinate to the whole, whether they are parts of cells or whole cells. This is the *organismal concept*, one of the most important concepts in biology.

CHARACTERISTICS OF THE MULTICELLULAR ORGANISM

Similarities with Unicellular Organisms.

INTERNAL COMPLEXITY. The idea that unicellular organisms are simple in structure because they are small is incorrect. Many protozoa, for example, are extremely complicated in internal structure, containing many different highly specialized *organelles* (diminutive for organ).

DIVISION OF LABOR. This is another characteristic common

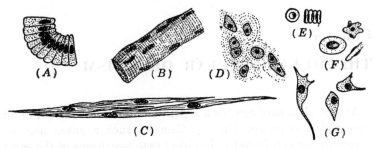

Fig. 10. Representative animal tissues. (A) Epithelium — cells of the mucosa lining the frog's intestine. (B) Striated muscle tissue from the leg of a grasshopper. (C) Smooth muscle tissue from the frog's intestine. (D) Cartilage (supporting tissue) from the frog. (E) Human red blood corpuscles. (F) Blood corpuscles of the frog. (G) Nerve cells from the spinal cord of a rabbit.

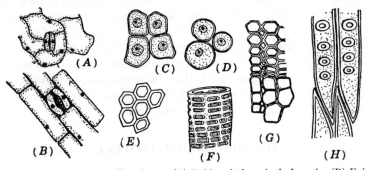

Fig. 11. Representative plant tissues. (A) Epidermis from leaf of turnip. (B) Epidermis from leaf of corn. (C) Wood parenchyma cells from stem of *Aristolochia* (Dutchman's pipe). (D) Parenchyma cells from cortex of corn root. (E) Sclerenchyma fibers (in cross section) from pericycle of stem of *Clematis*. (F) Pitted vessel from xylem (vascular tissue) of sycamore tree. (G) Cross section of tracheids (vascular tissue) from white pine — two adjacent annual rings; summer wood above, spring wood of the succeeding year below. (H) Longitudinal section of tracheids with bordered pits, from white pine.

to one-celled and many-celled organisms. Among the former, the different parts of a single cell illustrate the principle; in multicellular forms division of labor is among the different cells.

Differences from Unicellular Organisms.

SIZE. In general it is true that unicellular forms are smaller than multicellular ones, but the largest of the former are many times larger than the smallest of the latter.

KINDS OF DIFFERENTIATION. In one-celled organisms, differentiation is between the parts of a single cell; in multicellular organisms it takes the form of differences between individual cells and groups of cells.

Tissues. A tissue is a group of cells having the same structure and function. In multicellular animals these are epithelial, connective and supporting, blood, muscular, and nervous tissues. In multicellular plants they are epidermis, parenchyma, sclerenchyma, collenchyma, vascular tissues (xylem and phloem). (Figs. 10 and 11.)

Organs. An organ is a group of cells or tissues associated together for some common function. It is not necessarily of uniform structure throughout. The following are examples in animals: brain, stomach, foot, fin, wing, biceps muscle, femur. In plants examples are: root, stem, fruit, stamen, carpel, leaf, tendril. *Organ systems* are groups of organs involved in the same functions. The term is not satisfactorily applied to plants, but is common in describing animal structures, e.g., the circulatory, digestive, respiratory, nervous, and locomotor systems.

NATURE OF REPRODUCTION AND GROWTH.

Reproduction. Reproduction in one-celled forms is identical with cell division; growth is entirely associated with increase in size of the individual cell. Reproduction means death of the parent, for the parent goes into (or becomes) its own offspring.

Growth. In multicellular plants and animals growth has two aspects: (a) growth in size of individual cells and (b) increase in the number of cells, through division. Reproduction is a separate process, involving the activity of a specialized group of cells, the germ cells. Since reproduction involves only a few cells, the parent organism lives on.

Review Questions

1. Distinguish between a multicellular organism and a colony of unicellular forms.
2. What is the *organismal concept?*
3. Give similarities of, and differences between, unicellular and multicellular organisms.

Chapter VI
THE MORPHOLOGY OF MULTICELLULAR PLANTS

As previously stated, the Plant Kingdom is classified in four divisions by some authorities but in a relatively large number of phyla by other botanists. Some textbooks of general biology adopt one plan, some the other. Both plans, therefore, are included in this work. It will be necessary for the student to make the appropriate correlations with the classification used in his own course.

DIVISIONS OF THE PLANT KINGDOM

The four divisions are distinguished by the degree of differentiation into organs, the development of vascular (conducting) tissues, and the nature of the reproductive processes. The divisions are briefly characterized below.

Division Thallophyta. Plants in this division do not possess the specialized structures associated with higher plants. The form of the plant is a *thallus* — i.e., it is not differentiated into root, stem, and leaves. There are two subdivisions, the Algae and the Fungi, the former containing the thallus plants with chlorophyll, the latter including those without.

SUBDIVISION ALGAE. Algae are thallus plants that contain chlorophyll. In many cases, they contain other pigments as well. In color they appear blue-green, green, red, or brown, depending upon the supplementary pigments. Algae vary in size from microscopic species to large seaweeds that may be over a hundred feet long. Some are relatively complex in vegetative structure, and many have complex reproductive cycles. They are common in the sea and fresh water, but are limited on land to damp locales.

SUBDIVISION FUNGI. The fungi are thallus plants that lack chlorophyll. Most of them are saprophytic in nutrition. A few bacteria (which are in this subdivision) are autotrophic, some of these carrying on chemosynthesis, others photosynthesis (with pigments other than chlorophyll). Fungi vary in size from the smallest microscopic organisms to moderately large mushrooms and bracket fungi. Many of them are parasitic, and many cause animal and plant diseases. Varied, sometimes complex, reproductive cycles occur in the group.

Division Bryophyta. The mosses and liverworts constitute this division. They are small green plants in which a stem and leaves are developed. True roots and vascular tissue are absent. The plants are anchored in the substratum by threadlike *rhizoids*. The fertilized egg is retained in the female sex organ, where it develops into an *embryo* and the *sporophyte* (see p. 80). The *gametophyte* is independent, but the sporophyte is parasitic on the gametophyte. Mosses and liverworts are most abundant in shady, damp soil; a few are aquatic.

Division Pteridophyta. Ferns and plant types related to them are the members of this division. They have roots as well as stems and leaves, and they have vascular tissues, but they do not produce seeds. The gametophyte is independent, but the sporophyte is the more prominent stage in the life cycle and it is likewise independent. As in the bryophytes, the fertilized egg develops into an embryo in the female sex organ. Pteridophytes are most abundant in shady, damp soil.

Division Spermatophyta. These are the seed plants. They have well-developed organs and complex tissues. The prominent phase of the life cycle is the sporophyte, in which the gametophyte is parasitic. The fertilized egg develops into an embryo which is enclosed within the *seed*. Seed plants are widely distributed, but they are much more abundant on land than in the water. Two subdivisions of this division are recognized.

SUBDIVISION GYMNOSPERMAE. Cycads, the gingko, junipers, pines, and spruces are examples of gymnosperms. The specialized reproductive structures of the members of this group are usually *cones*. The Gymnospermae are seed plants in which the seeds are naked. All plants in this group are woody and perennial.

SUBDIVISION ANGIOSPERMAE. Grasses, palms, oaks, lilies, roses, and dandelions are examples of angiosperms. The specialized reproductive structures are *flowers*. The seeds are borne enclosed in a *carpel*. The plants in this group may be woody or herbaceous, perennial or annual.

PHYLA OF THE PLANT KINGDOM

Subdivision of the Plant Kingdom into phyla is based on an attempt to group together plants that have the same characteristics. Thallophytes are an assemblage of plants placed together because of what they lack rather than what they have. They are not necessarily closely related. Phyla, on the other hand, are groups of plants possessing similar characteristics and, therefore, presumably closely related. The division Thallophyta is made up of plants only superficially related, and when divided into phyla, it is seen to consist of ten of these groups — seven containing algae and three, fungi. The division Bryophyta corresponds directly with a phylum, but the pteridophytes and spermatophytes are so similar that they are placed in a single phylum. The twelve phyla are briefly summarized below. It should be noted that among the phyla listed are some whose members are all unicellular and others that include unicellular representatives, and that some of these microscopic plants have already been described in Chapter IV. In the remaining portion of this chapter, which deals with the morphology of multicellular plants, both classifications are given in connection with each plant type described.

Phylum Cyanophyta. These are the blue-green algae, unicellular (often colonial) or simple filamentous forms. The cells lack definite nuclei. Chlorophyll is present, but not in chloroplasts, and it is supplemented by a blue pigment (*phycocyanin*). Stored food is glycogen. Reproduction occurs only asexually. Most blue-green algae live in fresh water; some are marine.

Phylum Euglenophyta. This is the group of plants in which we classify *Euglena* (p. 33) when it is considered a plant rather than an animal. The description of *Euglena* will serve for the phylum.

Phylum Chlorophyta. This is a large group, including the many species of unicellular and multicellular green algae. Chloroplasts, containing chlorophyll like that of higher plants, are present, and starch is the stored food. Reproduction occurs both asexually and sexually, and in some species there is a complex life cycle. Most species live in fresh water, but some are marine, and some live in moist situations on land. The unicellular *Protococcus* and desmids have been described on pages 29 and 31.

Phylum Chrysophyta. These are the diatoms, unicellular yellow-green or yellow-brown algae already described briefly on page 31.

Phylum Pyrrophyta. Members of this phylum are unicellular marine and fresh-water flagellates known as dinoflagellates. They are considered protozoa by zoologists. They contain yellow-green or yellow-brown plastids, and their reserve food is starch or oil. Reproduction takes place asexually.

Phylum Phaeophyta. This phylum includes the brown algae. They are multicellular, sometimes quite large, and they may be complex for a thallus plant. Chlorophyll is masked by *fucoxanthin*, a brown pigment. Fats and soluble sugar are reserve foods. Reproduction often involves a complex life cycle. Practically all Phaeophyta are marine.

Phylum Rhodophyta. These are the red algae. Though never so large as the largest brown algae, they are multicellular and may be fairly large. A red pigment, *phycoerythrin*, occurs with chlorophyll. Reserve food is intermediate starch. Reproduction is complex. Practically all species are marine, algae of this phylum occurring at greater depths than any other photosynthetic plants.

Phylum Schizomycophyta. The bacteria, constituting this phylum, have already been described. (See Chap. IV.)

Phylum Myxomycophyta. These are the slime molds, already described in Chapter IV.

Phylum Eumycophyta. The true fungi — molds, rusts, mushrooms, yeasts — constitute this phylum. The body of a true fungus is made up of filaments called *hyphae*, the group of hyphae being called a *mycelium*. Nutrition is saprophytic. Food is stored in the form of glycogen. Reproduction is asexual or sexual and may involve a complex life cycle. The Eumycophyta occur in water, on land, in the bodies of dead organisms, and, as parasites, in the bodies of living organisms.

Phylum Bryophyta. Mosses and liverworts, constituting this phylum, are small green plants with stems and leaves but no true roots. *Rhizoids* anchor them to the soil. Vascular tissue is absent. In the life cycle, the sporophyte is parasitic on the gametophyte. A few plants of this phylum are aquatic but most of them are terrestrial, living in shady, damp soil.

Phylum Tracheophyta. These are small to large, chlorophyll-bearing plants with distinct roots, stem, and leaves. All have vascular tissue in a cylinder (*stele*), with both xylem and phloem. The sporophyte is the dominant stage in the life cycle. In primitive Tracheophyta the gametophyte may be metabolically independent, but in most plants in this group the gametophyte is parasitic in the sporophyte. Plants of this phylum dominate land habitats; a few species, however, are aquatic.

The phylum Tracheophyta is divided into four subphyla, the Psilopsida (primitive, mostly extinct forms), Lycopsida (club mosses), Sphenopsida (horsetails), and Pteropsida (ferns and seed plants). The subphylum Pteropsida is divided into three classes, the Filicineae (ferns), Gymnospermae (pine, etc.), and Angiospermae (flowering plants).

MORPHOLOGY OF MULTICELLULAR ALGAE

Examples of Blue-green Algae. (Class Cyanophyceae or Phylum Cyanophyta.)

Oscillatoria. (Fig. 12*a*.) This is a fresh-water alga in which the blue-green cells occur in unbranched filaments. Nuclei are absent but are apparently represented by chromatin granules. Chloro-

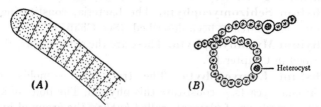

(A)   (B) — Heterocyst

Fig. 12. Blue-green algae. (A) Tip of a filament of *Oscillatoria*. (B) Part of a filament of *Nostoc*, with two heterocysts.

phyll, plus a blue pigment (phycocyanin), is present, but is not in plastids. A weaving or gliding movement of the filament is responsible for the name, *Oscillatoria*.

Nostoc. (Fig. 12*b*.) The filaments of beadlike cells are embedded in a common gelatinous mass, the *Nostoc* "marble." The ordinary cells are interrupted at intervals by *heterocysts*, large transparent dead cells at which breaks in the filament commonly occur. This organism occurs in fresh water.

Examples of Green Algae. (Class Chlorophyceae or Phylum Chlorophyta.) For reproduction in the following examples see Chapter VIII.

ULOTHRIX. (Fig. 13*A*.) This fresh-water alga consists of an unbranched filament of cells in linear order, each cell with a single chloroplast — the latter shaped like a broad transverse belt within the cytoplasm. Each chloroplast contains one or more small centers, *pyrenoids*. The filament is attached to the substrate by a modified basal cell, the *holdfast*.

ULVA. *Ulva* is a marine alga called sea lettuce. It is common between low and high tides on both coasts. The plant is a sheet-like thallus, two cells thick — the cells elongated at right angles to the surface. Rhizoids from some of the lower cells form a holdfast.

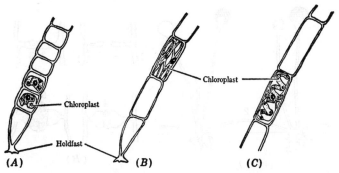

Fig. 13. Green algae. Parts of filaments showing vegetative cells of (A) Ulothrix, (B) Oedogonium, (C) Spirogyra. Cellular details are shown in only one or two cells of each filament. The dark ovoid bodies are the nuclei.

OEDOGONIUM. (Fig. 13*B*.) A filamentous, fresh-water alga, this is similar in appearance to *Ulothrix*. The chloroplast is a cylindrical network with many pyrenoids.

SPIROGYRA. (Fig. 13*C*.) This fresh-water form is not attached. It forms unbranched filaments of elongated cells in which the chlorophyll is in one or more spiral chloroplasts, each with pyrenoids. The nucleus is suspended in the center of the cell in cytoplasmic strands.

Examples of Brown Algae. (Class Phaeophyceae or Phylum Phaeophyta.) The rockweed (*Fucus*) and the kelp (*Laminaria*) attain relatively large size. The broad, ribbonlike thallus of the kelp may be over 100 feet in length. Differentiation into rootlike holdfast, a stemlike *stipe,* and leaflike structures occurs, but these are of simple form. In *Fucus*, air bladders (*floats*) are also present.

Specialized reproductive organs occur, and most brown algae have a complicated reproductive cycle.

MORPHOLOGY OF MULTICELLULAR FUNGI

The following examples are all members of the subdivision Fungi, phylum Eumycophyta. For reproduction in the fungi see Chapter VIII.

Black Bread Mold. (Class Phycomycetes.) (Fig. 14.) The plant body is a *mycelium,* which is a loose mass of cottony threads (*hyphae*) that extend down into moist bread as food absorbing

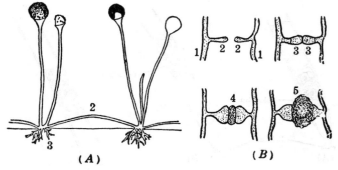

Fig. 14. *Rhizopus* (black bread mold). (A) Portion of *Rhizopus* mycelium. The vertical hyphae are sporangiophores, each bearing at its apex a sporangium which bears asexual spores. The horizontal hyphae (2) are called stolons, and those (3) extending into the substrate are rhizoids. (B) Stages in sexual reproduction involve two different hyphae (1). Steps in the formation of a zygote are shown in the details numbered 2–5. (Reprinted by permission from *General Botany* by Harry J. Fuller, copyright, 1950, by Barnes & Noble, Inc.)

structures, *rhizoids,* or extend upward as *sporangiophores* (spore-bearing structures). Cell cross walls are not present in the hyphae, and the latter are multinucleate. The genus name is *Rhizopus.*

Red Bread Mold. (Class Ascomycetes.) The mycelium of this tropical and subtropical mold is made up of hyphae with cross walls. The *ascospores,* characteristic of this class, are produced in groups of eight, each group in an elongated sac, an *ascus.* This mold is being extensively used in experimental studies in genetics. The genus name is *Neurospora.*

Mushrooms. (Class Basidiomycetes.) (Fig. 15.) A filamentous mycelium forms an underground portion. It consists of inter-

lacing hyphae, in which cross walls are present. From it grows
the fleshy, tough, parasol-shaped *sporophore*. This consists of
a *stalk* and a *cap*. On the under side of
the cap or *pileus* are borne thin plates,
the *gills*, which radiate outward from
the stalk. Extending out at right angles
to the surface of the gills are sterile
hyphae and swollen spore-bearing cells
known as *basidia*.

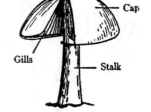

MORPHOLOGY OF BRYOPHYTA

Moss. (Fig. 16.)

Fig. 15. A mushroom, part
of cap removed to expose
gills.

VEGETATIVE PARTS. True roots are
absent in bryophytes, but rhizoids function as roots. There is an
erect stem, with scalelike leaves. Cells of the stem have little
differentiation; outer ones contain chloroplasts, inner ones form

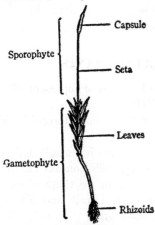

rudimentary conducting tissue. True
vascular tissue does not occur in
bryophytes. The leaves are thin and
narrow, and are usually only one cell
layer thick. The cells of leaves contain chloroplasts. These vegetative
structures occur only in the gametophyte generation.*

REPRODUCTIVE PARTS. (See Chap.
VIII for the life cycle.) At the
upper end of the stem of the gametophyte there is either a sperm-
producing organ (*antheridium*) or an
egg-producing organ (*archegonium*)
or both. The mature sperms and
eggs are known collectively as
gametes. From the fertilized egg

Fig. 16. A moss plant. The sporophyte is parasitic on the gametophyte.

(ovum), which remains in the archegonium, there grows out a
long stalk (*seta*) bearing at its upper end the *capsule*. Spores

* The gametophyte produces gametes (mature germ cells). These fuse in pairs
(the process is fertilization) to form a plant. The sporophyte produces spores,
which are able by cell division to form a plant. The two types of plants alternate
in the life history of every higher plant, the fused gametes developing into a sporophyte and the spore developing into a gametophyte. This concept, one of the most
important in botany, is further developed in Chapter VIII.

are formed in the capsule. The seta and capsule constitute the sporophyte. The cells of the sporophyte lack chlorophyll and are metabolically dependent upon the gametophyte.

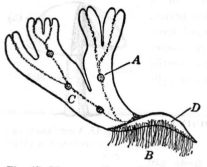

Liverworts. (Fig. 17.) Some liverworts have only a thallus body, with rhizoids. Others have a stem and leaves. In contrast to mosses, however, they have typically a prostrate rather than an erect form. Antheridia and archegonia are present. The sporophyte generation is relatively less conspicuous than in the mosses.

Fig. 17. Liverwort. Except for the small structures labeled *A*, this is all gametophyte. *A*, Sporophyte. *B*, Rhizoids. *C* and *D*, Upper and lower surfaces of thallus, respectively. (Reprinted by permission from *General Botany* by Harry J. Fuller, copyright, 1950, by Barnes & Noble, Inc.)

MORPHOLOGY OF VASCULAR PLANTS

Examples of Pteridophytes. (Life histories of representative pteridophytes are discussed in Chap. VIII.)

FERN. (Division Pteridophyta or subphylum Pteropsida of phylum Tracheophyta.) (Fig. 18.)

Vegetative Parts. The gametophytic generation is a small thallus plant, the *prothallium*, bearing rhizoids. Its cells contain chloroplasts. The sporophytic generation is the plant we think of as a fern, consisting of *fronds* (leaves) with central stalk and lateral leaflets, growing from a large underground stem (*rhizome*). The latter is anchored by small roots which have root hairs and in which there is differentiation into various types of tissues. *Epidermis*, the outer layer of cells from some of which the root hairs elongate, *parenchyma*, simple thin-walled cells, and *sclerenchyma*, thick-walled supporting cells, are present. Vascular tissue occurs, usually as two separate "bundles," one of *xylem*, large hollow woody cells, the other of *phloem*, small cells usually containing protoplasm. The *meristem* (growing part of the root tip) is a single cell. A *rootcap* is present. Epidermis, sclerenchyma, parenchyma. and vascular tissue are also present in the rhizome, and there is a *cortex* of sclerenchyma immediately under the epidermis. Internal bands of sclerenchyma are present. The

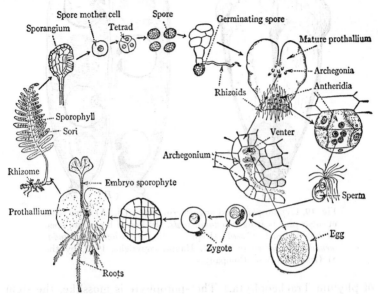

Fig. 18. Diagrams showing stages in the life cycle of a true fern (*Polypodium*). (Reprinted by permission from *A Textbook of General Botany* by R. M. Holman and W. W. Robbins, copyright, 1939, by John Wiley and Sons, Inc.)

xylem and phloem are combined in one *fibrovascular bundle*, the former usually surrounded by the latter. The leaf has an epidermis containing *stomata* (pores whose size is regulated by their marginal cells, the *guard cells*). Inner sclerenchyma is absent. The vascular bundles are branched to form *veins*. Chloroplasts are present in the nearly uniform parenchyma cells that occupy most of the leaf, and these constitute the *mesophyll*.

Reproductive Parts. Sperm cells are produced in antheridia, small spherical bodies on the under side of the prothallium. A single ovum develops in each of the archegonia, which are flask-shaped bodies also on the under side of the prothallium. Each sperm cell is spirally twisted, and motile through the action of many long cilia. Spores develop in *sporangia*. The latter occur in groups called *sori* (sing., *sorus*), brownish or yellowish, flattened ovoid structures on the under surface of the leaflets.

CLUB MOSSES. (Division Pteridophyta or subphylum Lycopsida

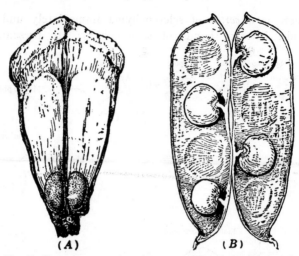

Fig. 19. Gymnosperm and angiosperm compared. (A) Cone scale of sugar pine bearing two *naked seeds*. (B) Pod of lima bean open to show the *enclosed seeds*. (Reprinted by permission from *Fundamentals of Biology* by A. W. Haupt, copyright, 1940, by the McGraw-Hill Book Company.)

of phylum Tracheophyta.) The sporophyte is mosslike, the stem bearing many small leaves. Club mosses are most common in the tropics; they were formerly more abundant than now and are important as fossils.

HORSETAILS OR SCOURING RUSHES. (Division Pteridophyta or subphylum Sphenopsida of phylum Tracheophyta.) The rhizome branches into jointed stems that bear rudimentary leaves in *whorls* (circles at one level) at the joints. Some branches are vegetative in function; others are reproductive, producing cone-like *strobili* (sing., *strobilus*) at the tips. A strobilus consists of an axis bearing shield-shaped *sporophylls*, which produce spores. The spores develop into either of two types of prothallia. One type produces antheridia, the other archegonia. The gametophytic generation is therefore *heterothallic*, the sperm cells and eggs being produced in different type plants.

Examples of Spermatophytes. (Classes Gymnospermae and Angiospermae of the Division Spermatophyta or the subphylum Pteropsida.) Reproductive cycles are described in Chapter VIII. Chapter VII is devoted largely to the physiology of angiosperms. (See Fig. 19.)

EXAMPLE OF CLASS GYMNOSPERMAE — PINE. The pine is described as an example of a gymnosperm. Other members of this class are cycads, the gingko ("maiden hair tree"), firs, spruces, hemlocks, cedars, redwood. Most gymnosperms are referred to collectively as conifers, and most of them are evergreens. They are abundant plants, particularly in the colder regions of the world; and they are of very great economic importance.

General Characteristics. A pine has a straight axial stem (*trunk*) with lateral branches, the trunk continued downward in a *taproot* with side roots. The leaves ("needles") are borne on dwarf shoots, in clusters or bundles — the number of needles in a bundle being characteristic of a species. Reproductive structures are confined to *strobili* (cones) of two kinds — ovule-producing and pollen-producing. The seeds mature in the former. The embryo contains several *cotyledons* (embryonic leaves).

Vegetative Parts. The roots and trunk and their branches attain considerable size, by secondary thickening. Xylem and phloem are produced on the two sides of a *cambium* layer (meristem tissue), phloem toward the outside, xylem inside. Annual rings are produced in both trunks and roots. Dwarf shoots occur on the trunk and branches. The leaves are elongated, needlelike structures. The epidermis of the leaves contains deeply sunken stomata and is underlaid by sclerenchyma. The vascular region (*stele*) of the leaf is surrounded by a sheath and contains two vascular bundles, each containing xylem and phloem.

Reproductive Parts. (Fig. 20.) The vegetative parts of the plant are limited to the sporophyte generation. The reproductive

(A) (C)

(B)

Fig. 20. Cones of the western yellow pine. (A) Staminate cone — natural size. (B) Ovulate cone — one-half natural size. (C) Single scale from the latter, bearing two winged seeds.

structures are cones of two types, borne on the sporophyte. The *staminate* (male) are smaller than the *ovulate* (female) cones. The staminate cones are made up of small scales, *microsporophylls*, each bearing two sporangia on the inner surface. In each sporangium are produced many *microspores* (*pollen grains*). The large cones, the ones commonly called "pine cones," are the ovulate cones. These are made up of large scales, *megasporophylls*, each bearing on its inner surface two *ovules*, structures that develop — after fertilization has occurred — into seeds.

EXAMPLES OF CLASS ANGIOSPERMAE. The descriptions given here are not based on one particular example but cover flowering plants in general. The major range of variations within the group is covered in this account.

General Characteristics. The angiosperms are differentiated into roots, stem, leaves, and *flowers*. A flower consists typically of four distinct elements — *calyx*, *corolla*, *stamens* (collectively the *androecium*), and *carpels* (collectively the *gynoecium*). The carpels are variously united to form one or more *pistils*. The gynoecium, sometimes combined with other structures, develops into a *fruit*, enclosing the seeds.

The class Angiospermae is divided into two subclasses, the Dicotyledoneae and the Monocotyledoneae. As the names suggest, the former have two *cotyledons* (seed leaves) in the embryo, and the latter have but one (Fig. 21). The leaves of dicots have

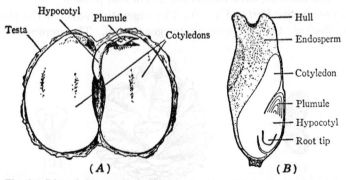

Fig. 21. Dicotyledonous (lima bean) and monocotyledonous (corn) seeds compared. Note: the absence of endosperm in the bean seed is not a characteristic of all dicotyledonous seeds. (Reprinted by permission from *Fundamentals of Biology* by A. W. Haupt, copyright, 1940, by the McGraw-Hill Book Company.)

netted veins (veins forming a network), those of monocots have parallel veins. Flower parts usually occur in fours and fives in dicots, in threes in monocots. The stem structure differs, too, in the arrangement of vascular tissue; in dicots the vascular bundles form a hollow cylinder, but in monocots they are scattered throughout.

Roots. The first root to develop from the embryo is called the *primary root*, and its branches are the *secondary roots.* Roots developing from leaves or branches are *adventitious;* they may develop into props or buttresses. A root growing straight down in the stem axis is a taproot. If enlarged for food storage (as in carrots or turnips), it is a *crown root.* Roots with swollen regions in which food is stored (for example, sweet potatoes) are *tuberous roots.*

If we examine the longitudinal section of a young root (Fig. 22), we can recognize a series of zones of cells of different types. The tip is covered by a rootcap. Immediately behind it is the meristem or region of cell division, and back of that is the zone of elongating cells. The elongating cells are gradually transformed further up the root into maturing cells. The epidermal

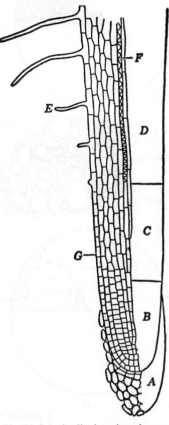

Fig. 22. Longitudinal section of young root. *A*, Rootcap. *B*, Meristematic region. *C*, Elongation region. *D*, Maturation region. *E*, Roothair. *F*, Stele. *G*, Epidermis. (Reprinted by permission from *General Botany* by Harry J. Fuller, copyright, 1950, by Barnes & Noble, Inc.)

cells in the zone of maturing cells bear elongations, the root hairs. If we examine a cross section (Fig. 23*A*, *B*), we see that the outer layer of cells of the root, the epidermis, surrounds a *cortex,* the inner layer of which is differentiated into the *endodermis.* The endodermis

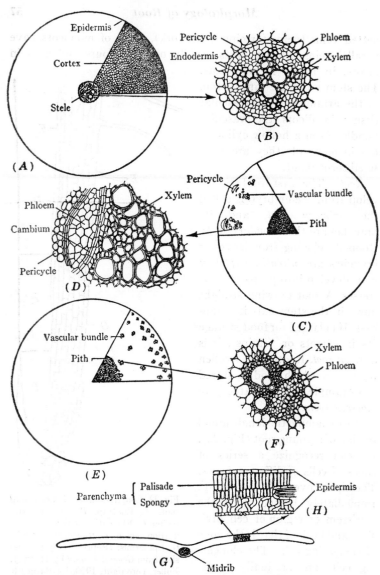

Fig. 23. Microscopic structure of root, stems, leaf. (A) Diagram of cross section of root of spiderwort (*Tradescantia*), with details shown in sector. (B) Stele of same section enlarged. (C) Diagram of cross section of dicotyledonous (*Clematis*) stem; the pith extends out to and between the vascular bundles. (D) Single vascular bundle enlarged. (E) Diagram of cross section of monocotyledonous (corn) stem — the pith (parenchyma of the stele, properly) extends around the vascular bundles. (F) Single vascular bundle enlarged. (G) Diagram of vertical section through leaf (privet). (H) Small section enlarged, part of a vein at the right.

surrounds the *stele* or cylinder of vascular tissue, consisting of its outer *pericycle* and alternate columns of xylem and phloem cells within it. Xylem may occupy the center of the root, or that region may be filled with a *pith* of parenchyma cells. In woody plants a cambium layer (of meristem cells) occurs between phloem and xylem, resulting in secondary thickening. In temperate and cold climates *annual rings* may be laid down.

Stems. The main stem may constitute a central axis of the plant or it may break up into many branches with no definite axis. The former type of development is *excurrent* (examples: pine, oak), the latter, *deliquescent* (example: elm). Some plants are erect, others are trailing or climbing — being incapable of supporting themselves. Leaves are attached along the stem at intervals characteristic for each particular species. Points of attachment are *nodes*, the stem between two nodes constituting an *internode*. The leaves may be *opposite* each other in pairs, or they may occur in *whorls* of three or more at a node; if they are single at each node, the arrangement is *spiral*. In the latter case, the angle between two adjacent leaves is characteristic for the species. (Fig. 24c, D.)

At the tip of each stem, and in the *axils* of the leaves (the upper angles between leaves and stem), occur meristem cells. These are enclosed in leafy outgrowths, the *buds*. The buds have the same arrangement on the stem as do the leaves. In trees and shrubs of colder regions, the outer parts of the buds are scalelike and protect the overwintering bud. When the scales drop off in the spring, scars are formed in the bark. These enable one to determine the age of a twig. For examples of winter twigs, see Figure 24.

Two distinct types of stem structure occur in the spermatophytes, the dicotyledonous and the monocotyledonous. (Fig. 23c–f.) In the gymnosperms and dicotyledonous plants, the vascular tissue is concentrated in a cylindrical sheath around the central *pith*. The xylem is internal to the phloem, the cambium lying between them. In woody plants the xylem and phloem are continuous around the periphery; in herbaceous plants, they are usually concentrated in vascular bundles. Outside the phloem lies the cortex, consisting of parenchyma cells and epidermis, and, in some cases, *cork*. The cork is interrupted by holes through it, the *lenticels*, by which the cells of the cortex are in contact with the atmosphere. In the monocotyledonous plants, the vascular

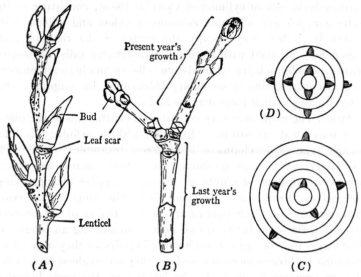

Fig. 24. Winter twigs. (A) Cottonwood. (B) Box elder. (C) Diagram showing the angles between adjacent bud scales, buds, leaves, or branches in
cottonwood. (D) Diagram showing the angles between the same structures
in the box elder.

tissue is scattered in bundles throughout the stem. There is no
central pith. Growth occurs between the vascular bundles, hence
they are gradually pushed further from each other.

Leaves. Leaves are typically broad, flattened structures attached to a branch by a *petiole* which divides in the leaf *blade*
into *veins.* If it has but one blade, the leaf is *simple;* if several
blades, it is *compound.* In the latter, the separate blades are
leaflets. A single prominent axial vein is usually present, the *midrib.* If the principal veins arise from the sides of the midrib, the
leaf is *pinnately* veined. If several prominent veins radiate from
the petiole, the leaf is *palmately* veined. In both these cases,
minute cross veins form a network, and the leaf is *netted-veined.*
If there are numerous parallel veins running lengthwise of the
blade, the venation is *parallel.* Simple leaves are of a great variety
of shapes — e.g., linear, elliptical, heart-shaped, with dentate,
crenate, or incised margins, etc. (See Fig. 25.) In compound
leaves, the leaflets may be pinnately or palmately arranged.
Leaves may be highly modified — to form tendrils, spines, etc.

The vascular tissue, in bundles, is contained in the petiole **and**

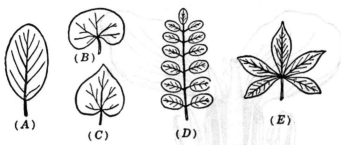

Fig. 25. Shapes of leaves. (A–C) Simple leaves: (A) elliptical, (B) kidney-shaped, (C) heart-shaped. (D–E) Compound leaves: (D) pinnately compound, (E) palmately compound.

veins. The blade is covered above and below with a layer of epidermis, containing at intervals the *stomata*. These consist of pores whose size is regulated by *guard cells*, a pair at each pore. The mid-portion of the leaf, the *mesophyll*, consists typically of one or two layers of vertically elongated cells under the upper epidermis, the *palisade cells*, and the irregular *spongy parenchyma* occupying the rest of the space. (Fig. 23G, H.)

Flowers. A typical flower, as previously stated, consists of four kinds of structures in concentric whorls. (See Figs. 26 and 27.) The structures of the two outer whorls are usually leaflike in form. Various degrees of reduction and fusion occur in either or both whorls. The outer whorl is the *calyx;* its separate elements are *sepals.* They are commonly green and scalelike. The inner whorl is the *corolla;* its separate elements are *petals.* They are usually delicately thin, and are often brightly colored. The calyx and corolla together constitute the *perianth.* If radially symmetrical, the flower is said to be *regular;* if it is only bilaterally symmetrical, it is *irregular.* The third whorl (from outside in) is made up of *stamens* and is called the *androecium.* Each stamen or *microsporophyll* consists of a basal stalk, the *filament*, and a sac in which the pollen grains form, the *anther.* The inner whorl, the *gynoecium*, consists of *carpels (megasporophylls).* In most flowers, the carpels have fused into a single central structure, the *pistil.* It consists of a basal expanded portion, the *ovary;* its vertical extension, the *style;* and the *stigma*, the specialized surface which receives the pollen grains. If the ovary has but a single cavity, it is "single-celled"; if the cavity is divided by one or more partitions,

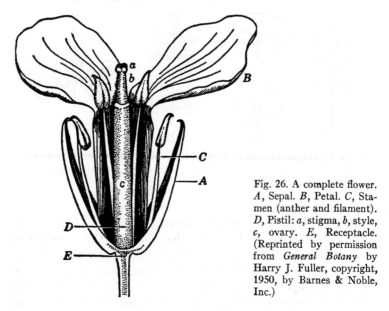

Fig. 26. A complete flower. *A*, Sepal. *B*, Petal. *C*, Stamen (anther and filament). *D*, Pistil: *a*, stigma, *b*, style, *c*, ovary. *E*, Receptacle. (Reprinted by permission from *General Botany* by Harry J. Fuller, copyright, 1950, by Barnes & Noble, Inc.)

it has several "cells." Several separate pistils are present in some flowers. The mature ovary constitutes the *fruit*.

Various types of floral variations occur. Three variations are related to the positions of attachment of floral structures to the *receptacle*, the organ to which they are attached. If the ovary is superior to (above) the bases of other floral parts, as in the bean and buttercup, the flower is *hypogynous*. *Perigyny* occurs if (as in the cherry) the ovary is surrounded by a cup upon the edge of which are borne the other floral parts. If the ovary is completely

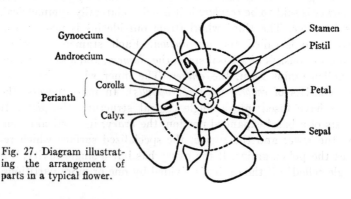

Fig. 27. Diagram illustrating the arrangement of parts in a typical flower.

inferior to (below) the other floral parts, the flower is *epigynous*. The flower of the evening primrose is an example of the last type.

Not all flowers have all typical parts. If staminate and carpellate structures are both present in the same flower, it is a *perfect flower;* and, if calyx and corolla are also both present, the flower is *complete* as well as perfect. Perfect flowers are called *monoclinous*. If stamens and carpels occur in different flowers, the flowers are called *diclinous*. Diclinous flowers — producing gametes of opposite sex — may occur on the same plant, in which case the plant

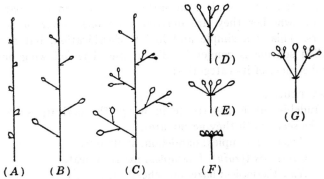

Fig. 28. Types of inflorescences. The ovals represent flowers: the larger ovals, the older flowers. (A) Spike. (B) Raceme. (C) Panicle. (D) Corymb. (E) Umble. (F) Head. (G) Cyme. (A–F) Indeterminate inflorescences. (G) Determinate inflorescence. (Modified from various authors.)

is said to be *monoecious*. If they occur on different plants, the condition is *dioecious*. Corn is monoecious; the cottonwood tree is dioecious.

Flowers do not necessarily occur as single structures at the end of a stem. They exist in many complex combinations called *inflorescences*. The pattern of occurrence of individual flowers in the major types of inflorescences is illustrated in Figure 28. These fall into two groups, *indeterminate inflorescences*, in which the terminal flower is the youngest (most recently formed), and *determinate* ones, in which the terminal flower is the oldest or first. Among inflorescences illustrated in the figure are the following indeterminate ones: *spike, raceme, panicle, corymb, umbel, head*. The *cyme* is a determinate inflorescence, as is also, of course, a single flower at the end of a single stem.

Fruits. A fruit is usually defined as a ripened ovary. It is that organ of the plant that ordinarily contains seeds. It may be derived from one ovary or many, and it may include other structures as well. Its development begins at pollination, and it may grow to a size enormously greater than the pistil or pistils of the flower. The wall of the ovary forms the *pericarp*, which encloses the seeds. The pericarp may be dry or fleshy, or both conditions may occur — in layers.

Fruits are classified as to type most simply by the following criteria: (a) whether they are from gynoecium alone or from gynoecium plus accessory structures; (b) whether they are from a single carpel or several — the latter either united or separated; and (c) whether they are derived from one flower or several flowers. This is a simple and logical classification, but a more detailed scheme is conventionally in use. The following outline includes most of its categories:

DRY FRUITS.
> Indehiscent Fruits (those in which the pericarp surrounds the seeds until they germinate).
>> *Achene*. Examples: dandelion, sunflower.
>> *Caryopsis (grain)*. Examples: maize, wheat.
>> *Nut*. Examples: hazelnut, chestnut.
>> *Samara*. Examples: maple, ash.
>> *Schizocarp*. Examples: carrot, parsnip.
> Dehiscent Fruits (those in which the pericarp opens along one or more sutures).
>> *Follicle*. Example: milkweed.
>> *Legume*. Examples: bean, pea.
>> *Capsule*. Examples: tulip, Jimson weed.

FLESHY FRUITS.
> *Drupe*. Examples: peach, cherry.
> *Pome*. Examples: apple, pear.
> *Berry*. Examples: gooseberry, orange, tomato.

AGGREGATE FRUITS (a collection of small drupelets together). Examples: blackberry, raspberry.

ACCESSORY FRUITS (in which the seeds are embedded in a modified receptacle). Example: strawberry.

MULTIPLE or COLLECTIVE FRUITS (derived from several flowers that occur close together). Examples: mulberry, pineapple.

Condensed Descriptions of Representative Flowers and Fruits. The following paragraphs summarize the characteristic features of the flowers and fruits of some of the most frequently studied plants. These illustrate various modifications in relations and numbers of flower parts. The first three types are of Dicotyledoneae, the last two of Monocotyledoneae. These examples are all monoclinous or perfect flowers. Common plants bearing diclinous flowers are the maize (Indian corn), which is monoecious, and the willows and cottonwoods, which are dioecious. (The catkins of "pussy willows" are inflorescences.)

Buttercups have complete, regular, hypogynous flowers. The calyx has five sepals, and the corolla five petals. There is a large and indefinite number of stamens and pistils, spirally arranged. The fruit is an aggregate of achenes.

Beans and peas have complete, hypogynous flowers that are irregular (papilionaceous — "butterfly-shaped"). There are five sepals and five petals. The petals are quite varied; there is an upper one, the *standard*, two lateral ones, the *wings*, and two lower ones that together form the *keel*. There are ten stamens, one of these free but the others fused along the filaments. There is a single pistil, the ovary one-celled. The fruit is a legume.

The dandelion "flower" is actually an inflorescence of the type called a head. The individual flowers are epigynous. A double involucre, the outer scales reflexed, surrounds the base of the head. The calyx is a whorl of bristles, and the corolla of each individual flower is tubular at the base but spread out into a *ligule* (flaplike structure) above. All flowers of the dandelion head are ligulate. There are five stamens, united into a tube around the style. There is a single pistil, with a one-celled ovary. The stigma bears two lobes. The fruit is an achene borne by a parachutelike structure derived from the calyx.

The flowers of tulips are complete, regular, hypogynous. There are three petal-like sepals and three petals. The six stamens occur in two circles. The pistil is single, but it is composed of three carpels and is three-celled. The stigma bears three lobes. The fruit is a capsule.

In bluegrass, one to several flowers occur in a spikelet — which has two sterile *glumes* at its base. Each flower is enclosed by two bracts, a lower one, the *lemma*, and an upper, the *palet*. There are three stamens. Each flower has a single pistil, with a one-celled ovary and a two-lobed stigma. The fruit is a caryopsis or grain.

Review Questions

1. What are the subdivisions of the Plant Kingdom and by what criteria are they classified? (Learn the classification used in your course.)
2. Compare typical representatives of the Algae and Fungi.
3. Describe in detail the morphology of a moss plant.
4. Describe in detail the morphology of a fern. Compare it with a moss and with a horsetail.
5. Compare and contrast gymnosperms and angiosperms, describing an example of each.
6. How do dicotyledonous and monocotyledonous plants differ?
7. Describe gross and microscopic structures of roots, stems, and leaves of angiosperms.
8. Describe the flowers of several different plants.
9. Give classifications of (a) kinds of flowers, (b) kinds of inflorescences, (c) kinds of fruits.

Chapter VII

THE PHYSIOLOGY
OF MULTICELLULAR PLANTS

The nonreproductive functions of multicellular plants are related to several aspects of the plants' activity. These include responses to environmental factors, metabolic activities related to maintenance, and the process of growth. The physiology of multicellular plants is here considered under these three subdivisions.

SENSITIVITY AND MOVEMENT

Plants do not show the same degree of sensitivity to stimuli shown by animals, but they are capable of movement. There are two kinds of movements in the higher plants, those accompanying growth and those due to turgor changes.

Growth Movements. Movements taking place during growth are due to continuous stimuli; they are irreversible, i.e., the shape of the parts moved is permanently affected. These movements consist of the turning of a growing region away from or toward a stimulus; the actual movement is accomplished by growth. These movements are *tropisms;* they are *positive* if toward the stimulus, *negative* if away from it. Local differences in concentrations of growth-promoting substances (*auxins* or *plant hormones*) are involved in such responses, for they are related to cell elongation.

PHOTOTROPISM ("light-turning"). Plant parts above ground are in general positively phototropic, bending toward a source of light. They may be so even in the absence of chlorophyll.

GEOTROPISM ("earth-turning"). Roots are positively geotropic at the growing tip, stems negatively so. The same response is shown to centrifugal force — suggesting a gravitational cause.

OTHER TROPISMS. The above two tropisms are of chief importance, but others have been demonstrated: *chemotropism,* response to chemicals; *hydrotropism,* response to water; *thermotropism,* response to heat, *thigmotropism,* response to touch.

NASTIC MOVEMENTS. Movements produced by differential growth

but not with a directional response (for example, opening and closing of flowers) are *nastic movements*.

Movements Due to Turgor Changes. Sudden, reversible changes, as the closing of the insect-capturing leaves of the Venus's-flytrap, or the closing and drooping of leaves of the sensitive plant (*Mimosa*), are due to sudden changes in cell turgor. In response to external stimuli, water moves from certain localized cells into intercellular spaces, the turgor pressure suddenly falling. The turgidity is restored by the water moving back into the cells.

METABOLISM AND RELATED FUNCTIONS

The absorption of water and inorganic nutrients, their transport, the synthesis of foods and of protoplasm, digestion, and respiration are considered in the following outline only in their special relations to multicellular plants. These functions in the individual cell are considered in Chapters III and IV.

Water Relations.

ABSORPTION. Water is absorbed by the root hairs, through which it is conveyed to and through the cortical cells to the xylem vessels. A gradient of osmotic pressure, increasing in the root cells from outside in, is the most important factor in this movement.

WATER MOVEMENT. The water, which with its solutes constitutes the *sap*, is conducted upward in the xylem. It may rise to considerable heights — over 300 feet in certain trees. Several factors supplementing each other are involved in the rise of sap: (1) root pressure — the osmotic pressure which brings the water into the plant; (2) capillary rise — the tendency of a liquid which wets its container to rise to a height dependent upon the surface tension of the liquid; (3) cohesion and transpiration — molecular attraction holding the column of liquid together, while its evaporation (transpiration) at the upper end tends to pull it upward.

TRANSPIRATION. This is the controlled evaporation of water from the leaves. The stomata are the mechanisms of control, their opening and closing by the guard cells regulating the amount of transpiration. Transpiration is greatest in the light, on warmest days, and at lowest relative humidities. It is possible that it may take place otherwise than through the stomata.

Nutrients. Nutrients are inorganic compounds essential to the life of the plant. (In animal physiology, the term is applied to the organic foods.) Nitrates, phosphates, sulfates, calcium, potassium, iron, and magnesium are important constituents of plant nutrients. Nutrients are absorbed in aqueous solution by the root hairs and are conveyed in the sap to the growing parts of the plant. They are used in the synthesis of foods and protoplasm and are involved in enzyme reactions.

Photosynthesis — "Carbon Assimilation." As used by the biologist, the term photosynthesis is applied to the synthesis of carbohydrates through the action of chlorophyll in the presence of sunlight. It is, then, a function limited to green plants. (Chemically, however, any synthesis for which light is the source of energy is photosynthesis.)

SIGNIFICANCE. Photosynthesis in green plants is the most important agency for maintaining the fitness of the earth's atmosphere for the support of life. The oxygen used up in the respiration of plants and animals is restored through the process of photosynthesis.

THE PROCESS. Carbon dioxide is absorbed from the atmosphere through the stomata of the leaves. Water is taken by the root hairs and conveyed to the leaves in the xylem vessels. Through the catalytic action of the green pigment, chlorophyll, with the sunlight as a source of energy, the two compounds are combined. Sugar is formed, and oxygen is given off as a by-product.

The process of photosynthesis begins with the absorption of light energy by chlorophyll, this energy being used to decompose the water molecules. The hydrogen atoms from the water are subsequently used in the process, but the oxygen is given off as a waste product. This is the first phase of the process. The second phase requires carbon dioxide, and this results in the formation of simple carbohydrate. This phase can, unlike the first phase, take place in darkness. By a series of steps, carbon dioxide is combined with the hydrogen from water to form carbohydrate. Phosphate-containing compounds are involved in the intermediate steps. The simple equation given in Chapter III was as follows:

$$6CO_2 + 6H_2O + \text{energy (from light)} \rightarrow C_6H_{12}O_6 + 6O_2$$

It now becomes apparent, however, that if the six molecules of oxygen are derived from the water, the above equation is not balanced. We now know that the equation for photosynthesis is more correctly represented as follows:

$$6CO_2 + 12H_2O + energy \text{ (from light)} \rightarrow C_6H_{12}O_6 + 6O_2 + 6H_2O$$

Even this, we should remember, is a shorthand representation of the reaction, for photosynthesis requires several distinct steps, different enzymes involved at each step.

The sugar, once formed, is basic material from which the many more complex compounds are synthesized by the plant.

CHLOROPHYLL. The green pigment involved in photosynthesis occurs in minute disc-shaped structures called *grana*, which compose the chloroplasts. Chlorophyll is of a compound nature, consisting, in the higher plants, of four chemically different pigments: chlorophyll a, chlorophyll b, carotin, xanthophyll. All contain carbon, hydrogen, and oxygen; and the two chlorophylls, nitrogen and magnesium in addition.

LIMITING FACTORS. The rate of photosynthesis is governed by that factor which is least available among those essential to the process. If either water, carbon dioxide, or light is available in below optimum quantity, the rate of photosynthesis will be limited. Temperature is an important factor in governing the rate of the reaction also, as it has a significant influence on the rate of the second phase of photosynthesis.

Assimilation. Simple sugars manufactured in photosynthesis may be condensed (by dehydration) to form double sugars (e.g., sucrose or cane sugar):

$$2C_6H_{12}O_6 \rightarrow C_{12}H_{22}O_{11} + H_2O$$

The formation of starch, the most important carbohydrate storage product in plants, is similar:

$$nC_6H_{12}O_6 \rightarrow (C_6H_{10}O_5)_n + nH_2O$$

Sugars are the basis for the synthesis of fats and other lipids. And some of their complex derivatives are combined with N-containing compounds to form amino acids and proteins. Plants (unlike animals) are able to synthesize their own proteins — from the nitrate and ammonia compounds absorbed from the soil and derivatives of the carbohydrates manufactured in photosynthesis. The plant thus functions as the ultimate source of amino acids for animal protein synthesis.

Transport and Storage. The manufactured food is conveyed from the leaf to other parts of the plant in the phloem cells. It is transported in a readily soluble form — viz., as a simple sugar. Starch may be formed and stored near to or far distant from the place of photosynthesis, but, being insoluble, may not be conveyed from one part of the plant to another without first undergoing digestion. All food material transported from one place to another in a plant must, of course, be in solution.

Digestion. The hydrolysis of complex foods (e.g., starch) is digestion. This process occurs in the cells in any part of a plant in which food storage takes place. The material stored may be used where it is digested, or it may be transported to some other part of the plant. The end products of digestion are then assimilated or oxidized.

Respiration. Respiration in plants, as in organisms in general, is the oxidation of food for the release of energy. In the higher plants, it is aerobic; in other words, it requires oxygen. The oxygen is absorbed through the roots (either from air spaces in the soil or in solution in water) and through the stomata of the leaves and the lenticels of the stem. The chief food used for oxidation is obtained through the process of photosynthesis, the most commonly oxidized food being a hexose (six-carbon) sugar like glucose:

$$C_6H_{12}O_6 + 6O_2 \rightarrow 6CO_2 + 6H_2O + \text{energy}$$

As in the process of photosynthesis, respiration takes place in a series of steps, each requiring particular enzymes. These steps are essentially similar in the cells of all aerobic organisms, plants and animals. The first steps can take place in the absence of oxygen. The sugar molecule is first transformed into a phosphorylated sugar (one containing phosphorus); and the phosphorus is of a special type, rich in energy. The phosphorus comes from ATP (adenosine triphosphate) — a common and very important cell constituent that is converted, by this process, to ADP (adenosine diphosphate). The phosphorylated sugar is next converted to pyruvic acid ($C_3H_4O_3$) by the loss of hydrogen. The hydrogen is passed along by a series of hydrogen acceptors, eventually combining with oxygen to form water — one of the by-products of respiration. The pyruvic acid undergoes a complicated series of reactions, in what is called Krebs cycle, giving off carbon dioxide and additional hydrogen atoms that, like those first given off, eventually combine with oxygen to form water. As the energy from the original sugar molecule is released, it is picked up by

ADP, which is converted to the more energy-rich ATP; and the net result of the whole process is that more energy is made available to the cell than was necessary to initiate any of the steps. The ADP–ATP mechanism is the most important mechanism in the cell for making energy available for various metabolic reactions — and energy is continually restored to this system by the process of respiration.

From the above account we can see that the equation for respiration describes the process in a general way, but it does not take into account the number of steps nor the fundamental complexity of the process.

GROWTH

Growth in plants is limited to certain regions of active metabolism — i.e., meristem tissues in the growing tips of root, stem, and bud, and in cambium. These tissues have access to water and nutrients from the xylem vessels and to manufactured food from the phloem vessels. Growth involves the multiplication of these meristem cells and their elongation. As the cells thus formed mature, they cease to have such active functions and no longer divide. Growth does not occur, therefore, in the older tissues.

Review Questions

1. What is a tropism? Name and define five tropisms of plants.
2. What are turgor movements?
3. Explain the water relations of a higher plant.
4. What are plant nutrients?
5. Discuss the nature of photosynthesis in green plants and explain the significance of the process for life in general.
6. Describe the process of cellular respiration.
7. Describe growth in plants and compare it with that in higher animals.

Chapter VIII

REPRODUCTION AND DEVELOPMENT IN MULTICELLULAR PLANTS

Reproduction in higher plants may take place either by *asexual* or *sexual* methods. In asexual reproduction, the progeny develops from a single parent. Only ordinary cell division (mitosis) occurs in the production of offspring. In sexual reproduction, two parents are involved, specialized cells from the two parents uniting to form a single cell, the *fertilized egg*. In this case a special form of cell division occurs, prior to fertilization, by which the chromosome number characteristic of the species (the *diploid number*) is reduced to half (the *haploid number*). This process of reduction, which requires two successive cell divisions, is called *meiosis*. The diploid chromosome number is restored at fertilization by the union of two haploid cells. Thus the major distinctions between asexual and sexual reproduction are: (a) the former is uniparental, the latter biparental; and (b) the former involves only mitosis, the latter meiosis and fertilization.

ASEXUAL REPRODUCTION

Reproduction of a unicellular organism by fission — ordinary cell division — is asexual reproduction. In multicellular organisms, the process may be almost as simple, but, in some cases, complex structures are involved. The following are forms of asexual reproduction in multicellular plants.

Multiple Division. Certain algae of definite cell number reproduce by a process of sudden cell division, each cell rapidly dividing until it forms as many cells as the original total. In this way an organism becomes as many separate organisms as it originally contained cells.

Reproduction from Specialized Structures.

ASEXUAL SPORES. Single cells called spores may be produced in specialized structures, sporangia. If these spores are formed by mitosis and germinate into a new plant by mitosis, they are asexual spores. (It is necessary to distinguish between asexual spores and spores formed by meiosis. See paragraph headed Alternation of Generations.)

GEMMAE. Among the bryophytes occur special structures, the *gemmae*, which, after detachment from the parent thallus, are capable of growing into new thalli.

Reproduction from Unspecialized Structures. Artificial propagation of desirable horticultural varieties of plants is often carried out by root, stem, or leaf cuttings — more commonly stem cuttings. This technique is commonly referred to as vegetative propagation. Strictly speaking, any form of asexual reproduction is vegetative reproduction.

ROOTS. The roots of some plants (e.g., wild plum, lilac) are capable of developing adventitious shoots from which new plants develop. Root cuttings are, in some species, more successful for artificial propagation than are stem cuttings.

STEMS. Artificial propagation by stem cuttings is familiar to all gardeners. Natural propagation of many species occurs — underground stems (*rhizomes*), surface runners (*stolons*), *bulbs*, and *tubers* being involved. Among plants commonly propagated by stem structures are iris (by rhizomes), strawberries (by stolons), tulips (by bulbs), and Irish potatoes (by tubers). Drooping branches covered by soil develop, in some species, new plants by the process of "layering." A new root system and vertical stem are developed from a node in these horizontal stems.

LEAVES. The ability of leaves to develop into complete plants is limited to a few species but does occur. African violets can be propagated artificially by this method.

SEXUAL REPRODUCTION

Sexual reproduction is associated with the formation of specialized, haploid, reproductive cells and their subsequent fusion to form a fertilized egg. The mature reproductive cells that fuse are called *gametes*. If they are alike in appearance, that condition is known as *isogamy*. Most plants are *heterogamous*, however, which means that the gametes are unlike in appearance. In such cases, the more active male gamete is called a *sperm cell;* the less active female gamete, an *egg cell* or *ovum*. The process of fusion

(A)   *(B)*   *(C)*   *(D)*

Fig. 29. A generalized diagram of meiosis. (A) The cell shown has four chromo-somes in the diploid complement, a pair of long ones and a pair of short ones. Each chromosome, prior to synapsis, consists of two chromatids. (The chromatids are marked differently to simplify following them in the succeeding steps.) (B) Synapsis. Homologous chromosomes fuse, each synaptic pair thus consisting of four chromatids (a tetrad of chromatids). In the division succeeding synapsis, each of the two daughter cells receives half of the chromatids from each pair, and when each of these cells divides (C), these two chromatids are also separated. Thus, each of the four daughter cells (D) has one chromatid from each tetrad in B. The net result is that the chromosome number is reduced from the diploid (four, in this case) to the haploid (two, in this case) condition; but in the process each kind of chromosome is retained in each daughter cell. The two homologous chromosomes are separated from each other at the first division.

is *fertilization,* and the cell formed as a product of fertilization is the fertilized egg or *zygote.* In plants exclusive of algae and fungi, the zygote develops, by repeated divisions, with differentiation, into an *embryo.* For this reason, the bryophytes and higher plants are sometimes collectively called the Embryophyta.

Gamete Formation. The haploid chromosome condition of gametes is acquired by a process of chromosome reduction called *meiosis* (Fig. 29). Although meiosis may be followed in plants by many ordinary mitotic divisions before the gametes are actually formed, it is as important in sexual reproduction as is the process of fertilization. For that reason one must understand meiosis to understand sexual reproduction. Meiosis begins with the fusion (*synapsis*) of *homologous chromosomes* (the diploid chromosome number being made up of pairs of homologous chromosomes). Because each chromosome consists of two chromatids, each fused chromosome pair contains four chromatids. In two, rapid, successive divisions these chromatids are separated into four cells. The net result of the two successive divisions that constitute meiosis is that only one of each pair of the original chromosomes is represented in each of the four daughter cells. Hence the haploid number is acquired without losing any particular kind of chromosome. (In mitosis, in contrast, each chromosome of each pair is represented by a chromatid in each daughter cell.)

In most plants, each daughter cell formed in meiosis divides by mitosis for several cell generations before forming the specialized gametes, and the haploid number of chromosomes is therefore already present when gamete differentiation takes place. In this respect, the cellular changes during sexual reproduction in most plants differ greatly from those that are characteristic of animals (Chap. XI).

Fertilization. The fusion of two gametes to form a zygote is fertilization. The diploid number of chromosomes is restored in this process. In higher plants, more than the fusion of two gamete nuclei is involved. Other nuclei may fuse to form cells involved in the nutrition of the embryo, the endosperm. Fertilization, with its related processes, is much more complicated in the higher plants than in any animals.

Seed Development. Two structures are involved in seed formation. One is the *embryo proper*, from the zygote; the other is the *endosperm*, which furnishes food for the growing embryo. In angiosperms they develop simultaneously, after fertilization; in gymnosperms the endosperm is formed before fertilization. The mature seed contains a relatively large embryo, somewhat differentiated into organs; it may or may not contain endosperm. If endosperm is absent, the embryo has consumed it in the process of development.

Germination. The seed remains for a shorter or longer time in a *dormant* condition, following which, under proper environmental conditions, it develops into a young plant or *seedling*. The process of rupturing the seed coat and beginning growth is *germination*.

ALTERNATION OF GENERATIONS

In the majority of plants the sequence of events in sexual reproduction is complicated by the occurrence of two different types of plants in the life cycle. (Fig. 30.) One type, the *gametophyte*, produces gametes. The gametes are haploid (n) in chromosome composition, but they are not produced in the gametophyte by meiosis. All of the cells of the gametophyte are haploid, and the gametes are therefore produced by ordinary mitosis. After the gametes of opposite sex unite, in the process of fertilization, they develop into a plant called a *sporophyte*. The cells of the sporophyte have the diploid (2n) chromosome number. This plant produces *spores*, but these are formed by meiosis and are, therefore, haploid. These spores, which we may call *meiotic spores*,

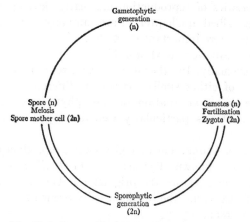

Fig. 30. A diagram illustrating the essential features in alternation of generations in plants. The haploid generation, the gametophytic, produces haploid gametes by mitosis. The gametes unite, by fertilization, to form the diploid zygote — from which the sporophytic generation develops. Haploid spores are produced by meiotic division of spore mother cells of the sporophyte, and a meiotic spore germinates into a gametophyte. (In this diagram, a single line indicates a single chromosome complement — the haploid condition; a double line indicates the diploid chromosome complement.)

germinate individually into gametophytes, and all of the cells of the gametophyte are, as previously stated, haploid. Thus the sexual cycle consists of an alternation between a diploid sporophyte that produces spores by meiosis and a haploid gametophyte that produces gametes by mitosis. The cycle appears to be a complex sexual cycle, but, because the spores develop individually, the sporophyte is sometimes called the asexual generation and the gametophyte the sexual generation. Such terminology will not be used in this book, however; the sporophyte and gametophyte will be considered two different phases in the complicated cycle of sexual reproduction. The expression asexual reproduction will be limited to reproduction not involving the sequence of meiosis and fertilization.

REPRODUCTION IN SPECIAL EXAMPLES

Characteristics of reproduction and early development of the examples described in Chapter VI are summarized here, in greater detail for the more important examples.

Reproduction in the Algae. The most primitive algae reproduce only asexually. In other forms sexual reproduction occurs — the gametes of either similar or widely different form. In some algae there is an alternation of sporophyte and gametophyte generations. This is particularly well developed among the red algae.

BLUE-GREEN ALGAE. The blue-green algae reproduce only asexually, so far as is known. The filaments of *Oscillatoria* and *Nostoc* break apart, then restore the original number of cells by simple cell division. In *Nostoc* the breaks usually occur at heterocysts.

GREEN ALGAE.

Ulothrix. The cells in a filament are all haploid. They are potentially either sporangia, producing *zoospores* (each with four flagella), or *gametangia*, producing gametes (each with two flagella). Both zoospores and gametes are, of course, haploid. Although the gametes appear to be alike they will not fuse unless derived from different filaments. The zygote divides by meiosis, forming zoospores, so there is no diploid stage except the zygote. Zoospores germinate into new filaments.

Ulva. In *Ulva* there is alternation of generations between a diploid sporophyte and a haploid gametophyte, both plants identical in appearance. The sporophyte produces zoospores with four flagella each. The zoospores are formed by meiosis and are, therefore, haploid. Each zoospore germinates into a gametophyte, in which the cells are all haploid. Gametes of opposite sex may be identical or may differ in size, depending upon the species of *Ulva*, but the two gametes taking part in fertilization must come from different thalli. *Ulva* is *heterothallic*, in other words.

Oedogonium. The life cycle is similar to that in *Ulothrix* but somewhat more advanced. *Oedogonium* is heterogamous. The egg cell is fertilized in the cell (*oögonium*) in which it formed — by a male gamete from another specialized cell (*antheridium*). The zygote develops a thick wall. It germinates later, forming, by meiosis, four zoospores — each germinating into a filament. Zoospores are also formed from cells of a filament.

Spirogyra. *Spirogyra* filaments reproduce asexually. In addi- tion, a form of sexual reproduction occurs. The contents of two similar cells of adjacent filaments may fuse in a fertilization process. (Fig. 31.) The fusion cell, a zygote, which is more or less resistant to drying, may develop later into a new filament. The

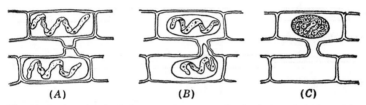

(A)   (B)   (C)

Fig. 31. Conjugation in *Spirogyra*. Three stages in the fusion of gametes. The gametes are the cell contents of cells of adjacent filaments. The zygote is shown in the upper cell at *C*.

cells of the filaments contain the haploid number of chromo- somes; the zygote contains the diploid number. Its first divisions are meiotic.

BROWN ALGAE. The thallus of the rockweed (*Fucus*) is diploid. It does not form asexual spores. Sperm and egg cells develop in specialized cavities (*conceptacles*) at tips of certain branches of the thallus; both escape into the water. Each sperm cell has two flagella. The fertilized egg divides into two cells: the holdfast and the thallus. The thallus of the kelp (*Laminaria*) develops from a zygote and is diploid. It produces spores in sporangia, grouped in sori. The spores develop into small filamentous gametophytes that are dioecious. Fertilization occurs in the water.

Reproduction in the Fungi.

BLACK BREAD MOLD. Bread mold mycelia are of two different sexual types, but the two types may develop from two spores found in the same sporangium. When the hyphae of mycelia of different sex come into contact they form zygotes. (**Fig. 14.**) Each zygote may contain many fusion nuclei rather than just one. From the zygote grows out a short hypha which forms a sporangium at its apex. The spores from the sporangium germinate into the two different sexual types of mycelia, in about equal numbers.

RED BREAD MOLD. Asexual reproduction occurs in *Neurospora* by the germination of asexual spores formed at the tips of hyphae, which are haploid. Sexual reproduction occurs when the tips of adjacent hyphae unite to form a zygote. The zygote divides by meiosis, and, with one additional mitotic division, forms eight haploid *ascospores* in an elongated sac, the *ascus*. Each ascospore can germinate into a new mycelium.

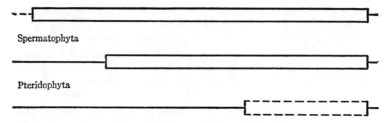

Spermatophyta

Pteridophyta

Bryophyta

Fig. 32. Diagrams illustrating the evolution of the relations between gametophyte and sporophyte generations in plants. Single lines represent the haploid (gametophyte) generation, double lines represent the diploid (sporophyte) generation. The lengths of the lines correspond roughly to the relative prominence of the two stages in the life cycle. Generations represented by unbroken lines are independent; those represented by broken lines are parasitic on the other stage in the life cycle.

MUSHROOMS. The basidia, from which the spores develop, are cells containing fusion nuclei and, therefore, the diploid number of chromosomes. Each basidium nucleus divides by meiosis; and the four nuclei go into four spores (basidiospores), each with the haploid chromosome number. The mycelium and sporophore, coming from the spore, contain the haploid number of chromosomes.

Reproduction in Mosses and Liverworts. The gametophyte generation is dominant and vegetatively independent. The sporophyte is parasitic on the gametophyte. (Figs. 16 and 32.)

Moss.

Sporophyte. All cells of the sporophyte contain the diploid chromosome number because it develops from a fertilized egg. It is parasitic on the gametophyte, remaining attached by its foot to the tip of the gametophyte stem. Spores develop in the capsule, from *spore mother cells*, each of which forms four spores by meiosis. Therefore, the spores are haploid. Each spore germinates to form a filamentous network, the *protonema*. (At intervals in the protonema develop *gemmae*, or buds, each of which is capable of giving rise to a gametophyte plant. When separated from each other, these plants are capable of independent survival.)

Gametophyte. All cells of the gametophyte contain the haploid chromosome number because it develops from a haploid spore by mitosis. The gamete-producing organs, *antheridia* and *archegonia*, occur at the apex of the same or different stems. The former are elongated, saclike organs in which are produced hundreds of two-flagellate sperm cells. The archegonia are bottle-shaped, each producing an egg cell in the expanded base, the *venter*. In rain or dew, the sperm cells swim to the archegonium, down the neck, and fertilize the egg cell. The sporophyte then grows from the zygote, which remains in the venter.

LIVERWORTS. Reproduction in liverworts does not differ in principle from that in the moss. The gametophyte is broad and thalluslike, not erect; the antheridia and archegonia are borne on discs elevated above the thallus by stalks. The sporophytes may or may not be stalked. Their capsules usually open by longitudinal slits.

Reproduction in Pteridophytes. The sporophyte generation is dominant and vegetatively independent. The gametophyte, though small, is independent of the sporophyte. It may or may not develop chlorophyll. Pteridophytes illustrate an intermediate stage in the evolution of sporophyte-gametophyte relations. (Figs. 18 and 32.)

FERN.

Sporophyte. The prominent, leafy fern plant is the sporophyte. Its cells are diploid. Spores are produced in sporangia in the *sori* from spore mother cells, each of which gives rise to four haploid spores. Upon germination, each spore forms a *prothallus*. Several independent sporophytes may develop from the nodes of a single rhizome. In some ferns, roots may develop from the tips of fronds in contact with the soil, and from them, other fronds.

Gametophyte. The cells of the prothallus, a small heart-shaped plant, contain the haploid chromosome number. The gametes are formed in antheridia and archegonia, both present on the underside of the same prothallus. The sperm cells are spirally twisted and flagellate. The egg cell is fertilized in the archegonium. From the zygote grows out the leafy sporophyte.

HORSETAILS OR SCOURING RUSHES. The prothallus is branched, rather than heart-shaped as in ferns. Spores are borne in *strobili*. Otherwise, reproduction is essentially as in ferns.

CLUB MOSSES. In some (not all) club mosses the spores are of two sizes, *microspores* and *megaspores*. The former develop in *microsporangia*, the latter in *megasporangia* — both types of sporangia in the same strobilus. Microspores are formed in the same manner as spores of ferns; but, in the megasporangium, only one spore mother cell forms megaspores, the four megaspores formed growing to a large size by ingesting the nonfunctional spore mother cells. Microspores produce male gametophytes which form sperm cells; megaspores produce female gametophytes which produce eggs. The gametophyte is very small. Club mosses bridge the evolutionary gap between ferns and seed plants.

Reproduction in Spermatophytes. The sporophyte is dominant and independent. The gametophyte is extremely small and is parasitic on the sporophyte. (Fig. 32.)

GYMNOSPERMAE: EXAMPLE, PINE. The specialized reproductive structures are cones (strobili). Seeds are formed, and these are borne naked on cone scales.

Sporophyte. Staminate and ovulate cones (Fig. 20) are borne on the same plant. Staminate cones consist of scales called *microsporophylls*, each bearing two *microsporangia* or *pollen sacs*. The pollen sacs contain *microspore mother cells (pollen mother cells)*. Each pollen mother cell divides by meiosis, forming four *pollen grains* or microspores. Each of these is, essentially, a male gametophyte. Ovulate cones, which are much larger than staminate ones, consist of scales called *megasporophylls*, each bearing two *ovules*. Each ovule contains one *megaspore mother cell*, surrounded by many spongy cells (the *nucellus*) and a coat (the *integument*). Through the latter extends an opening, the *micropyle*. The megaspore mother cell divides by meiosis to form a row of four cells, the basal one becoming the female gametophyte.

Gametophyte. Pollen grains (male gametophytes), after reaching the ovulate cones, are carried down the micropyle into a cavity, where they germinate. In germination, each pollen grain forms a *pollen tube* containing two sperm nuclei. The pollen tube grows down to the archegonium. The female gametophyte grows at the expense of surrounding tissue. Within it develop several archegonia, each containing an egg nucleus.

Fertilization is accomplished by the fusion of one pollen-tube sperm nucleus with an egg nucleus. Several eggs in one gametophyte may be fertilized, but only one completes development. The nucleus of the zygote divides to form four nuclei. From each of these begins the development of an embryo. Usually only one embryo completes its development in each ovule, and, therefore, only one embryo occurs in each seed. The embryo consists of a *hypocotyl* (from the lower end of which the root develops) and numerous *cotyledons*. It is surrounded by nutritive material and a hard seed coat and is attached to a "wing." In germination the seed coat is ruptured first by the developing root.

ANGIOSPERMAE. To illustrate reproduction in the angiosperms, only one account is given in detail — that a general one for the dicotyledons. Important differences between these and the monocotyledons are indicated. In both cases, the reproductive bodies are not cones, but flowers in the ordinary sense. (Figs. 26 and 33.)

Sporophyte. The sporophytes bear micro- and megasporophylls in their flowers, the former being the anthers, the latter, the carpels. Both may occur in the same flower, in different flowers on the same plant (monoecious), or in flowers on different plants (dioecious). Anthers contain cavities, the pollen sacs, in which pollen grains are formed. Pollen grains are haploid cells, each being one of four produced, by meiosis, from a pollen mother cell. As in gymnosperms, the cells produced by the pollen grain constitute, fundamentally, a male gametophyte. The carpels enclose cavities, the "cells," formed by the folding together of the megasporophylls or carpels. The seeds, therefore, are not borne naked on the megasporophylls as in gymnosperms, but are enclosed by them. The ovule grows from a point of attachment on the carpel which becomes the *placenta*. The ovule consists of spore mother cell, nucellus, and integument with micropyle, as in gymnosperms. The spore mother cell divides meiotically, forming a row of four megaspores, the basal one of which persists, becoming the female gametophyte.

Gametophyte. (Fig. 33.) The pollen grains are carried to the stigma of the pistil by gravity, insects, wind, or other agency. There they germinate, each pollen grain forming a pollen tube containing two sperm nuclei and a tube nucleus. The tube grows down through the style to and through the micropyle, carrying the sperm nuclei.

Meanwhile, the female gametophyte or *embryo sac* has been formed. As the basal megaspore enlarges, consuming the three nonfunctional megaspores and surrounding cells of the nucellus, its nucleus divides, one daughter nucleus moving into each end of the cell. Each nucleus then divides twice, four nuclei being formed in each end. One nucleus from each end moves to the

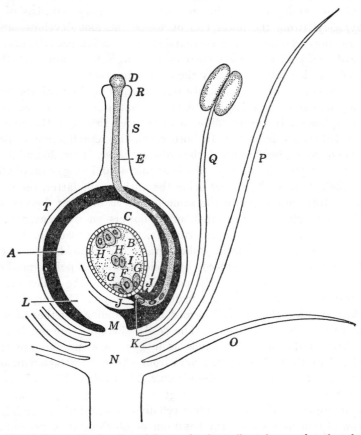

Fig. 33. Longitudinal section of flower, showing pollen-tube growth and ovule structure. *A*, Ovule. *B*, Embryo sac (megagametophyte). *C*, Nucellus. *D*, Pollen grain. *E*, Pollen tube. *F*, Egg nucleus. *G*, Synergids. *H*, Antipodals. *I*, Polar nuclei. *J*, Integuments. *K*, Pollen tube entering micropyle, with one tube and two sperm nuclei. *L*, Funiculus. *M*, Placenta. *N*, Receptacle. *O*, Sepal. *P*, Petal. *Q*, Stamen. *R*, Stigma. *S*, Style. *T*, Ovary. (Reprinted by permission from *General Botany* by Harry J. Fuller, copyright, 1950, by Barnes & Noble, Inc.)

center, these two constituting the *polar nuclei*. One nucleus near the micropyle becomes the nucleus of the *egg cell*, while the other two become the nuclei of the *synergids*. The three nuclei at the other end form the *antipodal cells*. This seven-celled structure is the *embryo sac*, the mature female gametophyte.

Fertilization. One of the sperm nuclei unites with the egg nucleus, forming the zygote, which develops into the embryo. In most cases, the other unites with the two polar nuclei to form a triploid endosperm nucleus. This is called double fertilization. The tube nucleus disintegrates.

Seed Formation. The endosperm is unicellular until after fertilization; and, unlike the condition in the gymnosperms, its growth occurs after fertilization. The embryo and endosperm develop at the same time; the former using part or all of the latter for food. The embryo of dicotyledons contains two cotyledons and the hypocotyl; that of monocotyledons, one cotyledon and the hypocotyl. (Fig. 21.) The seed is enclosed in the fruit, formed from the ovary wall. Endosperm may (castor bean, corn) or may not (bean, radish) be present in the mature seed.

Germination. Under proper conditions of temperature and moisture, and after a period of dormancy, the embryo swells, bursts the seed coat, and develops into the mature sporophyte.

Review Questions

1. Describe the different types of asexual reproduction in plants, giving examples.
2. What are the aspects of sexual reproduction common to all higher plants?
3. Discuss the evolution of sporophyte-gametophyte relations in plants.
4. Describe sexual reproduction in algae, fungi, mosses, ferns.
5. Compare in detail the sporophyte stage in gymnosperms and angiosperms.
6. Compare gymnosperms and angiosperms with reference to the gametophytes; describe fertilization in these two groups.

Chapter IX

THE MORPHOLOGY OF MULTICELLULAR ANIMALS

The most primitive group of animals, the phylum Protozoa, has been treated in Chapter IV. All other phyla are Metazoa — the term being inclusive of multicellular animals. The following phyla of Metazoa are of major importance, representatives being described in this chapter in some detail: Porifera, Coelenterata, Platyhelminthes, Nematoda, Echinodermata, Mollusca, Annelida, Arthropoda, Chordata. In addition, these phyla of minor importance are mentioned: Ctenophora, Nemertea, Rotatoria, Nematomorpha, Bryozoa, Brachiopoda, Onychophora. This list appears long, but several rather obscure and relatively unimportant phyla are not even mentioned, some authorities recognizing over thirty phyla in the Animal Kingdom.

THE PRINCIPAL CRITERIA FOR CLASSIFICATION INTO PHYLA

The phyla are distinguished from each other, not on the basis of a single set of characteristics, but by combinations of characteristics. These provide criteria for classification, and at the same time they are criteria of increasing complexity in an evolutionary series.

Number of Cells. The simplest phylum, the Protozoa, is distinguished from all others by the fact that each organism in it consists of a single cell. In general, too, members of the simplest phyla of Metazoa have fewer cells than do animals in more advanced phyla.

Tissue Differentiation. In metazoan phyla, the degree of differentiation of cells into tissue types varies. Porifera (sponges) have little tissue differentiation, but Coelenterata (jellyfishes and their relatives), though still primitive, show more tissue differentiation; and more advanced phyla have still more complex tissue variation.

Organ Differentiation. Distinct organs are poorly developed in primitive metazoan phyla, but they are progressively more complex in more advanced phyla. They differ in kind as well as complexity, too, thus providing positive distinctions between phyla.

Digestive System. Intracellular digestion occurs in sponges, but in other primitive Metazoa there is a *gastrovascular cavity* — with a single opening serving as both mouth and anus. A complete digestive tract with separate mouth and anus is a more advanced type.

Number of Germ Layers. Metazoa develop typically from either two or three germ layers (embryonic cell layers). Those of the former type are *diploblastic*, those of the latter type, *triploblastic*. The three embryonic cell layers are, in order from outside in, the *ectoderm, mesoderm,* and *endoderm.* The mesoderm is absent as a definite layer in diploblastic animals.

Coelom or Body Cavity. In the more advanced triploblastic animals a cavity develops within the mesoderm, lined with mesoderm. This is the true *body cavity* or *coelom.* A false body cavity or *pseudocoel* characterizes certain primitive phyla of triploblastic animals. The most primitive triploblastic animals, as well as diploblastic types, lack any kind of body cavity.

Metamerism. Several phyla are distinguished by more or less complete segmentation of the body. This condition is known as *metamerism,* each segment being a *metamere.* The metameres show various degress of independence from each other, but are subordinate for the most part to the whole organism.

Differentiation of Organ Systems. The presence, nature, and degree of development of particular organ systems vary from one phylum to another. Greater complexity is, in general, interpreted as meaning a more advanced or less primitive organism.

DESCRIPTIVE TERMINOLOGY

Kinds of Symmetry. Animals may show no plane of symmetry, being asymmetrical (e.g., *Paramecium*), or they may possess spherical, radial, or bilateral symmetry to a greater or lesser degree.

SPHERICAL SYMMETRY. (The symmetry of a ball.) Any section through the center divides the organism into symmetrical halves. Examples: certain marine protozoa of the class Sarcodina.

RADIAL SYMMETRY. (The symmetry of a wheel.) Any vertical section through the center divides the organism into symmetrical halves. Examples: jellyfish, sand dollar.

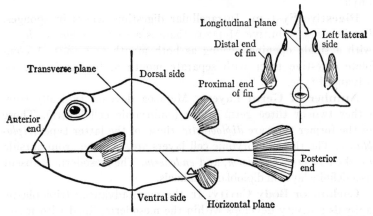

Fig. 34. Diagram illustrating descriptive terminology. An explanation of the names of *sections* occurs in the accompanying text. (The fish is a trunkfish, after Evermann and Marsh.)

BILATERAL SYMMETRY. (The symmetry of a plank.) Only one section, a vertical one in the longitudinal axis, divides the organism into symmetrical halves. Examples: earthworm, man.

Planes and Sections of the Animal Body. In a bilaterally symmetrical animal, a cut which follows any vertical plane parallel with the longitudinal axis is a *longitudinal section.* If exactly in the mid-longitudinal axis, it is a *sagittal section.* Sections in the vertical plane at right angles to the long axis are *transverse* or *cross sections.* Sections in the horizontal plane are *horizontal* or *frontal sections.* (Fig. 34.)

Names of Directions. The forward end is *anterior,* the opposite end, *posterior.* The back is *dorsal,* the lower surface, *ventral.* The sides are *lateral.* The point of attachment of a structure is its *proximal* end, the free end is *distal.* (Fig. 34.) All these terms are adjectives.

MORPHOLOGY OF THE PHYLUM PORIFERA

General Characteristics. The Porifera are the sponges; they are mostly marine, but some occur in fresh water. They are sessile (attached) organisms. A sponge contains a central cavity (the so-called *gastral cavity*) surrounded by a body wall penetrated by a series of canals of varying degrees of complexity. The internal cavity opens to the outside by the *osculum*, an opening at the distal end. A skeleton of *spicules* (of lime, glass, or

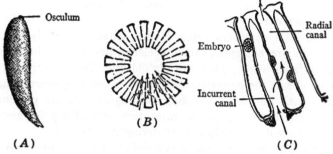

Fig. 35. A simple sponge (*Grantia*). (A) External appearance. (B) Diagram of a cross section. (C) Portion of body wall in cross section, enlarged. Arrows indicate the direction of water movement through the canals; water leaves the sponge through the osculum.

spongin) supports the organism. A single "sponge" may be a colony of individuals all of which have budded from one parent. The two germ layers are not truly comparable with ectoderm and endoderm of other Metazoa. Reproduction takes place sexually and by budding.

Example — Grantia.

GENERAL CHARACTERISTICS. *Grantia* is a simple, cylindrical sponge, about an inch long, common along the Atlantic Coast. It has no specialized organ systems, except perhaps the unique canal system characteristic of sponges. (Fig. 35*A*.)

CANAL SYSTEM. This is the *sycon* type — i.e., *incurrent* and *radial canals* parallel each other and are connected by pores, the *prosopyles*. Incurrent canals have smooth lining cells; radial canals are lined with flagellated *collar cells*, which ingest food. Water passes through incurrent canals, prosopyles, radial canals, internal cavity ("cloaca" or "gastral cavity"), and out through the osculum. (Fig. 35B, C.)

SKELETON. Calcareous spicules of mono- and triaxial forms are present.

MORPHOLOGY OF THE PHYLA COELENTERATA AND CTENOPHORA

Combined in one phylum by some authors, these are here separated but treated under a common heading.

Coelenterata.

GENERAL CHARACTERISTICS. Hydra, jellyfishes, corals, and sea anemones are examples. Most coelenterates are marine; a few inhabit fresh water. They are diploblastic. The digestive cavity is a blind sac, the *gastrovascular cavity*, its opening functioning as both mouth and anus. *Nettling* or *stinging cells* are present in the *epidermis*. Among coelenterates, two forms, the *polyp* and the *medusa*, may develop alternately during the life cycle.

Polyp. The general form is cylindrical, one end (proximal) attached, the distal end containing a mouth surrounded by *tentacles*. Polyps may occur in colonies, as, for example, in coral reefs. The *gonads* (gamete-producing organs) may be external or internal.

Medusa. The general form of a medusa is umbrella- or bell-shaped. The mouth is in the *manubrium*, which corresponds to the handle of the "umbrella." The digestive cavity has four main branches in the umbrella portion; these are the *radial canals*. They open into the *circular canal* around the rim. Tentacles hang from the margin of the umbrella surface. The gonads are suspended under the radial canals — opening internally in some medusae, externally in others.

EXAMPLE — HYDRA. (Fig. 36.) Hydra is a fresh-water coelenterate with the form of a polyp at all times. It is highly contractile and contains cells modified for conducting nerve impulses as well as for contraction. The gonads occur as swellings on the surface. Reproduction takes place sexually and by budding.

EXAMPLE — OBELIA. (Fig. 37.) This is a marine animal whose small individuals occur together as a colony of polyps. The colony develops asexually from a zygote, and the polyps in the colony are of two kinds — *vegetative* (feeding) and *reproductive*. Each polyp is surrounded by a transparent covering, the *hydrotheca* about the

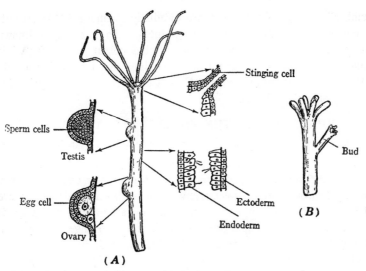

Fig. 36. *Hydra.* (A) Expanded individual, bearing gonads. Internal structures are shown in longitudinal section, enlarged, projected from four
regions (indicated by arrows). (B) A partially contracted individual, bearing a bud.

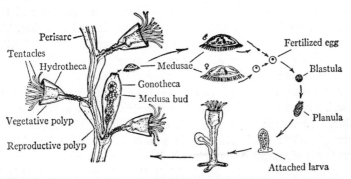

Fig. 37. *Obelia,* one of the colonial Hydrozoa. At the left, a portion of a
colony, which reproduces asexually, by budding; at the right, diagram-
matically shown, the sexual portion of the life cycle.

vegetative polyps, the *gonotheca* about reproductive ones. All
polyps are connected with each other by a hollow stem and
branches. Reproductive polyps produce, by budding, medusae —
which swim away when mature. They are sexually reproductive.

Ctenophora. All are marine. They are jellylike but not

umbrella-shaped. Ctenophora are biradially symmetrical or walnut-shaped — hence are called "sea walnuts." They are also known as "comb jellies," from the characteristic eight rows of paddle plates, the plates of each row resembling the teeth of a comb. Mesoderm cells are present, the Ctenophora being the most primitive of triploblastic animals.

MORPHOLOGY OF THE PHYLUM PLATYHELMINTHES

General Characteristics. This phylum comprises the flat-worms — elongated, bilaterally symmetrical animals, flattened in the horizontal plane. Examples are *Dugesia,* flukes, tapeworms. Most flatworms are parasitic and some are pathogenic. They are triploblastic, but without a coelom. A gastrovascular cavity is present, except in tapeworms — which have no digestive system. Several organ systems are definitely differentiated.

Examples.

DUGESIA (Fig. 38A.) *Dugesia* is a small, fresh-water, free-living flatworm. Its body surface is ciliated. Eyespots are present near the anterior end. From the mouth, on the ventral side near the center, a protrusible pharynx (*proboscis*) leads into the digestive cavity, an intestine of three main branches, one anterior and two posterior. Each main branch has many small lateral branches. The excretory system consists of two longitudinal excretory tubes leading from *flame cells,* and an anterior cross connection, the whole system opening to the outside through two dorsal *excretory pores.* There is a nervous system of two main longitudinal trunks, with an anterior cross connection, and two anterior *ganglia* under the eyespots. The reproductive system is quite complex, the animal being hermaphroditic (male and female gonads in the same individual). *Dugesia* is often called *Planaria.*

LIVER FLUKES. (Fig. 38B.) Adult liver flukes are parasitic in the bile ducts of vertebrates. For attachment they have anterior and posterior suckers. There is a mouth at the anterior end, opening into the gastrovascular cavity. Flukes are hermaphroditic, and they have complex life cycles. (See Chap. XI, under Metagenesis.)

TAPEWORMS. (Fig. 38C.) Adult tapeworms are parasites of the alimentary canal of vertebrates. Each consists of a *scolex* (head) — with hooks for attachment, followed by a chain of several to many hundreds of *proglottids* formed by budding. Each proglottid is an hermaphroditic individual. Excretory and nervous system are reduced, and there is no digestive system.

MORPHOLOGY OF THE PHYLUM NEMATODA

The Nematoda are the round- or threadworms. They have an elongated, cylindrical body, usually pointed at both ends, and with no segmentation. Some are important parasites — e.g., human hookworm and *Trichinella* (Fig. 38*D*) — but many are free-living. They are triploblastic, and they have a pseudocoel —

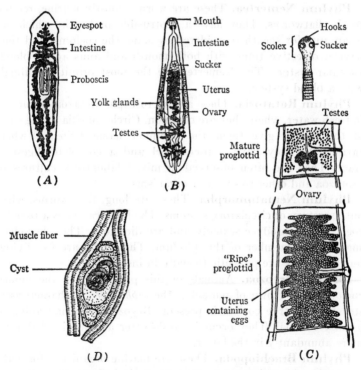

Fig. 38. Representatives of the Phyla Platyhelminthes (A–C) and Nematoda (D). (A) *Dugesia*—digestive system in black. (B) *Clonorchis,* a liver fluke which parasitizes man in the Orient. (C) *Taenia,* a tapeworm which parasitizes man; the three drawings are all of the same scale of magnification. (D) *Trichinella,* encysted in muscle, cause of a serious disease in man and other animals.

a body cavity that is not a true coelom, being lined with meso-derm only on the side next the body wall. The digestive tract is complete, both mouth and anus being present. They have both an excretory and a nervous system. Reproduction takes place sexually, and nematodes are dioecious, i.e., the sexes are separate.

MORPHOLOGY OF CERTAIN MINOR PHYLA

The relationships of the following phyla to each other and in an evolutionary sequence are not clear. All are triploblastic, but all are somewhat primitive in structure.

Phylum Nemertea. These are worms, mostly marine, related to the flatworms. They have a protrusible proboscis, which lies in an anterior sheath (considered by some the coelom); and they have a digestive tract with both mouth and anus and a blood-vascular system. The Nemertea are the most primitive animals with a blood system.

Phylum Rotatoria. These are microscopic Metazoa, occurring in fresh water, where they are common. Circles of cilia at the sides of the mouth give them the common name *rotifers* ("wheel carriers"). They have a pseudocoel and a complete digestive tract. They are often observed in mixed laboratory cultures of protozoa and other fresh-water organisms.

Phylum Nematomorpha. These are long, thin worms, without excretory or circulatory systems. The body cavity is a pseudo-coel. They reproduce sexually and are dioecious. The "horsehair snake" is a member of this phylum. The adults are free-living, but the larvae are parasitic (usually in insects).

Phylum Bryozoa. Animals of this phylum have the mouth enclosed in a crown of tentacles, the *lophophore*, a characteristic structure. A true coelom is present. Bryozoa are small animals, usually colonial. They occur in fresh-water and marine habitats, more abundantly in the latter.

Phylum Brachiopoda. These are marine organisms, formerly more abundant than in present geological time. They live in bivalve shells, the shells occupying dorsal and ventral surfaces rather than lateral surfaces as in clams and mussels (phylum Mollusca). They possess a lophophore in common with bryozoa and have a true coelom.

MORPHOLOGY OF THE PHYLUM ECHINODERMATA

Echinoderms are radially symmetrical marine organisms, possessing in most cases a spiny skin. Common examples are: starfish, brittle star, sea urchin, sand dollar, sea cucumber, crinoid. They are triploblastic, possess a coelom, and usually have an anus. A *water-vascular system* constitutes a hydrostatic pressure system regulating movements of the *tube feet*, locomotor organs characteristic of this phylum. The radial symmetry (usually on a plan of

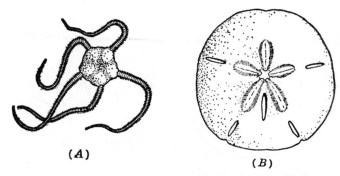

(A)

(B)

Fig. 39. Representatives of the Phylum Echinodermata. (A) Serpent star. (B) Keyhole sand dollar.

five antimeres) was probably derived from bilateral symmetry in the ancestral form. Some indications from developmental stages suggest that echinoderms and vertebrates had a common ancestry not very remote. (Fig. 39.)

MORPHOLOGY OF THE PHYLUM MOLLUSCA

General Characteristics. These are soft-bodied animals, usually protected by a calcareous shell of their own manufacture. They are marine, fresh-water, and terrestrial. Common examples are: mussel, clam, snail, slug, nautilus, squid, octopus. Mollusks are triploblastic, nonmetameric, possess a coelom, have a complete digestive system, and have complex nervous, respiratory, circulatory, and reproductive systems. They are the most highly developed of nonmetameric animals; they are more advanced in some characteristics than any group except the vertebrates. (Fig. 40.)

Example — Fresh-water Mussel.

EXTERNAL FEATURES AND GENERAL INTERNAL FORM. The mussel is enclosed in a *shell* consisting of two *valves*, on right and left sides, hinged at the dorsal side. Concentric lines of growth occur on each shell, centering at the *umbo*, the oldest part of the shell. Muscles, attached to the internal faces of the shells, close them and keep them together. The shells are lined with a delicate

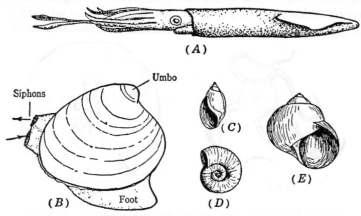

Fig. 40. Representatives of the Phylum Mollusca. (A) Squid. (B) Hard-shelled clam or "quohog" (*Venus*). (C) Shell of *Physa*, a pond snail. (D) Shell of *Planorbis*, a pond snail. (E) Shell of *Helix*, the edible land snail.

membrane, the *mantle*, the cavity within being the *mantle cavity*. A large muscular foot is capable of being extended between the valves at the anterior end. At its base is the large visceral mass, containing most of the organs, and suspended from this mass are four sheetlike, parallel *gill plates*. At the posterior end, leading into and from the mantle cavity are an *incurrent* (ventral) and an *excurrent* (dorsal) *siphon*. Water passes into the mantle cavity through the former and out through the latter.

ORGAN SYSTEMS.

Digestive System. There is a mouth at the anterior end of the visceral mass, opening from the mantle cavity. The digestive tract consists of a short *oesophagus*, *stomach*, long *intestine* coiled partly within the foot, and anus opening near the excurrent siphon.

Respiratory, Circulatory, and Excretory Systems. Oxygen, in solution, is taken up by the gills from water in the mantle cavity;

carbon dioxide is given off. The gill filaments contain blood vessels. Blood from the gills passes to the *heart*, through one of the two *atria* and into the *ventricle*. The heart is enclosed in a *pericardium*. From the ventricle blood is pumped both anteriorly and posteriorly through two *aortae* to various parts of the body. It is collected in the *vena cava*, carried through the *kidneys*, thence to the gills and back to the heart. (Fig. 41.) The kidneys or nephridia

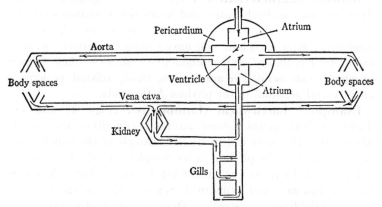

Fig. 41. Diagram illustrating the direction of blood flow in the fresh-water mussel. The gill circulation is represented on only one side of the body.

drain through excretory pores into the dorsal part of the mantle cavity, wastes being carried out through the dorsal siphon.

Nervous and Sensory Systems. Three pairs of ganglia (concentrations of nerve cells) are present, one pair near the oesophagus, one in the foot, the other near the posterior end of the visceral mass. These are connected by longitudinal fibers, the two anterior ones also connected transversely. Sensory cells, probably sensitive to touch and light, occur along the margin of the mantle; an organ for detecting disturbance in equilibrium is present. Sense organs, however, are less well developed in mussels than in many other mollusks.

Reproductive System. Mussels are usually dioecious; they may be hermaphroditic.

Land Snail. The shell is spirally coiled. The snail, fundamentally showing bilateral symmetry, is considerably modified to conform to the coiled shell. A well-defined *head* is present, bearing two pairs of tentacles, the longer pair with *eyes* at their tips. A peculiar rasping organ, the *radula*, occurs inside the mouth. Land snails are air-breathing, respiration involving the wall of the mantle cavity, air entering through a small opening, the *pulmonary aperture*. They are hermaphroditic, but not self-fertilizing.

MORPHOLOGY OF THE PHYLUM ANNELIDA

General Characteristics. These are the segmented worms. They are marine, fresh-water, and terrestrial. Common examples are: earthworm, clamworm, leech. Annelids are triploblastic, metameric, have a coelom, and have complex digestive, nervous, excretory, circulatory, and reproductive systems — these in part or wholly metameric. The annelids are closely related, perhaps in an ancestral position, to the phylum Arthropoda.

Example — Earthworm (Lumbricus). (Figs. 42 and 43.) *Lumbricus* is the genus of some (but not nearly all) common earthworms. It is the most widely studied example of the annelids but is not typical of the phylum in its complex reproductive system.

EXTERNAL FEATURES AND GENERAL INTERNAL FORM. An earthworm is elongate and cylindrical. Segmentation is visible externally as infoldings in the *cuticle*. Over one hundred metamers are present. The mouth is a slit at the anterior end, under a dorsal projection, the *prostomium*. The anus is at the posterior end. In sexually mature worms, a smooth swelling, the *clitellum*, occupies six or seven segments from about the thirty-second back. On each segment, except the first and last, there are four pairs of short bristles or *setae*. Internally, the coelom is divided into compartments by transverse partitions under external infoldings.

ORGAN SYSTEMS. (Figs. 42 and 43.)

Digestive System. The digestive system consists of: mouth; stout, swollen pharynx (segments 2–6); elongate, narrow oesophagus (6–14); thin-walled *crop* (15, 16); muscular *gizzard* (17, 18); intestine (segments 19 to end of body); anus. The intestine has a dorsal internal fold, the *typhlosole*, running its length. (Fig. 43.) The oesophagus has three pairs of *calciferous glands* along its sides. (Fig. 42B.)

Respiratory and Circulatory Systems. The earthworm breathes through the moist cuticle covering the entire surface, blood *capillaries* in the body wall taking up oxygen and giving off carbon dioxide. The blood-vascular system includes two main and

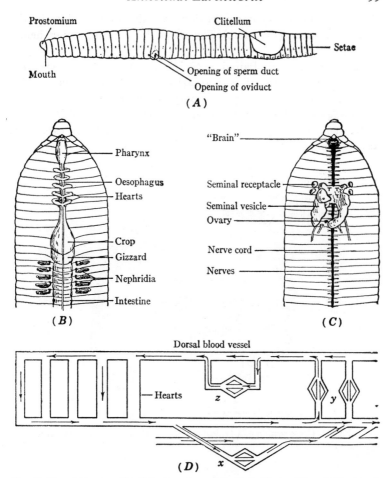

Fig. 42. The earthworm. (A) Side view of anterior third of body. (B) and (C) Dorsal views of dissections, with body wall spread out. (B) Digestive, circulatory, and excretory organs — the nephridia shown in only five segments, however. (C) Nervous and reproductive systems; the four testes lie under the spots marked T. (D) Diagram illustrating the directions of blood flow; the capillary systems marked *x*, *y*, and *z* are alternative routes; there is not general agreement concerning the direction of flow in the smaller vessels.

three smaller longitudinal vessels. Blood flows forward in the dorsal vessel, through the five pairs of muscular hearts (segments 7–11) to the ventral vessel, thence to the body wall, thence to the dorsal vessel by way of the three smaller longitudinal vessels.

There is disagreement concerning the direction of flow in the smaller vessels. (Fig. 42D.) The blood is red, containing hemoglobin in solution.

Excretory System. Paired *nephridia* are present in every segment except the first three and last one. Each nephridium drains material from the coelomic cavity anterior to it through its *nephrostome* and coiled *tubule* out through a ventral excretory pore. It also receives material by diffusion from blood capillaries surrounding the tubule. (Fig. 42B.)

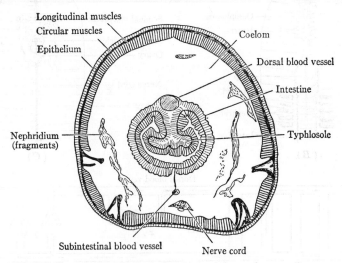

Fig. 43. Cross section of a typical segment of the earthworm, diagrammatic.

Nervous and Sensory Systems. Sense organs in the skin are sensitive to contact and light. The nervous system is a ventral chain of ganglia, one in each segment beginning with the fourth, and an anterior *suprapharyngeal ganglion*, the "brain," in segment three. Nerve cords around the pharynx connect the "brain" with the first ventral ganglion. Three pairs of *nerves* in each metamer arise from the ventral nerve cord. (Fig. 42c.)

Reproductive System. Earthworms are hermaphroditic, but not self-fertilizing. (Fig. 42c.) Reproductive organs are complicated and variable in different kinds of earthworms. Some annelids are monoecious, the gonads duplicated segmentally.

MORPHOLOGY OF THE PHYLUM ONYCHOPHORA

The Onychophora constitute a phylum of wormlike, terrestrial animals that are clearly intermediate between the Annelida and the Arthropoda. Its members have a soft integument and they have nephridia like those of segmented worms, but their respiratory system (tracheae) and circulatory system are like those of arthropods. They are metameric, but this condition is evident externally only in the paired, segmentally-arranged legs. The genus *Peripatus* is a member of this phylum. It, and the other members of the group, occur in moist tropical and subtropical regions.

MORPHOLOGY OF THE PHYLUM ARTHROPODA

The greatest variety in species and perhaps the greatest abundance in individual animals occurs in this phylum which numbers more known species than all other animals and all plants combined. Furthermore, the insects, man's greatest rivals economically, are the dominant representatives of the arthropods. For these reasons, the subdivisions of this phylum are treated here in some detail.

General Characteristics. Arthropods are segmented animals with jointed appendages and, in most cases, hard exoskeletons. They are found in marine and fresh-water habitats and on land, most species being terrestrial. The following are common examples of the phylum: crayfish, crab, centipede, spider, mite, cricket, fly, beetle, butterfly, wasp. Arthropods are triploblastic and metameric. They have a true coelom but it is ill defined, and they have complex organ systems. They are, with the exception of the vertebrates, the most highly developed metameric animals — a peak in the evolution of segmentation with an external skeleton.

Classes of the Phylum Arthropoda. Five classes of arthropods are recognized in the following scheme. The Diplopoda and Chilopoda, here separated, are sometimes combined in one class, the Myriapoda. The phylum Onychophora is sometimes considered a class under the phylum Arthropoda, rather than a separate phylum as in this book. (Fig. 44.)

CLASS CRUSTACEA. Members of the class Crustacea are chiefly marine, but many live in fresh water and a few on land in damp

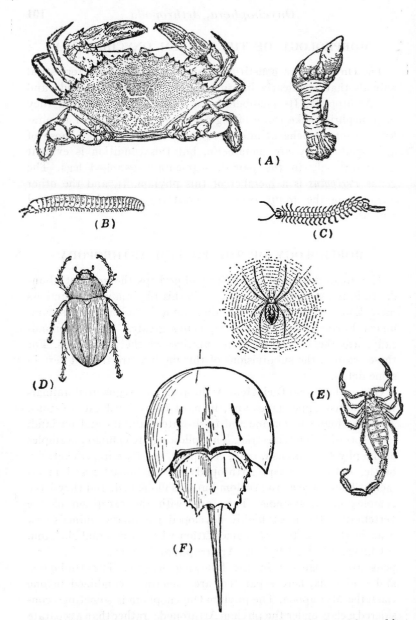

Fig. 44. Representatives of the Arthropoda. (A) Crustacea (crab and barnacle).
(B) Diplopoda (millipede). (C) Chilopoda (centipede). (D) Insecta (beetle).
(E) Arachnida (spider, scorpion). (F) Horseshoe crab. (A–E, copyright by General Biological Supply House, Chicago, and used by permission.)

places. They breathe through *gills*. Two pairs of *antennae* are present, and the larger crustacea have *compound eyes*. The appendages are derived from a common, *biramous* plan. Examples include: lobster, crab, pill bug, sow bug, water flea, barnacle.

CLASS DIPLOPODA. These are terrestrial forms with a cylindrical, elongated, wormlike body (but with a hard exoskeleton). They are distinctly segmented, with two pairs of similar legs on most segments. They have one pair of short antennae. The respiratory organs are *tracheae*, air tubes extending through the body. Millipedes are members of this class.

CLASS CHILOPODA. Members of this class are terrestrial forms with an elongated, flattened body, and with a hard exoskeleton. They are distinctly segmented, like the Diplopoda, but with only one pair of similar legs on each body segment. They have a single pair of long antennae. They breathe through tracheae. Centipedes constitute this class.

CLASS INSECTA. These are mostly terrestrial, though many species occur in fresh water and some are, rarely, marine. The body is divided into *head, thorax*, and *abdomen*. There is one pair of antennae — on the head; there are three pairs of legs attached to the thorax; and there are usually two pairs of *wings*, also attached to the thorax. The respiratory organs may be tracheae or, in aquatic forms, *tracheal gills*. The mouth parts are variously modified for chewing solid food or sucking plant and animal juices. Development may be fairly direct or may involve a complete transformation through several unlike stages, the former type being called *indirect* and the latter *direct metamorphosis*. Members of this class are collectively called insects. Examples of insects are given in the following summary of the principal orders. (See Fig. 45.)

Order Orthoptera. Straight-winged insects with well-developed jumping legs constitute this order. They have chewing mouth parts, and their metamorphosis is incomplete. Examples include crickets, katydids, and grasshoppers.

Order Blattariae. Running insects with flattened bodies, the cockroaches, form the order Blattariae. The four wings, when present, are flattened and overlap on the abdomen. They have chewing mouth parts, and their metamorphosis is incomplete.

Order Isoptera. The termites ("white ants") are the members of this order. They are small, soft-bodied insects that live in colonies. They have large, prominent jaws. Their four membranous wings are lost at maturity. The metamorphosis of termites is incomplete.

Order Homoptera. Small to medium-sized insects of somewhat varied form are members of this order. They have four, similar, membranous wings; they have sucking mouth parts; and their

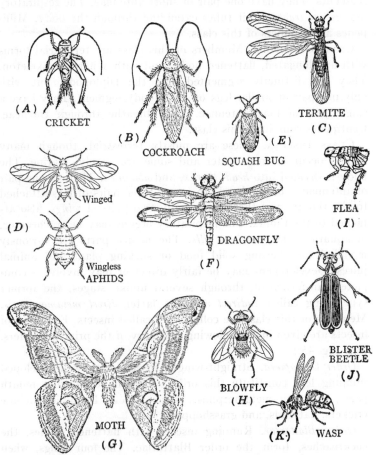

Fig. 45. Representatives of the principal orders of insects. (A) Orthoptera. (B) Blattariae. (C) Isoptera. (D) Homoptera. (E) Hemiptera. (F) Odonata. (G) Lepidoptera. (H) Diptera. (I) Siphonaptera. (J) Coleoptera. (K) Hymenoptera. (B–H, J, K, copyright by General Biological Supply House, Chicago, and used by permission.)

metamorphosis is incomplete. Examples include such diverse forms as cicadas, leaf hoppers, aphids, and mealy bugs.

Order Hemiptera. These are the true bugs. They are similar to members of the last group except that the forewings, which overlap on the abdomen, are thickened in the basal half — not membranous.

Order Odonata. These are the dragonflies and damsel flies, large predatory insects with movable head and large compound eyes. There are four membranous wings, similar in size. Metamorphosis is incomplete, but there is an aquatic nymphal stage superficially unlike the adult.

Order Lepidoptera. The insects that constitute this large order are the moths and butterflies. Their wings are covered with scales — these forming color patterns. Sucking mouth parts are coiled under the head. Metamorphosis is complete, involving egg, several larval (caterpillar) stages, a pupa (cocoon or chrysalis), and the adult.

Order Diptera. The Diptera, as their name suggests, have only two wings. They have sucking and piercing mouth parts, and their metamorphosis is complete. Flies, gnats, and mosquitoes belong to this order.

Order Siphonaptera. These are the fleas — small, wingless, jumping insects. They have piercing and sucking mouth parts and a complete metamorphosis.

Order Coleoptera. This very large order is made up of the beetles. They vary greatly in size but all have hardened forewings. The mouth parts are modified for chewing. Metamorphosis is complete.

Order Hymenoptera. The insects in this group have four membranous wings, the wings of the anterior pair being larger than those of the posterior pair. The head is free, and the mouth parts are chewing, but adapted for lapping. Metamorphosis is complete. Many colonial insects are in this order, which includes ants, bees, and wasps.

CLASS ARACHNIDA. The arthropods in this class have a body of two divisions, *cephalothorax* and abdomen. Many arachnids have a soft exoskeleton. The cephalothorax bears six pairs of appendages, four pairs being legs. Antennae, however, are absent. Arachnids have simple eyes but no compound eyes. They breathe through tracheae, *lung books*, or *gill books*. Most arachnids are terrestrial, but a few are aquatic. Ticks, mites, spiders, and scorpions are all members of the class Arachnida.

Example of the Class Crustacea — Crayfish. The following account applies equally well to *Cambarus*, the genus of crayfishes of the eastern United States, *Astacus*, the genus found in Europe and the Pacific Coast section of North America, and the lobster *Homarus*.

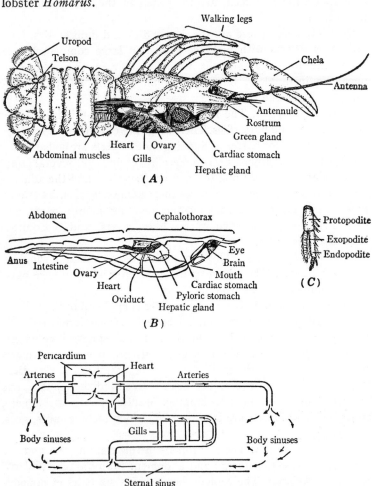

Fig. 46. The crayfish. (A) External features — part of the carapace removed to expose the internal organs in place. (B) Diagrammatic longitudinal section, showing internal organs in relative positions. (C) The fourth swimmeret, an appendage showing the primitive biramous condition. (D) Diagram illustrating the direction of blood flow.

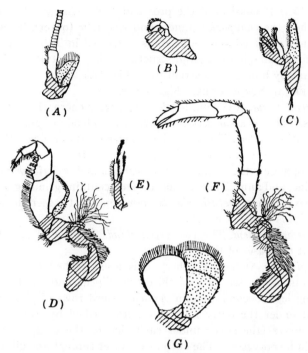

Fig. 47. Homology, as illustrated in the appendages of the cray-fish, *Astacus*. Typical appendages from the left side of the body. (A) Antenna. (B) Mandible. (C) Second maxilla. (D) Third max-illiped. (E) Third abdominal appendage of female. (F) Second walking leg. (G) Uropod. The protopodite is shaded with parallel lines; the exopodite, with dots; the endopodite is unmarked. (Modified after Huxley.)

EXTERNAL FEATURES. (Figs. 46*A* and 47.)

Divisions of the Body. The major divisions are *cephalothorax* and *abdomen*. The former is covered by a hard shield, the *carapace*, which projects forward between the eyes as the *rostrum*. The first thirteen pairs of appendages, and the eyes, are attached to the cephalothorax; the remaining six are attached to the abdomen, which terminates in a horizontal fin, the *telson*. The abdomen is divided into segments, each protected dorsally and laterally by an arched skeleton. This consists of the dorsal *tergite* and two lateral *pleurae*. The ventral plates are known as *sternites*.

Appendages. Each appendage, except possibly the eye, is modi-fied from the *biramous* type, which is ancestral and embryonic.

(Fig. 46c.) It consists of the proximal *protopodite* and two distal branches, the *endopodite* (inner) and *exopodite* (outer). These are variously modified and reduced, as suggested in Table I, but are essentially alike in origin and structure. They illustrate well what is meant by homologous structures. (Fig. 47.)

INTERNAL STRUCTURES. (Fig. 46A, B.)

General Form. A coelom is present, largely encroached upon by organs. There is a *haemocoel* — part of the blood system.

Digestive System. The digestive tract consists of a mouth, surrounded by several pairs of appendages — the "mouth parts," an oesophagus, the stomach (with *cardiac* and *pyloric chambers*), intestine, and anus. The cardiac stomach contains grinding organs. Digestive glands (*hepatic glands*) pour enzymatic secretions into the pylorus of the stomach.

Excretory System. The two *green glands*, nephridial structures, open at the bases of the antennae.

Respiratory System. Feathery gills are attached to the basal segments of the second and third maxillipeds and the first four walking legs. Second and (in *Astacus*) third rows of gills are attached under the outer row. These are bathed by water in the *gill chamber* (the space under each side of the carapace); they contain blood vessels. The current of water through the gill chamber is maintained by the "bailer," a branch of the second maxilla.

Circulatory System. (Fig. 46D.) There is a dorsal heart, in a pericardium. Blood enters the heart through three pairs of *ostia*, valvular openings. It is pumped out through seven *arteries*, which empty into open spaces, the *sinuses*. These sinuses drain into the capillaries of the gills from which the blood enters the heart through the pericardium.

Nervous System. This consists of a dorsal brain, two *circumoesophageal connectives*, and a ventral chain of ganglia. The first ventral ganglion is large, representing the fusion of several. Nerves branch from the brain and ventral nerve cord.

Sensory System. The sense of touch and the chemical senses of taste and smell are highly developed on the anterior appendages. Two *compound eyes* (consisting of many optical units, the *ommatidia*) are present, each eye on the end of a stalk. Organs of equilibration, *statocysts*, occur at the bases of the antennules.

Reproductive System. The sexes are separate (dioecious). The *testis* and *ovary* are bilobed. The testis empties by *sperm ducts*

Table I. Homologies of the Appendages of the Crayfish

Number of Appendage	Name of Appendage	Modifications from Primitive Biramous Condition (Protopodite Always Present)
1	Antennule	Ex- and endopodites both elongated sensory filaments.
2	Antenna	Endopodite a long sensory filament, exopodite a short basal blade.
3	Mandible	Exopodite absent; remainder a strong food-crushing organ with a palp.
4	1st Maxilla	Exopodite absent. A thin organ lying just behind the mandible.
5	2nd Maxilla	Exopodite constitutes "bailer" of gill chamber.
6	1st Maxilliped	All parts present. Modified for manipulation of food.
7	2nd Maxilliped	
8	3rd Maxilliped	
9	Cheliped or 1st Walking Leg	Exopodite absent. Endopodite forms heavy pincher.
10	2nd Walking Leg	Endopodite forms small pincher. Exopodite absent
11	3rd Walking Leg	
12	4th Walking Leg	No pincher on endopodite.
13	5th Walking Leg	
14	1st Swimmeret	In female very small or absent; in male modified for transfer of sperm.
15	2nd Swimmeret	In male modified for transfer of sperm; in female like next three appendages.
16	3rd Swimmeret	All parts present — most nearly approach primitive form. Used in swimming and, in females, for egg attachment.
17	4th Swimmeret	
18	5th Swimmeret	
19	Uropod	All parts present, but broadened for swimming. Together with telson, constitutes tail fin.

through pores at the base of the fifth pair of walking legs; *oviducts* convey eggs from the ovary to openings at the base of the third pair of walking legs. (Fig. 46*b*.)

Example of the Class Insecta — Grasshopper.

EXTERNAL FEATURES. (Fig. 48*a*.)

Divisions of the Body. Bodies of all insects have three major divisions — *head, thorax,* and *abdomen.* Each division consists embryonically of several segments. In the adult, three divisions of the thorax are visible — *prothorax, mesothorax,* and *metathorax.* In the grasshopper, the dorsal part of the prothorax is a saddle-like covering, the *pronotum.* The abdomen is divided into numerous segments, all distinct except the last few, which are fused and modified to form the *external genitalia.* About nine segments are clearly evident.

Appendages. The grasshopper has one pair of antennae, on the head, each antenna consisting of numerous segments.

The mouth parts are as follows: The *labrum* (upper lip) is suspended from the *clypeus.* Immediately under it are the two *mandibles* — heavy, chewing jaws. Under these are the two *maxillae,* each bearing a jointed *palp.* Between the basal parts of the maxillae is the pear-shaped *hypoglossus.* The divided lower lip, the *labium,* bears a pair of jointed palps. The maxillary and labial palps are sensory; the remaining parts function in food manipulation and mastication.

There are three pairs of legs, one pair on each of the three divisions of the thorax. The third pair (metathoracic legs) are strong and elongated, with a swollen femur, and are adapted for leaping. Each leg consists of the following segments, from proximal to distal end: *coxa, trochanter, femur, tibia, tarsus* — the latter having three segments in grasshoppers. The tarsus terminates in a pad (*pulvillus*) and two *claws.*

There are usually two pairs of wings, one each on meso- and metathorax, but they may be absent or reduced. The anterior pair, the *tegmina* (sing., *tegmen*), are hard, leathery, and more or less opaque. The posterior two are enlarged, membranous, transparent except when bearing color pattern or bands, and folded when at rest. There are numerous *veins* in the wings.

External Genitalia. In the male, the posterior tip of the abdomen is rounded below. Copulatory structures are largely concealed but include exposed lateral projections, the *cerci,* that are of varied

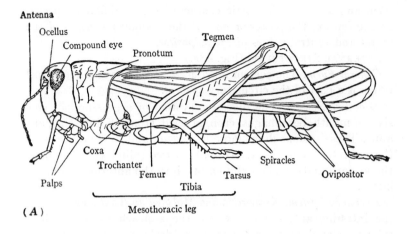

(A)

Mesothoracic leg

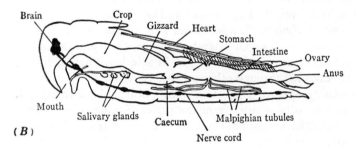

(B)

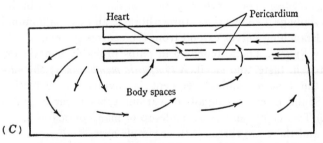

(C)

Fig. 48. The grasshopper. (A) External features — the segments of a typical insect leg being labelled in connection with the mesothoracic leg. (B) Diagrammatic longitudinal section, showing the organs in their relative positions. (C) Diagram illustrating the direction of blood flow.

form and serve as diagnostic characteristics of different species. In the female, the posterior end of the abdomen consists of the dorsal and ventral valves of the *ovipositor*.

INTERNAL STRUCTURES. (Fig. 48*B*.)

General Form. The coelom is reduced, and there is a haemocoel which is a part of the circulatory system.

Digestive System. The digestive system of a grasshopper consists of mouth, oesophagus, crop, gizzard, stomach, intestine, and anus. These regions differ more in texture and thickness of walls than of internal diameter. Six double *caeca* (blind sacs) surround the gizzard and stomach and empty into the anterior end of the latter.

Excretory System. Numerous fine *Malpighian tubules* empty into the intestine at the point where the stomach joins it. These tubules, closed at their upper ends, drain excretory materials which diffuse from the haemocoel into the intestine.

Respiratory System. Tracheal tubes and *air sacs* are connected with the outside through lateral openings, the *spiracles.* Air is carried to cells as air, not as oxygen in solution. Carbon dioxide is partly excreted through other organs, however.

Circulatory System. There is a dorsal heart, blood entering it through five pairs of ostia from the pericardial sinus in which it is enclosed. The pericardial sinus receives blood from all parts of the body, from sinuses which blood reaches after being pumped out of the anterior end of the heart. (Fig. 48*c*.)

Nervous System. The nervous system consists of a dorsal brain, circumoesophageal connectives, three thoracic and five abdominal ganglia. Branching nerves extend from the central system.

Sensory System. The antennae and palps probably contain organs of touch, taste, and smell. A *tympanic membrane* on the surface of the first abdominal segment is involved in detecting sound. (Sound producing organs of various types occur in grasshoppers.) Two compound eyes, made up of many ommatidia, are present, and there are three *ocelli*, or simple eyes.

Reproductive System. The sexes are separate. There are two testes or two ovaries present, in the dorsal part of the body cavity. Sperm ducts from the testes, or oviducts from the ovaries, open ventral to the anus.

Example of the Class Insecta — Honey Bee.

KINDS OF INDIVIDUALS (CASTES). The males, which are fertile, are called *drones;* the fertile females are the *queens;* the sterile females are the *workers. Pollen baskets* are present only in workers. Drones have a broad abdomen; queens, a somewhat narrow, long abdomen.

EXTERNAL FEATURES.

Divisions of Body. These are the head, thorax, and abdomen. The thorax consists of prothorax, mesothorax, and metathorax. Six visible segments are present in the abdomen.

Appendages. The single pair of antennae consists of twelve segments in the male, thirteen in the female.

The following summary will describe the mouth parts. The labrum is broad and short, and the fleshy *epipharynx* projects beneath it. Two mandibles, horny jaws, lie lateral to the labrum and extend beyond it. Two maxillae extend much beyond the mandibles; they are covered with stiff hairs. Small maxillary palps are present. The labium is modified into a much elongated central portion, the *tongue,* and a large palp on each side.

There are, of course, three pairs of legs. Each leg consists of five joints — coxa, trochanter, femur, tibia, and a tarsus. The tarsus terminates in a pulvillus and lateral claws. The legs are covered with bristles and other structures used in collecting and carrying pollen and in cleaning pollen from the body. An antenna cleaner and an eye brush are present on the prothoracic legs. A spur on the mesothoracic legs is used to pry pollen from the pollen baskets, which are on the tibia of the metathoracic legs.

Two pairs of wings are present, both meso- and metathoracic wings being membranous. Veins divide each wing into "cells."

External Genitalia. The *sting,* present in queens and workers, is a modified ovipositor. In the male, copulatory apparatus is present.

INTERNAL STRUCTURES. (Fig. 49.)

General Form. The general form is typical of insects. A reduced coelom is present and there is a hemocoel.

Digestive System. This consists of mouth, oesophagus, *honey sac,* stomach, intestine, *rectum,* and anus. The oesophagus is elongated and thin; the honey sac is a globular region; the stomach is large and long; the intestine is narrow; and the rectum is enlarged. Digestive glands occur in the wall of the stomach.

Excretory System. Malpighian tubules drain into the intestine at its anterior end.

Respiratory System. Oxygen is not transported in the blood, but is carried in air in the tracheae. Lateral openings (spiracles) admit air into the tracheae and air sacs, branches of which convey it to all parts of the body.

Circulatory System. There is a dorsal heart in a pericardial sinus, receiving blood through five pairs of ostia. Blood is pumped

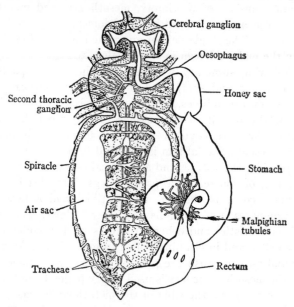

Fig. 49. Internal morphology of the honey bee, respiratory system partly eliminated on the right. (Redrawn from Henne-guy, after Leuckart.)

anteriorly from the heart. After leaving the heart it diffuses through the hemocoel into the pericardial sinus.

Nervous System. A dorsal brain, a ventral chain of ganglia, and commissures or connectives around the oesophagus constitute the major structures of the nervous system. Nerves branch from these.

Sensory System. Antennae probably bear end organs of smell, hearing, and touch. Taste organs are located near the mouth and on the tongue. There are two compound eyes and three ocelli.

Reproductive System. The sexes are separate. Fertilization is internal. There are two testes or two ovaries. The two ducts in either case join before reaching the genital opening.

MORPHOLOGY OF THE PHYLUM CHORDATA

Man and all his nearest relatives are members of this phylum, the majority of its members being vertebrates. The most highly developed of all animals belong to the phylum Chordata.

General Characteristics. Chordates are triploblastic, have a coelom, evident metamerism, and highly developed organ systems. An *endoskeleton* is always present at some stage. Its

(A)   **(B)**

Fig. 50. (A) *Dolichoglossus.* (B) *Molgula,* a sea squirt. (Reprinted by permission from *General Zoology* by Gordon Alexander, copyright, 1951, by Barnes & Noble, Inc.)

characteristic form is the *notochord*, a gelatinous, longitudinal, dorsal rod, replaced in higher forms by a chain of vertebrae. Respiration always involves the *pharynx* — the region at the back of the mouth cavity. A dorsal, hollow, nerve cord is present.

Major Divisions of the Phylum Chordata. Four subphyla are recognized, the first three sometimes combined under the name Prochordata. The fourth subphylum, the Vertebrata, may be conveniently divided into seven classes, but more than seven are often recognized.

SUBPHYLA OF THE PHYLUM CHORDATA.

Subphylum Hemichorda (Enteropneusta). Example: *Dolichoglossus.* The notochord is hollow, short, not typical; it is an anterior projection of the alimentary canal. (Fig. 50A.)

Subphylum Urochorda (Tunicata). Examples: sea squirt, sea pork. The notochord is present in the tail of the larva or tadpole; it is absent in the adult, which is sessile (attached). (Fig. 50B.)

Subphylum Cephalochorda. Example: *Amphioxus.* These have a fishlike, elongated body. The notochord is well developed, extending practically the full length of the body. (Fig. 51.)

Subphylum Vertebrata. Examples: lamprey, shark, perch, frog, turtle, bird, man. The notochord, if persistent, is surrounded by cartilage; if not persistent, it is replaced by a segmented, dorsal skeleton (*vertebral column*) of *vertebrae*, composed of cartilage or bone. Vertebrates have a central heart, red blood *corpuscles*,

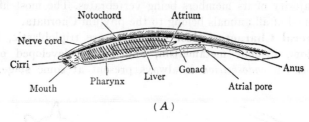

(*A*)

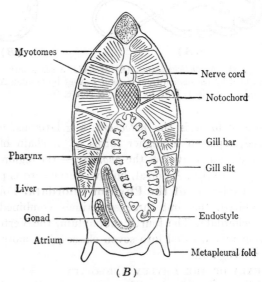

(*B*)

Fig. 51. *Amphioxus* (*Branchiostoma*). (A) Diagrammatic sketch of the right half, as exposed by sectioning in the sagittal plane (redrawn after Krause). (B) Diagrammatic sketch of a cross section through the posterior part of the pharynx.

and an *hepatic portal system*. They usually have paired appendages with internal skeletal structures, but they never have more than two pairs of paired appendages.

CLASSES OF THE SUBPHYLUM VERTEBRATA.

Class Agnatha. Examples: lamprey, hagfish. These have a persistent notochord, a round mouth without jaws, and numerous *gill slits*. Paired fins are absent.

Class Chondrichthyes. Examples: shark, ray, sawfish. These are the cartilaginous fishes — the skeleton being of cartilage. Jaws are present (as in all succeeding classes). There are numerous gill slits. The body is covered with *placoid scales,* and paired *fins* are present. (Fig. 52.)

Class Osteichthyes. Examples: pike, perch, trout, cod, eel. In these fishes the skeleton is of bone or bone and cartilage. The gills are covered by a flap or *operculum,* leaving apparently only one gill slit. There is usually a covering of scales, but they are not placoid scales. Paired fins are usually present.

Class Amphibia. Examples: salamander, frog, toad, caecilian. (Fig. 54.) A smooth, moist skin, without scales, is characteristic of members of this group. Respiration is usually by gills in the young (which are aquatic), by *lungs* in the adult. There is a three-chambered heart (only two chambers being present in the heart in the three preceding classes). The eggs have a gelatinous covering.

Class Reptilia. Examples: turtle, snake, lizard, alligator. In reptiles, the skin is dry and covered with *epidermal scales.* Respiration takes place through lungs. There is a three-chambered heart. The eggs have tough shells.

Class Aves. Examples: gull, snipe, pigeon, chicken, ostrich. Birds have a body covering of *feathers,* and the anterior appendages are modified for flight (with few exceptions). Birds are warm-blooded animals, having a four-chambered heart. Their eggs are covered with a hard shell.

Class Mammalia. Examples: opossum, rabbit, cat, whale, man. Mammals have a body covering of *hair* — which may be limited to certain areas or be almost entirely absent. *Mammary glands* (milk glands) are present in all female mammals. The young in most cases undergo embryonic development in the *uterus* of the female. This is *viviparous* development. (See Chaps. XI and XII.)

Example of a Vertebrate — Dogfish Shark. (In this and the following section, two examples of vertebrates are described, the dogfish shark and the frog. Repetition of similar details in the two accounts is avoided by cross references.)

EXTERNAL FEATURES. (Fig. 52.) The body is long, cylindrical, tapering, the head somewhat flattened. The appendages are as follows: two median *dorsal fins,* a *caudal fin* (tail fin) — which is heterocercal (the upper half being longer than the lower), a pair

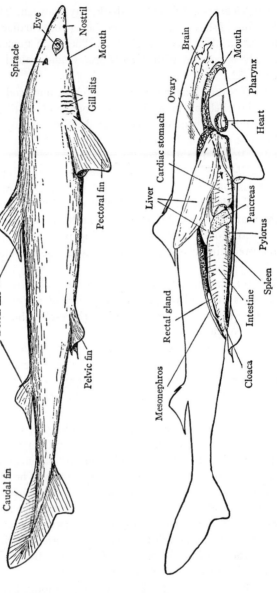

Fig. 52. Dogfish shark. Above, external features. Below, lateral view of a dissection in which the relative positions of organs are shown (one liver lobe has been moved to expose certain organs otherwise concealed by it).

of anterior *pectoral fins*, and a pair of posterior *pelvic fins*. In the male, the pelvic fins are modified along the inner margins to form *claspers*, which are copulatory organs. The mouth is ventral in position. The nostrils are pits on the ventral margin of the head. The eyes are lateral in position. There are five gill slits on each side, posterior to and somewhat ventral to the eyes. The *cloaca* opens between the pelvic fins. The body is covered with small placoid scales.

INTERNAL STRUCTURES. (Fig. 52.)

General Form. The coelom is divided into two compartments, a small anterior one enclosing the heart, the *pericardial cavity*, and a larger posterior chamber containing the rest of the viscera, the *peritoneal cavity*. The coelom opens to the outside through two *abdominal pores* at the posterior end.

Skeletal System. The brain and principal sense organs are enclosed or protected by a cartilaginous box, the *chondrocranium*. Beneath it is suspended the skeleton of the jaws and gill arches, this part of the skeleton being referred to collectively as the *visceral skeleton*. The vertebral column is made up of a chain of cartilaginous vertebrae extending from the chondrocranium into the tail. Rudimentary *ribs* are attached to vertebrae. The fins are supported by *rays* of cartilage proximally and numerous fin rays of keratin distally. *Pectoral* and *pelvic girdles* support the pectoral and pelvic fins, respectively, and connect them with the axial skeleton.

Muscular System. Regularly metameric muscle segments or *myotomes* occur through the body, but they are considerably modified in the head and appendages.

Digestive System. The mouth has jaws covered with *teeth*, these teeth being homologous with placoid scales. The pharynx opens into the respiratory chambers laterally, and the oesophagus posteriorly. The oesophagus merges into the cardiac portion, then into the pyloric portion of the stomach, which bends anteriorly in a U. This empties into the *duodenum*, then into an expanded portion of the intestine containing a *spiral valve*, then into the *rectum* and the *cloaca* — the latter being a common drainage channel for digestive, excretory, and reproductive systems. A *pancreas* and *liver* are present, their ducts (*pancreatic* and *bile*) emptying into the duodenum. A large *rectal gland* (function unknown) is present.

Excretory System. Two long narrow *mesonephroi* (sing., *mesonephros*, a type of primitive kidney) drain into the cloaca through the *Wolffian ducts.* These lie dorsal to the coelom, embedded in the muscles of the body wall.

Respiratory System. Gills are in lateral compartments of the pharynx, washed over by water from the mouth, which passes out through gill slits. Each half gill is a *demibranch.* Nine demibranches occur on each side, each containing blood capillaries.

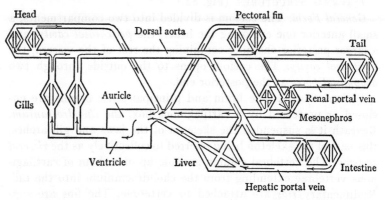

Fig. 53. Diagram illustrating the direction of blood flow in the dogfish shark. Applies equally well to all fishes.

Circulatory System. (Fig. 53.) The heart has two chambers, a dorsal *auricle* and a ventral *ventricle.* The blood is pumped forward from the ventricle through the *ventral aorta* to and through the gills (*afferent arteries* to gill capillaries to *efferent arteries*), to the *dorsal aorta*, and thence over the body through its branches. Blood enters the auricle from the *sinus venosus*, draining the two anterior and two posterior *cardinal veins* and the two *hepatic sinuses* (from the liver). Blood reaches the liver directly, from the dorsal aorta, or indirectly, through the hepatic portal vein (which drains the capillaries of the intestine). The posterior cardinal veins drain the capillaries of the mesonephroi, which receive their blood from the posterior end of the body.

Nervous System. The nervous system consists of the brain and *spinal cord*, nerves as branches of each, and the *autonomic nervous system.* Nerve centers of the latter are more or less independent of the central nervous system. See Table II for names of embryonic brain divisions, common names of parts they include, and sources

Table II. Divisions of Brain and Their Relations to Cranial Nerves

DIVISIONS OF BRAIN		CRANIAL NERVES	
In Early Embryo	*In Late Embryo or Adult*	*Number and Name*	*Peripheral Distribution and Function*
Prosencephalon	Telencephalon (Cerebrum)	I. Olfactory	Olfactory membrane; sensory.
	Diencephalon	II. Optic	Retina of eye; sensory.
Mesencephalon	Mesencephalon (Midbrain)	III. Oculomotor	Four eye muscles; motor.
		IV. Trochlear	One eye muscle; motor.
Rhombencephalon	Mesencephalon (Cerebellum)		
	Myelencephalon (Medulla oblongata)	V. Trigeminal	Muscles and skin of face; mainly sensory.
		VI. Abducens	One eye muscle; motor.
		VII. Facial	Chiefly motor, to muscles of face.
		VIII. Auditory	Cochlea and semicircular canals; sensory.
		IX. Glosso-pharyngeal	Pharyngeal or gill region; sensory and motor.
		X. Vagus	Heart, lungs, digestive tract; sensory and motor.

and distributions of the ten pairs of *cranial nerves*. Also see Figure 56A. *Spinal* nerves are distributed one pair to each body segment.

Sensory System. The eyes differ from those of the frog (*q.v.*) chiefly in the absence of lids. The nostrils open to the outside, having no connection with the pharynx. They are lined with the *olfactory membrane*, from which nerves pass to the *olfactory lobes* of the brain. *Lateral line organs* probably function in hearing and in determining the direction of water currents. The *semicircular canals*, organs that function in detecting disturbances in equilibrium, are enclosed in the sides of the chondrocranium. There are three semicircular canals, an anterior vertical, a posterior vertical, and a horizontal one. Organs of taste are located in the skin.

Reproductive System. The sexes are separate and fertilization is internal. Embryos develop in the uterus of the female until able to swim. The female has two ovaries, in the anterior end of the abdominal cavity. Eggs, when mature, escape into the coelom, whence they are drawn into the oviducts through the *ostia* (funnel-like openings at the anterior ends of the oviducts). The lower end of each oviduct is swollen into a *uterus*, its walls extremely well supplied with blood vessels. The male has two testes, and mature sperm cells leave the body through the mesonephric or Wolffian ducts.

Example of a Vertebrate — Frog.

EXTERNAL FEATURES. (Fig. 54.) The body of a frog is made up of the head, trunk, and two pairs of appendages — the hind pair much elongated. The skin is smooth and scaleless. The nostrils are anterior, the eyes dorsal, and the mouth a broad anterior slit. The *tympanic membrane*, flush with the skin, is behind the eye on top of the head. There are four fingers, plus a rudiment, on each hand, and five toes, webbed, on each foot. The *cloacal aperture* appears on the dorsal side between the hind legs.

INTERNAL STRUCTURES. (Fig. 54.)

General Form. The coelom of the frog has two compartments, the pericardial and the *pleuroperitoneal* (abdominal) cavities. The latter contains the lungs as well as the abdominal viscera.

Skeletal System. The *skull* of the frog consists of a small *cranium* (brain case) and a broad portion constituting the skeleton of jaws and face. The vertebral column consists of ten *vertebrae*, the first being the *atlas*, the ninth, the *sacrum*, and the tenth (greatly

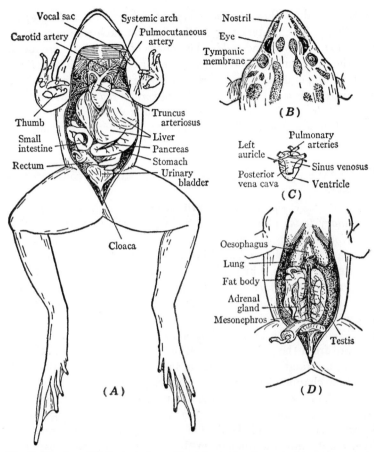

Fig. 54. The frog. (A) Ventral view, with abdominal wall removed to expose organs in place. (B) Dorsal surface of head. (C) Dorsal side of heart. (D) Ventral view, abdominal wall and some organs removed to expose organs of the dorsal part of the abdominal cavity.

elongated), the *urostyle*. All vertebrae except the first, ninth, and tenth bear elongated *transverse processes* — the so-called "ribs." A *sternum* is present, connected with the rest of the axial skeleton through the pectoral girdle. The skull, vertebral column, and sternum constitute the *axial skeleton*.

The *appendicular skeleton* of the frog is made up of the skeletal structures of the two pairs of appendages and their attachments (girdles) to the axial skeleton. Each anterior or *pectoral girdle* consists of the following: *clavicle, coracoid, scapula, suprascapula* (cartilage). The posterior or *pelvic girdle* on each side consists of the *ilium, ischium,* and *pubis.* The bones of each girdle are fused, and the right and left pelvic girdles are fused in the midline. Each pectoral appendage contains the following bones, in order from the proximal to the distal end: *humerus, radio-ulna, carpals, metacarpals, phalanges.* The corresponding bones in the pelvic appendage are: *femur, tibiofibula, tarsals, metatarsals, phalanges.*

Muscular System. Muscles show much greater differentiation from the primitive metameric pattern than in the shark, particularly in the appendicular muscles. No details are considered in this work.

Digestive System. In the mouth there are numerous fine teeth (*maxillary teeth*) along the upper jaw, as well as two groups of *vomerine teeth* in the roof of the mouth. The *tongue* is fleshy, bifurcate at the tip, and attached anteriorly. It is flipped forward in catching insects, which adhere to its sticky tip. The oesophagus is a straight-walled, rather large tube, terminating in the stomach. The latter is an elongated muscular sac, curved toward the animal's left side. The intestine consists of a moderately long, coiled *small intestine,* the first portion of which, the *duodenum,* extends forward from the *pyloric* or posterior end of the stomach, and the *rectum,* a straight section merging into the *cloaca.* The latter is a common channel for digestive, excretory, and reproductive systems. The *liver* has three lobes, the median one containing a *gall bladder.* The pancreas lies in the *mesentery* (supporting tissue) between stomach and duodenum. Ducts from the pancreas and liver empty into the duodenum. In cross section, the intestine or stomach is seen to consist of four layers; these are, from the outside in, the *peritoneum* (continuous with the mesentery), the *muscular layer* (of smooth muscle, as in Fig. 10), the *submucosa,* and the *mucosa* (the lining).

Excretory System. Primitive kidneys or *mesonephroi* empty into the cloaca through the two *Wolffian ducts.* The kidneys lie dorsal to the peritoneum of the dorsal body wall. A *urinary bladder* is present on the ventral side of the cloaca; the Wolffian ducts do not empty directly into it.

Respiratory System. External and (later) internal gills are present in the tadpole. These are replaced by lungs at the time of metamorphosis, the adult frog breathing through lungs (and the skin).

Each lung is a sac with numerous hollows in its walls. The lungs communicate with the outside through *bronchi*, a *larynx* (voice box), the pharynx, and the nasal passages between internal and external *nares*. The pharynx communicates with the larynx through the *glottis*, a longitudinal slit in the floor of the mouth behind the tongue.

Circulatory System. (Fig. 55.) The heart of the frog has three chambers, two *atria* (also called auricles) and one *ventricle*. Blood

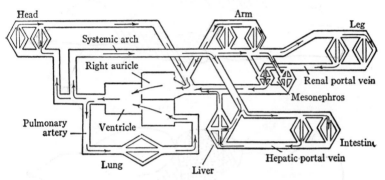

Fig. 55. Diagram illustrating the direction of blood flow in a frog. Applies equally well to toads, but not to all salamanders.

is pumped out of the heart by the ventricle, leaving through the *conus arteriosus* (also called truncus arteriosus). The conus bifurcates anterior to the heart and then divides on each side into three trunks. From anterior to posterior branch these are the *common carotid artery*, the *systemic arch*, and the *pulmocutaneous artery*. Each common carotid divides immediately into an *internal* and an *external carotid artery*, both going forward into the head. Each pulmocutaneous artery sends branches to the lung and skin of the corresponding side. The systemic arches unite dorsally to form the *dorsal* aorta, after giving off branches to the arm and back. The principal arteries from the dorsal aorta are, in approximate order, the *coeliaco-mesenteric* (to stomach, liver, and intestine), *segmental* (to the body wall), *renal* (to the kidneys), and the two *iliacs* (to the legs).

Blood from the lungs returns in the *pulmonary veins*, emptying into the left auricle. All other blood enters the right auricle, passing through the *sinus venosus*, a large sac on the dorsal side. The sinus venosus receives two *anterior venae cavae*, with blood from the anterior part of the body, and one *posterior vena cava*, which originates between the mesonephroi and flows through the liver to the heart. Blood from the liver enters the posterior vena cava near the heart, through the *hepatic vein*. Blood reaches the liver from the *hepatic artery* (a branch of the coeliaco-mesenteric), or from the hepatic portal vein, draining the walls of the intestine.

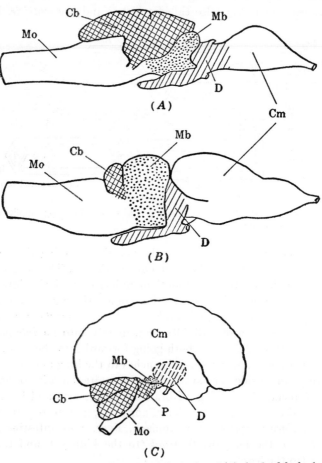

Fig. 56. Diagrammatic side views of the brains of (A) the dogfish shark, (B) the frog, and (C) man. From anterior to posterior (right to left) the five major divisions distinguished are: telencephalon, diencephalon, mesencephalon, metencephalon, myelencephalon. Abbreviations: Cb, cerebellum; Cm, cerebrum; D, diencephalon; Mb, midbrain; Mo, medulla oblongata; P, pons.

As a dogfish, there is a *renal portal system,* carrying venous blood to the "kidneys" from the posterior part of the body. There is also a *ventral abdominal vein,* carrying blood from the legs to the hepatic portal system.

Endocrine System. The glands of internal secretion produce *hormones.* The *pituitary gland,* beneath the brain, secretes hormones that regulate growth and metamorphosis, sexual cycles, pigment changes in the skin, and water relations. The *thyroid gland,* which is behind and below the tongue, is related to metamorphosis and, perhaps, general metabolism. The *islets of Langerhans,* in the pancreas, are related to glycogen storage. The *adrenal glands,* embedded in the ventral side of the kidneys, have few known functions in frogs but are essential for life. The gonads secrete sex hormones.

Nervous System. The names of the divisions of the brain and the spinal nerves are in Table II. Differences in proportions of parts between brains of dogfish, frog, and man are indicated in Figure 56. Spinal nerves of the frog are ten in number; the first three have interlacing fibers constituting the *brachial plexus;* the seventh, eighth, and ninth form in the same way the *sciatic plexus.* Each plexus originates in an enlarged portion of the cord, the *brachial* and *lumbar enlargements.*

Sensory System. The *eyes* have upper and lower *eyelids* and a transparent third eyelid, the *nictitating membrane.* The *eyeball* is approximately spherical; its outer face is covered with the thin transparent *conjunctiva* (reflexed under the lids) and under it the transparent but thicker *cornea.* The *cornea* is continuous with the *sclera,* the outer opaque covering of the sides and back of the eyeball. Under the sclera lies the *choroid,* which, in front, merges into a doughnut-shaped shelf not in contact with the cornea, the *iris.* The hole in the iris is the *pupil.* The *crystalline lens* fits against the back of the iris, closing the pupil. The back of the inside of the eyeball is lined with nerve tissue, the *retina,* directly continuous with the *optic nerve.* The cavity in front of the lens and iris contains the *aqueous humor;* that behind, the *vitreous humor.* The eye is moved by six muscles. (See Fig. 64.)

The *ear* includes organs both for hearing and the sense of equilibrium, the latter in the semicircular canals (see account of dogfish). A *tympanic membrane* (with no external ear) conveys impulses set up by sound waves to the *columella,* a thin bone in the *middle ear,* which transmits impulses to the *cochlea,* the organ of hearing. The middle ear communicates with the pharynx through the *Eustachian tube.*

Reproductive System. The sexes are separate and fertilization is external. The female has two ovaries, ventral to the "kidneys." Mature ova escape into the coelum and are drawn into two oviducts, which lead to the cloaca. Gelatinous envelopes are deposited around eggs in the oviducts. In the male there are two testes, from which the sperm cells reach the cloaca in the Wolffian ducts.

Review Questions

1. What are the criteria used in classifying animals into phyla?
2. Give a classification of the kinds of symmetry shown by animals.
3. What is the general body form of a sponge? Describe the canal system of *Grantia.*
4. Compare *Hydra* and *Obelia* with reference to structure and life history.
5. Describe typical flatworms, both free-living and parasitic kinds.
6. Name common Echinodermata and give the characteristics of the phylum.
7. Describe in detail the structures of the fresh-water mussel.
8. Describe the organ systems of the earthworm.
9. Give the general characteristics of the phylum Arthropoda.
10. In what ways are the Annelida and the Arthropoda similar, and in what ways do they differ? What are the Onychophora?
11. Name the classes of Arthropoda, and give characteristics and examples of each.
12. Explain the principle of homologous structure, as illustrated in the appendages of the crayfish or the frog.
13. Describe in detail the morphology, external and internal, of a typical insect.
14. What are the characteristics of the phylum Chordata?
15. Name and distinguish between (1) the subphyla of the phylum Chordata and (2) the classes of the subphylum Vertebrata.
16. Compare, with reference to each organ system in turn: *Planaria,* fresh-water mussel, earthworm, crayfish, grasshopper, dogfish shark, and frog.
17. Compare the different phyla on the occurrence of a coelom, metamerism, and the nature of skeletal, digestive, circulatory, and nervous systems.

Chapter X

THE PHYSIOLOGY
OF MULTICELLULAR ANIMALS

In discussing animal physiology one may consider either the physiology of different animal types or the physiology of separate functions. In this chapter the latter plan is followed, as a device for summarizing functional relations. The material bearing specifically on human physiology is summarized in Chapter XII. General principles already given in Chapters II and III are not repeated here, nor are functional details that are obvious from the discussion of morphology in the preceding chapter.

A SUMMARY OF FUNCTIONS
IN MULTICELLULAR ANIMALS

Protection and Support. Protection is attained in many organisms through the development of a hard exoskeleton. This may be a shell of lime (in mollusks, corals), a hard covering of chitin (in arthropods), a series of bony plates (turtles), or a coat of scales (fishes, snakes, lizards). Feathers and hair of birds and mammals are protective, as well as means of conservation of heat for warm-blooded animals. Protection of internal organs may also be given by an endoskeleton; e.g., in vertebrates the cranium protects the brain, and the ribs protect the thoracic viscera. Both endo- and exoskeletons help maintain body form, furnish support for organs, and furnish places for the origin and insertion of locomotor muscles.

Movement and Locomotion. Locomotion in Metazoa is usually due to contraction of muscles but may not be (ciliary movement in *Dugesia*).

Mechanics of Muscle Contraction. Muscular contraction involves no change in total volume of tissue; it thickens at the same time it shortens. The shortening may take place across a skeletal joint, resulting in movement at the joint. The movable part behaves like a mechanical lever, the joint being the fulcrum. (See Fig. 60.)

CHEMISTRY OF MUSCLE CONTRACTION. Muscle contraction is a type of trigger reaction, initiated by transformation of ATP to ADP. The state of internal stress which is disturbed on stimulation is restored by energy released in the decomposition of phosphocreatine, a muscle constituent. The phosphoric acid and creatine are then recombined, the energy for this coming from the oxidation of sugar or the formation of lactic acid from glycogen (the latter process nonoxidative). Most of the lactic acid may later be reconverted into glycogen. Only the recovery phase involves oxidation. (For a fuller account, see page 148.)

Digestion.

MECHANICAL PROCESSES INVOLVED IN DIGESTION. These include *mastication,* which may occur in the mouth (grasshopper, crayfish, man), or independently, or in addition farther along in the alimentary canal (in gizzard of earthworm, stomach of crayfish, or gizzard of bird). There may be no thorough mastication (frog). Swallowing, the next process, is voluntary; but food movements through the alimentary canal, largely by *peristalsis,* are involuntary. Food is retained in the stomach of vertebrates until thoroughly acidified, a small bit at a time being then passed through the pyloric valve. *Defecation* (egestion), discharge of undigested or unabsorbed materials, is voluntary.

CHEMICAL PROCESSES INVOLVED IN DIGESTION. These are essentially hydrolyses of foods through the action of specific enzymes. The enzymes are referred to as carbohydrases (if they digest carbohydrates), lipases (if they digest fats), and proteinases (if they digest proteins). Not a great deal is known about the course of digestion in most invertebrate types, but, in general, a variety of digestive enzymes must be present. The description of the digestive enzymes in man (in Chap. XII) will serve as a pattern for the variations within this group of substances.

Respiration.

DEFINITION. Respiration involves all processes bringing oxygen into the body and removing carbon dioxide, together with the process of oxidation within the cells. (Cellular respiration is described in Chapter VII.)

KINDS OF EXTERNAL AND INTERNAL RESPIRATION. Respiration

involves a diffusion gradient of oxygen and carbon dioxide across a thin moist membrane, the oxygen being in greater concentration away from the cells, the carbon dioxide in greater concentration within the cells. Diffusion between the external environment and the animal constitutes *external respiration,* in some cases called *breathing.* It may occur across the walls of the alveoli or air sacs of lungs (air-breathing vertebrates), of lung books (spiders), of gills (fishes, mussels, larval amphibia), or of tracheal gills (in early stages of some insects, e.g., dragonflies). There may be no specialized structures, respiration occurring over the whole surface (*Hydra, Dugesia,* earthworm). The exchange with the individual cells is *internal respiration.* In lower Metazoa, oxygen diffuses in from cell to cell; in insects, air is carried directly to the cells through tracheae; but in other higher animals (earthworm, mussel, all vertebrates), the blood-vascular system carries oxygen to the cells and carbon dioxide away. The gases may be in solution or may be carried in loose combination with a respiratory pigment, e.g., hemoglobin. In lower coelomate forms, having no circulatory system, the coelomic fluid may convey oxygen to the cells and carbon dioxide away.

MECHANICS OF BREATHING IN THE FROG. The mechanisms by which air is brought into the lungs vary considerably with different vertebrates. In the frog, breathing can not occur with the mouth open, for it is by pressure within the mouth cavity, plus the opening of the glottis, that air is pushed into the lungs. The mechanism of breathing in man, which is quite different, is described in Chapter XII.

Circulation.

BLOOD-VASCULAR SYSTEM. This involves a heart and a system of blood vessels. The system of vessels may be completely closed — arteries from the heart branching into capillaries, then reuniting in veins to return the blood (mussel, earthworm, vertebrates); or the heart may pump blood through arteries which do not merge into capillaries but empty their contents into large spaces through which the blood is drawn back to the heart (crayfish); or the blood may flow directly from the heart through irregular spaces in the coelom and back to the heart (insects). Differences between typical animals in the course of circulation are illustrated in Figures 41, 42, 46, 48, 53, 55, and 62. A blood-vascular system functions in carrying food and oxygen to cells or to organs of storage (e.g., liver), in carrying waste products to excretory organs, and in carrying hormones (see p. 157).

CORPUSCLES. Blood cells occur in many forms. These may remove foreign matter or, as in vertebrates, carry oxygen. Amoeboid forms (*amoebocytes*) occur in the greatest variety of animals. In the vertebrates these are "white corpuscles" or *leucocytes*. The "red corpuscles" or *erythrocytes* are of more stable form. The latter have no nuclei in man, but those in the frog and dogfish are nucleate. A third type in vertebrates, the blood platelets or *thrombocytes*, are involved in coagulation of blood.

Excretion.

DEFINITION. Excretion is the discharge of the waste products of metabolism. (It is distinct from egestion — the discharge of undigested or unabsorbed materials.)

ORGANS OF EXCRETION. Carbon dioxide and water are excreted by the lungs; water, urea, and some inorganic salts, by the sweat glands in the skin; certain proteins, by the liver; but the chief excretory organ is the kidney. This functions not only as an excretory organ but as a regulator of osmotic pressure. (In fishes, gills also function in both capacities.) The liquid formed by the kidney is the *urine*, which may or may not be stored in a urinary bladder and discharged at intervals.

KIDNEY FUNCTION. The unit of the kidney, primitive or complex, is the *nephridium*, a more or less coiled tubule. This may have an opening into the coelom (the typical condition in invertebrates and lower vertebrates), or it may receive excretory products solely from the blood stream. For kidney function in man see Chapter XII.

Conduction.

DEFINITION. The transmission of a nerve impulse from one part of the body to another is conduction.

THE STRUCTURAL BASIS FOR CONDUCTION. In primitive Metazoa, nerve impulses are conducted through cells little or not at all differentiated for the purpose. In higher animals, the cells are highly specialized — the *neurons*. A typical neuron consists of three parts: *cell body, dendron, axon*. (Fig. 63.) Neurons are associated together in *nerve tracts* and *reflex arcs*.

PROPERTIES OF THE NERVE IMPULSE. The impulse which passes along a nerve as the result of a stimulus moves at a measurable speed; in man, about 120 meters per second; in the frog, about thirty meters; in the nerve net of a jellyfish, less than one meter per second. The impulse may pass in either direction within a neuron, but only from the axon of one neuron to the dendron of the next in a reflex arc. The impulse is accompanied by a wave of negativity which may be detected by a galvanometer. The recovery of a nerve after excitation (in preparation for next impulse), which takes place in a small fraction of a second in mammals, involves the oxidation of food; it is a chemical as well as a physical process.

THE MECHANISM OF A REFLEX ARC. A simple reflex arc involves at the least: a *receptor* (sense organ), an *afferent neuron*, an *efferent neuron*, and an *effector* (motor organ). From a few to many *associating* or *internuncial neurons* are nearly always present between afferent and efferent neurons. The connections between neurons, the *synapses*, are not intimate; most of the delay in a nervous response is due to the number of synapses rather than the total distance the impulse must travel. (Fig. 63.)

Sensation. A nerve impulse is the result of a stimulus, the latter being received usually by an external sense organ. The sensory system is the system which, more than any other, keeps the individual animal in contact with its environment.

SIGHT. In primitive organisms, sensitivity to light may occur in complete absence of specialized organs. In other animals, an organ which distinguishes between light and darkness may be present. In higher animals, an image from the outside world may be perceived by an eye. The eye is best understood in analogy with a camera. In a camera, light is refracted by a lens; the eye also has a lens, but in addition two liquid refractive media, the aqueous and vitreous humors. One obtains sharp focus in a camera by moving the lens a greater or lesser distance from the sensitive plate; in primitive vertebrates, the lens may be moved a short distance within the eyeball, but in the human eye the shape itself of the lens is modified. An iris diaphragm is present in both camera and eye, concentrating the rays of light on the center of the lens. In the *retina*, the vertebrate eye possesses a sensitive plate containing a light-sensitive chemical (*visual purple*). The analogy does not explain sight itself, however, for a camera can not see. The animal sees with its brain centers, not its eyes; the eyes merely contain the centers for stimulation of the optic nerve tracts.

EQUILIBRIUM AND HEARING. Organs of equilibrium occur in vertebrates, arthropods, and mollusks, at least. They all depend in function on movements of granules or liquids or both across sensitive nerve endings. In higher vertebrates, this function is associated with hearing, the ear housing both sense organs. Organs of hearing present in arthropods as well as vertebrates include membranes which can be set in motion by alternate condensations and rarefactions of the air. The impulse thus set up is conducted by an intermediary, e.g., the chain of ossicles in the human ear, to the real end organ of hearing, which contains the nerve endings. Ability to distinguish between sounds of different pitch involves a very complicated end organ, which, according to some theories, responds by sympathetic vibration to different frequencies at different points along its surface.

CHEMICAL SENSES. The senses of smell and taste involve the exposure of nerve endings to volatile and nonvolatile materials respectively, in solution. Such sense organs occur only in moist membranes — e.g., frog skin.

TACTILE SENSES. End organs of a corpuscular nature, detecting sensations of pressure, pain, heat, and cold, occur in the skin and various body membranes.

PROPRIOCEPTORS. Sense organs similar to the last type in structure occur in muscles and tendons. Impulses set up in them during the contraction of muscles help maintain reciprocal action of antagonistic muscles — preventing muscles of opposite effects from working against each other.

Internal Secretion — Endocrine Secretion. In the higher vertebrates, and less strikingly in other forms (arthropods, in particular), there occur glands that empty their secretions directly into the blood stream. These secretions are carried in the blood to all parts of the body, and they influence activities at a distance from their place of origin. The glands are called *endocrine glands*, or glands of internal secretion. Their products are called *hormones* ("chemical messengers"). In the arthropods, they induce color changes and are influential in regulating development. In vertebrates they control a variety of metabolic, developmental, and reproductive functions. The endocrine glands of man, and the functions of the hormones secreted by them, are summarized in Chapter XII.

Reproduction. (See Chap. XI and, for man, Chap. XII.)

Review Questions

1. What are the functions of animal skeletons?
2. Name and explain the basic mechanical and chemical processes involved in digestion.
3. Compare respiratory mechanisms in different animals.
4. Contrast the course of the blood in earthworm, mussel, insect, fish, and amphibian.
5. Contrast excretion and egestion.
6. Define: nerve impulse, neuron, reflex arc.
7. Give a classification of sense organs.
8. Compare and contrast the eye and a camera.
9. Define endocrine glands, hormones.

Chapter XI

REPRODUCTION, EMBRYOLOGY, AND DEVELOPMENT OF MULTICELLULAR ANIMALS

Reproduction in multicellular animals may occur by either sexual or asexual means; in the higher animals it is exclusively sexual. The two methods differ in that asexual reproduction is uniparental and only mitotic divisions are involved between parent and progeny whereas sexual reproduction is biparental and is accompanied by meiosis and fertilization. (See Chap. VIII.)

ASEXUAL REPRODUCTION

In Metazoa, asexual reproduction involves development of offspring from a relatively small part of the parent — not equal division of parent into two offspring, as in Protozoa.

Budding. In sponges, coelenterates, and bryozoa, new individuals may form as outgrowths from the parent. They may later become separate individuals (*Hydra*) or remain attached as parts of a colony (*Obelia*). In cestodes (tapeworms) new individuals (proglottids) bud from the neck, but remain attached together, distal proglottids dropping off when mature. Certain annelids divide transversely into individuals which separate, becoming independent — a form of reproduction intermediate between budding and fragmentation; a similar method occurs among planarians.

Fragmentation. Some planarians break into fragments, each of which reorganizes into a new individual.

Gemmule Formation. In certain sponges, particularly freshwater forms, at the onset of unfavorable weather, germinal cells become grouped into balls surrounded by spicules. The parent sponge dies, but the balls or *gemmules* survive the unfavorable period, developing into sponges during the next season.

Statoblast Formation. Fresh-water bryozoa form disc-shaped resistant structures, *statoblasts*, which after an unfavorable period (which may have killed the parent colony) germinate into new colonies.

SEXUAL REPRODUCTION

Normal Sexual Reproduction. Two mature germ cells (gametes) fuse to form a *zygote.* The gametes have developed in parents of different *sex.* The male gamete is a *sperm cell (spermatozoon)*; the female, an *egg cell (ovum).* By a process called *maturation* or *gametogenesis*, each gamete develops into an organ called a *gonad.* The gonad of the male is the *testis;* of the female, the *ovary.* The fusion of the gametes, particularly of their nuclei, constitutes *fertilization.* The zygote becomes the mature animal through the process of *embryogeny.*

Variations from Normal Sexual Reproduction.

HERMAPHRODITISM. One individual, a *hermaphrodite*, may produce both eggs and sperm cells. The eggs may be fertilized by sperm cells of the same animal (*self-fertilization*) or by those of another (*cross-fertilization*). (Examples: *Hydra*, flatworm, earthworm, snail.)

PARTHENOGENESIS. This is reproduction through the development of an unfertilized egg — so-called virgin reproduction. (Examples: bees, plant lice. *Artificial parthenogenesis* has been induced by chemical or physical methods in many animals.)

PAEDOGENESIS. Reproduction by an animal in a young or larval condition is called *paedogenesis.* (Examples: liver fluke, tiger salamander.)

Gametogenesis or Maturation. This is the process by which gametes are formed. Structurally, the male gamete is modified for active movement and for penetration of the egg. The female gamete contains a large amount of food material (yolk) for the developing embryo and is passive in movement. In both, the chromosome number has been reduced from diploid to haploid. (Fig. 57.)

SPERMATOGENESIS. Following the period of cellular multiplication which increases the number of germ cells in the testis, there occurs the growth period. The growing cell (destined to form

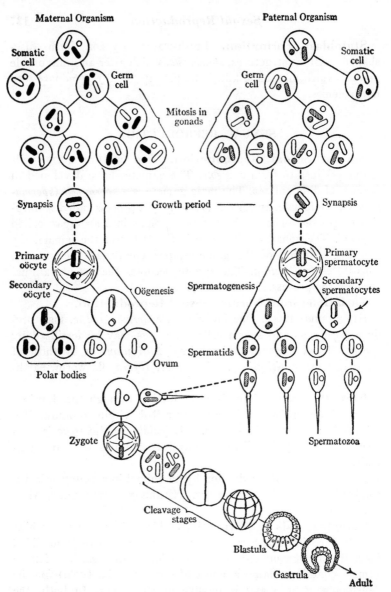

Fig. 57. Diagram illustrating maturation or gametogenesis (oögenesis in female, spermatogenesis in male) and the stages of embryogeny in animals. Also illustrated is the continuity of chromosomes from the gametes which form two parents, through the germ cells in the gonads of these individuals, to the embryo which is their progeny. Reduction division (meiosis) is represented here as occurring during the first maturation division; it may occur during the second instead. (See text for explanation.)

spermatozoa) is the *primary spermatocyte*. It divides, forming two *secondary spermatocytes*. Each of these divides, forming two *spermatids*. Each spermatid, by a process of differentiation without any division, becomes a sperm cell or spermatozoon. Two cell divisions have occurred, together constituting *meiosis*. End result: four functional sperm cells, each with the haploid (n) chromosome number.

Oögenesis. Following the period of multiplication in the ovary, there occurs the growth period, the enlarged cell being the *primary oöcyte*. It divides unequally, forming one (large) *secondary oöcyte* and a (small) *polar body*. The size difference is not due to nuclear size difference, but to cytoplasmic. The polar body may or may not divide again; its fate is unimportant. The secondary oöcyte divides to form a second small polar body and the mature egg cell or ovum. The divisions result in one ovum with the haploid (n) chromosome number, and two or three nonfunctional polar bodies.

Fertilization. Fertilization of the egg is completed when the two *pronuclei,* one from the sperm cell, one already in the ovum, fuse. The sperm may penetrate the egg cell before the first polar body is formed, between the formation of first and second polar bodies, or after the egg is mature; in the first two cases it does not fuse with the egg pronucleus until maturation is complete. The time of *penetration* is characteristic for different species. Fertilization merges immediately into the first division of the zygote, the chromosomes from the two pronuclei being combined on the mitotic spindle, restoring the diploid (2n) chromosome number and giving to the new individual equal numbers of chromosomes from paternal and maternal parents. (Fig. 57.)

Accessory Processes. Various processes adapted to insure fertilization occur. If fertilization occurs outside the female's body, both egg and sperm cells may be shed into the surrounding medium (in every case, water). In some cases where fertilization is external, behavior patterns exist which insure a greater percentage of fertile eggs: In the earthworm, eggs are discharged into a cocoon, into which are then ejected sperm cells received previously during copulation with another worm; in frogs, a male clasps a female during spawning, so that the sperm cells as discharged come immediately into contact with the egg mass. In animals in which fertilization is internal, the male discharges the sperm cells directly into the genital tract of the female during *copulation*. In some forms, this involves merely the apposition of the genital openings, neither being specialized. In others, the male discharges packets of sperm cells which are later picked up by the cloaca of the female (salamanders). An *intromittent organ* or *penis*, introduced into the female genital tract during copulation, may convey packets of sperm cells (grasshopper) or sperm cells in a liquid medium produced by various accessory glands (higher vertebrates).

EMBRYOLOGY OF METAZOA

Definition of Embryogeny. Strictly speaking, the whole course of development from the fertilized egg throughout life is embryogeny. Ordinarily, embryogeny is considered the process of development from the fertilized egg to a stage approximating the adult condition, e.g., to hatching in birds or birth in mammals.

Embryology is the study of the process of development.

General Principles. The zygote divides by a sequence of mitoses characteristic for each animal, this constituting a differentiation pattern which produces the adult form. The process of early development is governed by the nature of the egg.

Kinds of Egg Cells. The nucleus of egg cells is usually excentric, its position being near the side on which polar bodies are formed — the *animal pole*. The cytoplasm is concentrated toward the same side, the yolk being concentrated nearer the opposite pole — the *vegetative pole*. If the yolk is small in amount and rather evenly distributed, the egg is *homolecithal*. If it is large in amount and concentrated toward one pole, the egg is *telolecithal*. In insect eggs, the nucleus with a little cytoplasm lies in the yolk, which is central, the whole being surrounded by a layer of cytoplasm. Such an egg is *centrolecithal*. In the first case, *cleavage* (cell division) may be equal and total, the cells formed being completely divided and of about equal size. In telolecithal eggs, cleavage may be more or less confined to a disclike region at the animal pole. In centrolecithal eggs, cleavage may be confined to the surface all over the egg.

Stages in Embryogeny. The following stages merge one into another; they are given different names for convenience only. (Figs. 57 and 58.)

EARLY CLEAVAGE. The cells as they divide remain attached; the original mass does not increase in size, it simply subdivides. The zygote forms two cells, each of these two making four; in some cases this geometric progression continues some time: 2—4—8—16—32; but in most cases, greater division rates at the animal

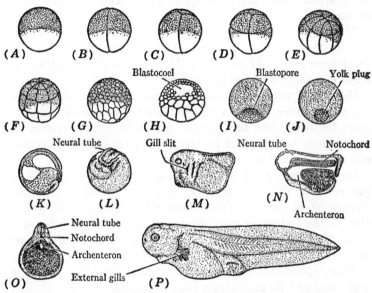

Fig. 58. Stages in the embryology of the frog: (A) the uncleaved egg, (B–F) early cleavage stages, (G–H) blastula, (I–K) gastrula, (L–P) organ formation, (N) a longitudinal section and (O) a cross section of the embryo shown at (M). (Adapted from figure copyright by General Biological Supply House, Chicago, and used by permission.)

pole disturb the regularity. Embryos of approximately sixteen cells look like mulberries; hence the name *morula* for that stage.

BLASTULA. Continued cleavage results in the formation of a hollow ball of cells, the *blastula*, its cavity being the *blastocoel* or *segmentation cavity*.

GASTRULA. More rapid division of cells at animal than at vegetal pole results in a pushing in or *invagination* of the cells near the vegetal pole. This results in a reduction of the blasto- coel as the outer cells push inward, the embryo becoming a ball of cells whose cavity (*archenteron*) opens to the outside but is surrounded elsewhere than at the opening (the *blastopore*) by two layers of cells, the outer *ectoderm* and the inner *endoderm*. In some animals invagination does not occur, but the endoderm is formed by delamination — an internal layering-off from the cells of the blastula. The internal cavity in such embryos becomes secondarily open to the outside (*Hydra*). From an evolutionary standpoint, the gastrula represents the stage to which the adult coelenterate attains.

MESODERM FORMATION. Between ectoderm and endoderm, cells proliferate to occupy the segmentation cavity. These form the third germ layer, the *mesoderm*. The platyhelminthes attain this stage in evolution but go no further.

COELOM FORMATION. Mesoderm cells may separate into two layers, an outer (*somatic*) and an inner (*splanchnic*), leaving a space between which becomes the true *body cavity* or *coelom*. The coelom may be separated by transverse partitions into segmentally-arranged cavities (e.g., earthworm).

ORGANOGENY. With the beginning of coelom formation, *organogeny* or differentiation of organs commences. (Example: Formation of nervous system from ridge of ectoderm.) Derivatives of the embryonic germ layers are, in general, as follows:

From ectoderm: Integument, nervous system, lining of mouth and anus.

From endoderm: Lining of alimentary canal (except mouth and anus) and its appendages (e.g., lungs, bile ducts).

From mesoderm: Internal skeleton, muscles, heart and blood vessels, kidneys, gonads, muscular and connective tissue layers of alimentary canal and its appendages.

Accessory Processes. In some animals the young are retained in an expanded portion of the oviduct, the *uterus*, during a period of development. They may merely be protected, having no nutritional dependence on the maternal organism, as in some fishes and reptiles; or they may receive nourishment from the mother, as in most mammals. The organ which provides for nutrition in mammals is the *placenta*, of partly foetal (embryonic) and partly maternal tissue. Food and oxygen may diffuse through the placental membranes from the maternal into the foetal blood, and waste material may diffuse in the opposite direction, but there is no direct connection. The connection between embryo and placenta is the *umbilical cord*.

COMPLEXITIES IN ANIMAL DEVELOPMENT

Metagenesis. Alternation of a sexually-reproducing with an asexually-reproducing generation occurs in some animals. It is best illustrated in colonial coelenterates like *Obelia* where it is called *metagenesis*. The animals of the colony are formed asexually, by budding; certain of these buds produce, also by budding, the medusae; the medusae reproduce sexually, the fertilized eggs developing into polyps which, by budding, produce new colonies. (Fig. 37.) Metagenesis also occurs among the parasitic flatworms: (1) The adult sheep liver-fluke reproduces sexually; from the egg develops a ciliated larva which bores into a snail; inside, it becomes a *sporocyst* which produces *rediae* asexually; these produce more rediae, and then *cercariae*, asexually; from the cercariae adults develop. (2) In the tapeworm life history, the proglottids are sexually reproducing individuals, but these have been derived from the scolex by an asexual method, viz., budding.

Indirect Development. Many animals attain adult form only after passing through a series of stages more or less unlike the adult. If these stages are very unlike the adult, development is said to be indirect (*complete metamorphosis*); if these stages are present but quite like the adult, in general, development is said to be direct (*incomplete metamorphosis*). Common examples of the former are (1) frogs and toads — which pass through a tadpole stage and (2) bees and butterflies — which have larval and pupal stages. (Among insects having complete metamorphosis, four stages may be recognized: egg, larva — during which stage there may be several molts, pupa, adult.) A common example of incomplete metamorphosis is furnished by the grasshopper, which passes through a series of nymphal stages all of which look somewhat like the adult. The differences are in body proportions and presence and nature of wings or wingpads.

Review Questions

1. Describe asexual reproduction in the Metazoa.
2. Give the steps in gametogenesis, distinguishing between the processes of spermatogenesis and oögenesis.
3. What is the normal course of embryological development from fertilization on?
4. Give examples of various types of complexities in animal development.

Chapter XII

MORPHOLOGY, PHYSIOLOGY, AND
REPRODUCTION OF MAN

Man is an animal. As an animal, he belongs to the species *Homo sapiens* of the order Primates, class Mammalia, phylum Chordata. His anatomy and physiology lend themselves to the same kind of study carried out on other animals. Man is distinct from other animals in the possession of conceptual thought and speech; and, in connection with these, he has a highly organized social system and such distinctly human developments as government and law, education, and religion. Man is, therefore, a unique creature; but the biologists' concern with him is not in his uniqueness but in the ways in which he is a typical animal. This chapter concerns itself with metabolism, irritability, and reproduction in man; and each organ system will be considered from the twin aspects of morphology and physiology.

GENERAL CHARACTERISTICS

Body Divisions. The major divisions of the human body are the *head, neck, trunk*, and two pairs of appendages, the *arms* and *legs*. Five *digits* are present on each appendage. The trunk is commonly divided into two regions, the *thorax*, containing the heart and lungs, and the *abdomen*, containing the liver, stomach, intestine, and other viscera. The axis of the head is horizontal — at right angles to the axis of the rest of the body, which is vertical. The ventral surface of the trunk is in front (apparently anterior), the dorsal surface, in back. The head is actually anterior to the trunk, not dorsal to it.

Coelom. The coelom, in man and other mammals, has four compartments. These are the *pericardial cavity* (containing the heart), two *pleural cavities* (each containing a lung), and the *peritoneal cavity* (containing the abdominal viscera). The peritoneal cavity is bounded anteriorly by the *diaphragm*, a transverse muscle.

ORGAN SYSTEMS OF METABOLISM AND IRRITABILITY

Integumentary System. The *skin* consists of two layers, an outer thin *epidermis* and an inner thick *corium* (or *dermis*). The inner layer, but not the epidermis, contains a variety of tissue types, including blood vessels and nerves. The epidermis, of epithelial tissue, protects underlying structures from loss of moisture and from injury. Specialized structures of the integument include *hair, nails,* and *glands.* The hair of man is distributed on the head, in the axillae (armpits), and. in the pubic region in both sexes, and has a somewhat wider distribution in the male, including the face. Hair and finger and toe nails are derived from the epidermis. The principal glands in the skin are *sweat glands,* which function in temperature regulation (evaporation being a cooling process) and in excretion. Other integumentary glands include *oil glands* and, in the female, *mammary* or *milk glands.* Hair and mammary glands are characteristics man shares with all other mammals.

Skeletal System.

MORPHOLOGY. The bones of the human skeleton comprise an *axial* and an *appendicular skeleton.* The former includes the *skull, vertebral column,* and *thoracic basket;* and the appendicular skeleton comprises the bones of the appendages and *girdles.* All bones of the human skeleton are summarized in Table III, and their general relations are indicated in Figure 59.

PHYSIOLOGY. The major functions of the skeleton are support, protection, and movement (supplying points of attachment for the skeletal muscles). The normal formation of bone in a developing child depends upon the presence of a dietary element, vitamin D, contained plentifully in cod-liver oil and capable of being formed in one's body on exposure to sunlight. The ratio of calcium in blood and bone is regulated by the hormone secreted by the parathyroid glands. A growth-regulating hormone from the anterior lobe of the pituitary gland is involved in bone growth; its excessive secretion may cause gigantism; inadequate secretion may be associated with dwarfism.

Muscular System.

MORPHOLOGY. A skeletal muscle consists typically of a mass of

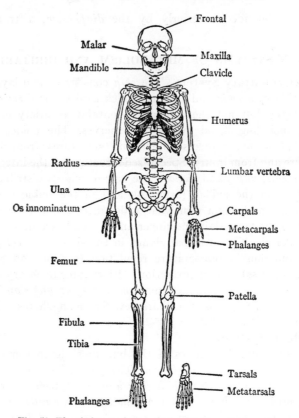

Fig. 59. The skeleton of man. (Adapted from figure copyright by General Biological Supply House, Chicago, and used by permission.)

striated muscle fibers extending across a joint of the skeleton. The end that moves least during contraction is the *origin;* the end moving most, the *insertion.* The movement accomplished constitutes the *action.* Table IV gives origins, insertions, and actions of a few typical skeletal muscles. Some striated muscles are not associated with the skeleton. The diaphragm has a circular origin; its insertion is a central tendon. The tongue is a mass of striated muscle fibers extending in three planes. Nonstriated muscle and cardiac muscle are not ordinarily considered parts of the muscular system because their major activities are related to other functions than locomotion.

Table III. Bones of the Human Skeleton

Axial Skeleton	Skull	Cranium	1 occipital, 2 parietals, 1 frontal, 2 temporals (each containing 3 ossicles of middle ear), 1 sphenoid, 1 ethmoid.
		Face	2 nasals, 1 vomer, 2 inferior turbinals, 2 lacrimals, 2 malars, 2 palatines, 2 maxillae, 1 mandible, 1 hyoid.
	Vertebral Column		Vertebrae: 7 cervical, 12 thoracic, 5 lumbar, 5 sacral (fused into 1), 1+ coccygeal.
	Thoracic Basket		24 ribs, 1 sternum (of 3 elements).
Appendicular Skeleton*	Pectoral Girdle		1 clavicle, 1 scapula.
	Pectoral Appendage		1 humerus, 1 radius, 1 ulna, 8 carpals, 5 metacarpals, 14 phalanges.
	Pelvic Girdle		1 os innominatum, consisting of ilium, ischium, and pubis.
	Pelvic Appendage		1 femur, 1 patella, 1 tibia, 1 fibula, 7 tarsals, 5 metatarsals, 14 phalanges.

* Bones of the appendicular skeleton are given from only one side; to arrive at the total number of bones each of these figures should be multiplied by two.

PHYSIOLOGY.

Mechanical Relations. Muscular contraction involves no change in total volume of tissue; the muscle thickens at the same time it shortens. The process is due to the sudden folding of elongated protein molecules that constitute the microscopic structure of the contractile elements. The shortening of a skeletal muscle takes place across a joint in the skeleton, resulting in a bending at the joint. The movable part behaves like a mechanical lever, the joint

Table IV. Origins, Insertions, and Actions of Representative Muscles of the Human Body

NAME OF MUSCLE	ORIGIN	INSERTION	ACTION
Masseter	Zygomatic arch; temporal and malar bones	Mandible, at angle of jaw	Closes jaws
Biceps	Two points on scapula	Tubercle on radius	Flexes arm at elbow
Triceps	One point on scapula; two on back of humerus	Proximal end of ulna	Extends arm at elbow
Deltoid	Clavicle and scapula	Outer surface of humerus	Raises arm outward from body
Pectoralis major	Clavicle, sternum, cartilages of ribs	Ridge on outer surface of humerus	Pulls arm forward
Gastrocnemius	Two spots on distal end of femur at back	Calcaneum — the tarsal bone of the heel	Extends foot at ankle

being the fulcrum. All three types occur in the human body, the types, with corresponding muscle-skeleton examples, being illustrated in Figure 60. The actions of the diaphragm and tongue do not depend upon skeletal relations. The former is conical when relaxed; contraction transforms the cone into a flattened disc, increasing the vertical diameter of the thoracic cavity. Tongue movements are brought about by the contraction of muscle groups that extend in different directions.

Chemistry of Muscular Activity. The chemical processes in muscle contraction involve a type of trigger reaction in which stored energy is released suddenly, this energy being used to pro-

duce the contraction. The stored energy is released by the break-
down of ATP (adenosine triphosphate) and phosphocreatine. Both
are common constituents of muscle. The ATP and phosphocreatine
are then resynthesized, the energy for this coming from the
oxidation of sugar or the formation of lactic acid from glycogen
(the latter process being anaerobic). Glycogen is the form in
which carbohydrate food is stored in muscle. Most of the lactic

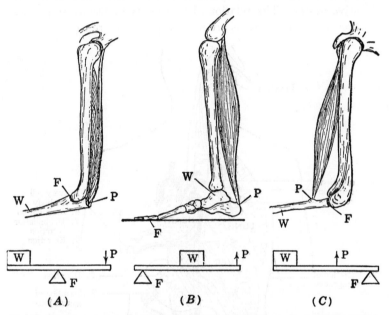

Fig. 60. Diagrams to suggest the relations between the three classes of levers and
the actions of skeletal muscles. (A) First class lever, illustrated by the triceps muscle
extending the arm at the elbow. (B) Second class lever, illustrated by the gastrocne-
mius muscle raising the weight of the body on the toes. (C) Third class lever, illustrated by the biceps muscle flexing the arm at the elbow. Abbreviations: F, fulcrum,
P, power, W, weight.

acid may later be reconverted into glycogen, the energy for that
process coming from the aerobic oxidation of a part of the lactic
acid. Thus only the recovery phase involves oxygen, and a muscle
can contract vigorously for some time in the absence of oxygen. A
muscle becomes fatigued, however, and ceases to contract, if
contractions occur so frequently that oxidative recovery can not
take place.

Digestive System. Metabolic activity depends upon food as a source of energy. Man's specific needs in this respect constitute proper *nutrition*. The digestive process is basic to all other metabolic activities because man, like other animals, can not manufacture his own food. He acquires it in complex form from plants (either directly or indirectly — from other animals) and, in order to use it, must reduce it to chemically simpler form. The process of preparing food for absorption and use is the function of the digestive system. The relations between its functions and those of other metabolic systems are illustrated in Figure 61.

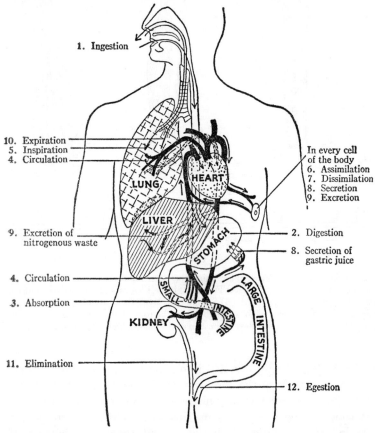

Fig. 61. Diagram to suggest the steps in metabolism as they occur in the human body. (Compare with Figure 8.) (Reprinted by permission from *Animal Biology* by R. H. Wolcott, copyright, 1946, by the McGraw-Hill Book Company.)

MORPHOLOGY.

Alimentary Canal. The digestive tract or alimentary canal consists, in order, of the *mouth, pharynx, oesophagus, stomach, small intestine, large intestine* or *colon, rectum,* and *anus.* The mouth is closed by fleshy lips, and these and the tongue function in moving food so that the masticating organs, the *teeth,* can break it up. There are thirty-two teeth, of four types: eight *incisors,* four *canines,* eight *premolars,* and twelve *molars,* equally distributed in upper and lower jaws. These constitute the *permanent dentition.* The first or *milk dentition* lacks the twelve molars. The tongue bears *taste buds.* The mouth merges into the pharynx, the region in which air passing to and from the lungs crosses the food passage. The oesophagus is a straight, muscular tube opening into the stomach. The latter is curved, its *greater curvature* to the left. The upper end of the stomach is the *cardiac end;* the lower, the *pyloric end,* terminates in a circular muscle, the *pyloric valve.* The small intestine consists of three parts, the *duodenum, jejunum,* and *ileum.* The large intestine or colon consists of ascending, transverse, and descending portions. A *caecum* (blind pouch) is present at the junction of colon and ileum, and the *vermiform appendix* is a projection from the caecum. The descending portion of the colon merges into the *sigmoid flexure* and rectum, the latter opening to the outside through the anus. There is no cloaca.

Digestive Glands. Three pairs of *salivary glands* empty into the mouth. The specialized digestive glands of the peritoneal cavity are the *liver* and *pancreas.* The liver, which is very large, consists of four lobes; it contains a *gall bladder* (in which bile is stored) in the right lobe. The pancreas is a smaller, transverse organ lying behind the stomach. The *bile duct* (from the liver) and the *pancreatic duct* meet, their contents entering the duodenum together, not far from the pyloric valve. Other digestive glands are present in the stomach wall and the lining of the small intestine.

PHYSIOLOGY.

Mechanical Processes. The food, after being masticated in the mouth and mixed with *saliva* from the salivary glands, is swallowed by voluntary movements. Its passage through the alimentary canal is, however, largely involuntary. Food is retained in the stomach until thoroughly acidified. It is passed into the duodenum through the pyloric valve a small amount at a time. The acidified food in the duodenum causes the secretion of two hormones, one stimulating secretion of the pancreas and the other causing the flow of bile from the gall bladder. Mechanical actions of the intestine involve forward movement of the contents by *peristalsis* (muscle waves) and a rhythmic segmentation, the latter process allowing for complete mixing of the food mass or *chyme* with intestinal enzymes and complete absorption of digested food through the intestinal walls. Water is resorbed through the walls of the colon, concentrating the undigested material to form *feces*. *Defecation*, the discharge of fecal material, is voluntary.

Chemical Processes — the Digestive Enzymes. Digestion is accomplished by a series of specific hydrolyzing enzymes. The first enzyme activity is in the mouth, where *salivary amylase (ptyalin)* converts starch into maltose (a double sugar), but its action is stopped by high acidity when the food reaches the stomach. In the stomach, *pepsin*, in the presence of hydrochloric acid, hydrolyzes proteins to peptones and proteoses — simple compounds of amino acids. The pancreatic juice contains several enzymes. One of these is *pancreatic amylase*, with the same function as salivary amylase. Another is *lipase*, which hydrolyzes fats to glycerol and fatty acids. In addition to these there is a substance called *trypsin* that appears to be a mixture of protein-hydrolyzing enzymes; it can carry out the complete digestion of a protein to amino acids. The bile does not contain a digestive enzyme but does aid in fat digestion, emulsifying fat particles. Four other enzymes are secreted by glands in the wall of the small intestine. Three of these digest the common double sugars, maltose, sucrose, and lactose. The other, *erepsin*, is a protein-splitting enzyme, completing the digestion of partially digested proteins.

Food Absorption. The small intestine contains in its lining minute fingerlike projections called *villi* (sing., *villus*). These contain microscopic branches of the circulatory system — both blood capillaries and lymphatics. In general, the end products of carbohydrate and protein digestion are absorbed in the blood capillaries and fat in the lymphatics. The blood capillaries carry food to the liver in the portal system; the lymphatic system empties directly into the veins near the heart.

NUTRITION. Nutritional requirements include food for energy, specific foods, water and mineral needs, and vitamins.

Energy Requirements. Man's food requirements for energy are measured in *Calories* per day. *Total metabolism* requires 2,500 to

5,000 Calories per day, depending upon the kind of physical exertion involved. *Basal metabolism*, energy use during complete rest, involves 1,600 to 1,800 Calories per day. Carbohydrates and proteins yield four Calories per gram, fats nine Calories per gram.

Specific Food Requirements. A minimum protein intake is necessary to offset continuous nitrogen excretion — to maintain *nitrogen equilibrium*. Specific amino acids are required, too, particularly in growing individuals.

Water and Mineral Requirements. A human being requires about one quart of water per day, in addition to water contained in food. Most mineral requirements are present in an average diet in sufficient quantity, but phosphorus, calcium, and iron are three important elements in which a diet may be deficient.

Vitamins. These are complex substances of plant origin required in man's diet but not needed in large quantity. Water-soluble vitamins include those of the vitamin B-complex (thiamine, riboflavin, and others) and vitamin C (ascorbic acid). These are involved in cellular respiration. The fat-soluble vitamins include vitamin A, related to visual activity, vitamin D, involved in bone formation, and vitamin K, important in blood clotting. Certain diseases (called *deficiency diseases*) occur in the absence of an adequate quantity of vitamins in the diet. Thus, scurvy is a result of inadequate vitamin C, and rickets is due to a deficiency of vitamin D. (Vitamin E is related to normal reproduction in some mammals, but its necessity in the human diet has not been demonstrated.)

Circulatory System.

MORPHOLOGY. The circulatory system consists of a circulating medium, the *blood*, the channels through which it flows, and a *lymphatic system*.

Blood. The blood consists of a liquid substrate, the *plasma*, in which are contained *erythrocytes* (*red corpuscles*), *leucocytes* (*white corpuscles*), and *thrombocytes* (*blood platelets*).

Heart and Blood Vessels. Circulation of the blood is maintained by the rhythmic contraction of the *heart*, the rate of the heart beat being intrinsic but subject to modification by autonomic nervous control. There are two *auricles* or *atria* in the heart, both thin-walled, and two *ventricles*, the latter with thick, muscular walls. Blood to the lungs leaves from the *right ventricle* and passes through the two *pulmonary arteries*. It is returned to the *left auricle* of the heart through the *right* and *left pulmonary veins*. From the left auricle it enters the *left ventricle*, passing through the opening guarded by the *mitral valve*. The left ventricle pumps the blood into the *systemic circulation*, through the *aorta*, whose main arch is to the left. Branches from the arch of the aorta are: the *innominate artery* — dividing into *right subclavian* and *right carotid arteries*, the *left carotid artery*, and the *left subclavian artery*. The carotids extend into the head; the subclavians, through the shoulder into the arm. The *descending aorta* gives off branches to muscles, lungs, and abdominal viscera, and divides in the lower portion of the abdominal cavity into the *common iliac arteries*, which carry the blood into the legs.

The venous system consists of: a *portal vein*, carrying blood from the alimentary canal to the liver (a renal portal vein — such as occurs in the frog — is absent); the *inferior vena cava*, a large vein draining the lower part of the body and emptying into the *right auricle;* and the *superior vena cava*, formed by the union of the *right* and *left innominate veins*, each of these formed by a *jugular* and a *subclavian vein*. The jugulars drain the head; the subclavians, the arms. Microscopic blood vessels, the *capillaries*, carry the blood directly to the tissues of all parts of the body. They provide the connection between arteries and veins and between the portal system and the inferior vena cava, and, from the point of view of circulatory function, are the most important structures of the circulatory system.

Lymphatic System. Intercellular spaces, which are filled with material that diffuses from the capillaries, are drained by a set of channels called *lymph vessels* that empty into the subclavian veins near the heart. The lymph vessel on the left side, the *thoracic duct*, drains all the body below the diaphragm as well as the left side above it. The right lymphatic duct, which drains the right side of the body above the diaphragm, is smaller.

PHYSIOLOGY. The course of the blood, outlined in the description of the morphology of the heart and blood vessels, is diagrammed in Figure 62. Functions of the blood include (1) transport of food material and oxygen to the cells and waste material away from them, (2) regulation of body temperature, (3) transport of hormones, and (4) disease resistance. Blood capillaries in the walls of the intestine absorb end products of carbohydrate and protein digestion. These are conveyed to the liver by the portal vein. Products of fat digestion are absorbed by the *lacteals* (small lymph channels in the villi), through which they are conducted to the veins by way of the thoracic duct. The disease-resisting function is accomplished by the *antigen-antibody reactions* of the blood, a foreign protein (antigen) in the blood stimulating the formation of an antibody. The latter may *precipitate* the foreign protein if the protein is in solution or *agglutinate* the foreign bodies into clumps if they are insoluble. In the latter case, *phagocytosis* (the engulfing of the foreign material by white corpuscles)

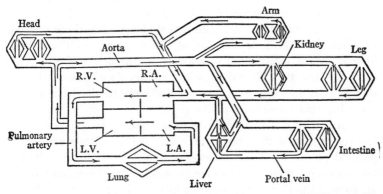

Fig. 62. Diagram illustrating the direction of blood flow in man. Applies equally well to all mammals and (by substituting "wing" for "arm") to all birds. The aortic arch swings to the left in mammals, to the right in birds.

is increased. A poison (*toxin*) produced by a foreign organism stimulates production of an *antitoxin*, a kind of antibody. The thrombocytes are functionally important in blood clotting, whereas the erythrocytes, which contain hemoglobin, carry oxygen from the lungs to the cells.

Respiratory System.

MORPHOLOGY. The air passages in the nose are increased in surface area by *turbinal bones*, over which extends the olfactory membrane. The passages open into the roof of the *pharynx* at the back of the *soft palate*. From the pharynx, the air passage leads into the *larynx* ("voice box") through an opening covered by a flap, the *epiglottis*. The larynx is at the upper end of the *trachea* or windpipe. The latter bifurcates, forming two *bronchi*, one entering each *lung*, where it repeatedly divides into the smaller *bronchial tubes;* these terminate in thin-walled pockets, the *alveoli,* arranged in groups. The pulmonary capillaries are in the walls of the alveoli.

Each lung is covered by a membrane, the *visceral pleura,* which is reflected back at its root to line the cavity in which the lung lies. The outer wall of the cavity is lined with the *parietal pleura.* Each of the two pleural cavities is separate, and neither communicates with any other portion of the coelom.

PHYSIOLOGY.

Breathing. The movement of air into and out of the lungs properly constitutes *breathing,* not "respiration," in spite of popular usage to the contrary. The mechanics of breathing involve movements of the floor and wall of the chest cavity. The floor is formed by the diaphragm; increase in height of the chest cavity (actually the two pleural cavities) results from contraction of this muscle. Increase in transverse diameter results from raising the ribs, this movement produced by contraction of *intercostal muscles.* Because the parietal pleura is attached to the outer wall, increase in size of the chest is accompanied by withdrawal of the parietal pleura from the lungs. Decrease of air pressure in the pleural cavity then decreases air pressure in the lungs, and, if the air passages are open, air is drawn into the lungs.

Oxygen Transport. Because alveolar air normally contains more oxygen and less carbon dioxide than does the blood in the pulmonary capillaries, oxygen tends to diffuse into the blood and carbon dioxide from the blood into the alveoli. Once in the blood, most of the oxygen is picked up and carried in loose combination with *hemoglobin,* the reddish pigment of the erythrocytes, the combination being called *oxyhemoglobin.* In the capillaries in the systemic (nonpulmonary) portion of the blood system the concentration gradient is in the opposite direction from that in the lung wall, the oxygen being more concentrated in the blood than in the cells. The oxyhemoglobin is spontaneously reduced, under the lower oxygen pressure, and the oxygen diffuses into the cells. Carbon dioxide, more concentrated in the cells than in the blood, diffuses into the blood and is carried to the lungs.

Cell Respiration. The oxidation that takes place within the individual cells is, properly speaking, cell respiration. This process, essentially the same in all animals and plants, has already been described in Chapter VII.

Excretory System.

MORPHOLOGY. There are two, moderately large, bean-shaped *kidneys*, in the posterior wall of the peritoneal cavity. Each has a duct, the *ureter*, that conveys urine to the *urinary bladder*. The channel by which urine leaves the urinary bladder is the *urethra*. The urinary and reproductive ducts have a common external opening.

In the kidney each secretory unit consists of a *Bowman's capsule*, the *proximal* and *distal convoluted tubules*, and the *loop of Henle* intervening. Blood capillaries form a knot within the capsule and around the tubules.

All excretion does not take place through the kidneys. The sweat glands of the skin, and the lungs, are both partly excretory in function. Certain nitrogenous compounds discharged into the blood by the liver are excretory products; hence the liver, too, is a part of the excretory system.

PHYSIOLOGY. Bowman's capsule, which surrounds a knot of capillaries called a *glomerulus*, functions as a filter. The convoluted tubules have a more active function, in that they secrete additional materials into the cavity of the tubule, and remove others from the tubule. The urine is the product, therefore, both of filtration and secretion.

The sweat glands are of great importance in temperature regulation, the act of perspiring being important, through the effect of evaporation, in reducing surface temperature. The rate of perspiration is determined by the blood supply of the sweat glands, which, in turn, is under autonomic nervous control.

Endocrine System. Although not constituting a definite organ system, the *endocrine glands*, which secrete *hormones*, may be summarized together. In all cases their secretory products are picked up and carried in the blood stream rather than in specialized ducts; hence they are called endocrine glands, meaning glands of internal secretion. The hormones, which produce effects remote from their place of origin, are chemical co-ordinators.

The *pituitary gland*, at the base of the brain, consists of two main divisions, the *anterior* and *posterior lobes*. The former secretes hormones that regulate growth, sexual development, and the activity of other endocrine glands. The posterior lobe secretes hormones that affect smooth muscle activity and the water relations of the circulatory system. The *thyroid gland*, a bilobed structure in front of the trachea, secretes a hormone (*thyroxin*) that regulates basal metabolism. The *parathyroid glands*, four small bodies that may be embedded in the thyroid, secrete a hormone that regulates calcium balance between the bones and the blood. In the pancreas occur scattered groups of endocrine cells, the *islets of Langerhans*, which secrete *insulin*, a hormone involved in glycogen storage in the liver — and therefore in the sugar balance in the blood. The *adrenal glands*, which are endocrine, lie anterior to and in contact with the kidneys. They secrete a hormone (*epinephrine* or *adrenalin*) from the *medulla* or central portion and a mixture of hormones (collectively called *cortin*) from the *cortex*. Epinephrine produces the same effects as those accomplished by stimulation of the sympathetic portion of the autonomic nervous system — acceleration of the heart beat, heightened blood pressure, inhibition of secretion of certain glands, and other effects. Cortin is involved in the regulation of metabolism and in reproduction. The parathyroid secretion, insulin, and cortin are essential to life. A few hormones that regulate the production of digestive. secretions are formed in the walls of the duodenum. Hormones responsible for the development of secondary sexual characteristics are secreted by cells in the gonads of both sexes, and from the ovary arise hormones involved in the regulation of menstruation, pregnancy, and lactation. In addition to the glands of known endocrine function there are a few suspected of having such function. These include, particularly, the *thymus gland*, in the throat, and the *pineal body*, on the dorsal side of the brain.

Nervous System. The nervous system consists of the *central nervous system* (*brain* and *spinal cord*), the *peripheral nervous system* (*cranial* and *spinal nerves*), and the *autonomic nervous system*.

MORPHOLOGY.

Central Nervous System. The brain has five major divisions. The *cerebral hemispheres* (derived from the embryonic *telencephalon*) are so large in the human brain that the *diencephalon* and *midbrain* (*mesencephalon*), the next two divisions, are completely concealed by them. The *cerebellum* (*metencephalon*) is, however, relatively large. These four, with the *medulla oblongata* (*myelencephalon*), constitute the five divisions of the brain. The medulla merges into the *spinal cord*, which has two enlarged regions, the *cervical* and *lumbar enlargements*. (See Fig. 56.)

The brain and spinal cord are surrounded by three membranes or *meninges*. These are the *pia mater*, next the brain or cord, the *dura mater*, lining the cranium and neural canal of the vertebrae, and the loose *arachnoid membrane* between them.

Peripheral Nervous System. There are twelve cranial nerves, as in reptiles, birds, and other mammals, with essentially the same distribution. Three are purely sensory: I, *olfactory;* II, *optic;* VIII, *auditory.* Three (III, IV, and VI) serve the eye muscles.

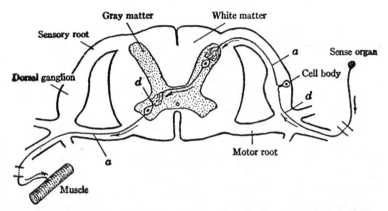

Fig. 63. Diagram illustrating relations between spinal cord and spinal nerves. Three neurons, constituting a simple reflex arc, are represented. The direction of the nerve impulse through these neurons is indicated by arrows. Abbreviations: a, axon; d, dendron.

The *vagus nerve* (X) extends into the thoracic and peritoneal cavities from the head. The other cranial nerves supply head and neck with sensory and motor fibers. Of these nerves, the *trigeminal* (V) and the *facial* (VII) are quite important. Man has thirty-one spinal nerves: eight *cervical*, twelve *thoracic*, five *lumbar*, five *sacral*, and one *coccygeal*. The spinal nerves join to form *cervical*, *brachial*, *lumbar*, and *sacral plexuses* in man. Each spinal nerve has two *roots*, a *dorsal* or *sensory root* and a *ventral* or *motor root*. The nerve branches into three *rami*, a dorsal, a ventral, and a communicating ramus (containing fibers of the autonomic nervous system). (See Fig. 63.)

Autonomic Nervous System. The autonomic nervous system is related structurally to the central nervous system but the actions it controls are independent of the will. The system consists of two parts, the *sympathetic system*, arising in the thoracic region, and the *parasympathetic system*, arising in the cranial and sacral regions. Fibers from both systems invade all parts of the body, and the impulses they carry are mutually antagonistic.

PHYSIOLOGY. The principal function of the nervous system is the conduction of *nerve impulses* from one part of the body to another, thus bringing about co-ordinated responses. The cells involved are the highly specialized *neurons*, typically consisting of a *cell body*, and a *dendron* and an *axon*. Neurons are associated together in *nerve tracts* and *reflex arcs*. The nerve impulse may pass over a single neuron in either direction, but only from the axon of one neuron to the dendron of the next in an association tract or reflex arc. Such a connection is a *synapse*. A simple reflex (Fig. 63) involves at least a *receptor* (sense organ), an *afferent* (sensory) *neuron*, an *efferent* (motor) *neuron*, and an *effector* (motor organ). From a few to many *associating* or *internuncial neurons* are nearly always present between afferent and efferent neurons. The connections between neurons (synapses) are not intimate. Most of the delay in the passage of a nerve impulse through a reflex arc is due to the number of synapses over which it must pass rather than the total distance it travels. The nerve impulse travels at a measurable speed, about 120 meters per second in man. It is accompanied by a wave of negative electricity which can be detected by a galvanometer. The recovery of a nerve after excitation (in preparation for conducting the next impulse), which takes place in a small fraction of a second, involves the oxidation of food. Transmission of a nerve impulse is, therefore, a chemical as well as a physical process.

Sensory System.

EYE. (Fig. 64.) The eye is best understood in analogy with a camera. In a camera, light is refracted by a lens; the eye also has a *lens*, but it has, in addition, two liquid refractive media, the *aqueous humor* and the *vitreous humor*. While in a camera focussing is accomplished by moving the lens forward and backward, in the eye it is accomplished by changing the shape of the lens. An *iris* diaphragm, concentrating the rays of light in the center of the lens, is present in both eye and camera. In the *retina*, the human eye possesses a sensitive plate containing a light-sensitive chemical (*visual purple*). This analogy does not, of course, explain sight itself. A camera can not see. The brain gives man the final interpretation of visual stimuli, after impulses set up in the retina are conducted to the brain over the optic nerve.

EAR. Two different sense organs are contained in the ear, the organ for the sense of equilibrium and the organ of hearing. The former consists of three *semicircular canals* at right angles to each other (two vertical and one horizontal), containing nerve endings stimulated by the flow of liquid in the canals. The organ of hearing involves three regions, the *outer ear*, *middle ear*, and

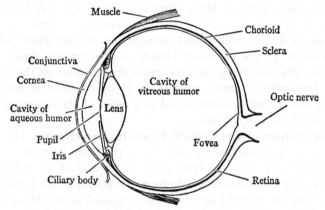

Fig. 64. Vertical section through the human eye. The relations, though not the proportions, are typical of vertebrates in general. (Modified from various authors.)

inner ear. The outer ear includes the *pinna*, or ear flap, and the *external auditory meatus* or canal, terminating at its inner end with the *tympanic membrane*. Movement of the tympanic membrane is conveyed as vibrations across the middle ear through a chain of three small bones or auditory ossicles, the *malleus* ("hammer"), *incus* ("anvil"), and *stapes* ("stirrup"). These vibrations are transferred to liquid in the inner ear, which contains the real organ of hearing, the *organ of Corti*. Ability to distinguish between sounds of different pitch involves, according to a widely-held theory, response by sympathetic vibration to different frequencies at different levels along the organ of Corti. The interpretation of the sensation of sound, as of sight, rests, of course, in the brain.

OTHER SENSE ORGANS. In general, other sense organs involve relatively simple terminal nerve elements that do not occur in complexly differentiated organs. The senses of taste, smell, pain, pressure, temperature, and others are of this general type.

REPRODUCTION AND DEVELOPMENT

Morphology of the Male Reproductive Organs. The gonads of the male, the *testes*, are contained in a saclike extension of the coelom, the *scrotum*. Each testis contains many tubules in which spermatozoa are formed and from which numerous *vasa efferentia* drain into the single *vas deferens* from each of the two testes. Each vas deferens or sperm duct extends into the peritoneal cavity, where it meets the urethra and the sperm duct from the opposite side, after receiving the secretions of a *seminal vesicle*. The ducts in this region pass through the *prostate gland*, which contributes to the secretion known as the *seminal fluid*. The urethra, after receiving the two sperm ducts, traverses the *penis*. This intromittent organ consists of three columns of spongy, *erectile tissue* that becomes turgid as a result of the concentration of blood in its vascular spaces.

Morphology of the Female Reproductive Organs. The two gonads of the female, the *ovaries*, lie in the lower part of the abdominal cavity near the open ends of the *oviducts* or *Fallopian tubules*. The two tubules join to form the *uterus*, which communicates with the external opening, the *urogenital sinus*, through the *vagina*. The opening of the urogenital sinus is bounded laterally by two pairs of folds, the inner *labia minora* and the outer *labia majora*. The *clitoris*, homologous with the penis of the male, lies at the anterior margin of the urogenital sinus, and the urethra opens into the sinus just posterior to it.

Physiology of Reproduction and Development. The developing *ovum* is contained in a *follicle* in the ovary, and this follicle grows as the egg cell grows. When fully formed, the follicle ruptures, releasing the ovum. This process is *ovulation*. The ovum is drawn into the Fallopian tubule, where fertilization (conception) may occur if motile sperm cells are present. (The sperm cells move through the uterus from the vagina, and up the Fallopian tubules, following copulation, and fertilization normally occurs at the upper end of the Fallopian tubule.) If fertilization does not occur, the ovum is carried down the tubule, through the uterus, and it leaves the body through the vagina. In that case, the *corpus luteum*, formed at the surface of the ovary from the ruptured follicle, gradually decreases in size; and in about two weeks after ovulation the lining of the uterus goes through a process of rapid disintegration, the process of *menstruation*. Ovulation and menstruation, two events in the *menstrual cycle* of approximately twenty-eight days, are normal aspects of the sex cycle of a woman between *puberty* and *menopause*, except when interrupted by *pregnancy*.

If fertilization of the ovum occurs, development begins in the Fallopian tubule; when the embryo reaches the uterus, it is *implanted* in the wall of the uterus. In this case the corpus luteum persists and grows, forming an endocrine gland whose hormone provides for maintenance of the embryo in the uterus and inhibits the menstrual cycle. As the embryo (*foetus*) develops, part of its tissue becomes embedded in the maternal tissue lining the uterus, the embryonic and maternal tissues there forming the *placenta*, an organ in which substances in the maternal and foetal blood may diffuse back and forth through relatively few intervening cell layers. The embryo is connected with the placenta by the *umbilical cord*. There is no direct connection of blood stream, nervous system, or any other system between embryo and mother. At the end of the period of pregnancy, about ten lunar months after fertilization, *birth* or *parturition* occurs. This is calculated as 280 days after the beginning of the last menstruation (since menstruation ceases during pregnancy). Shortly after parturition, *lactation* or milk secretion begins. This is continued through stimulation caused by the drainage of the ducts of the *mammary glands*.

Review Questions

1. Is man a typical animal? a typical mammal?
2. Describe the human skeleton.
3. How are skeletal muscles involved in movement?
4. What is the chemistry of muscle contraction?
5. Trace the path of food through the digestive tract, giving in order the names of the enzymes acting upon it and their effects.
6. What are the nutritional requirements of man?
7. What are the functions of the circulatory system, and, in that connection, why are capillaries important?
8. Describe the course of the blood in the human circulatory system.
9. Describe in detail the various mechanisms involved in the transport of oxygen from the outside air to the cells of the body.
10. What structures are involved in the formation of urine, and how do they function?
11. Describe the interrelations of digestive, circulatory, respiratory, and excretory systems.

12. Name, locate, and give the functions of the endocrine glands.
13. Name and describe the principal parts of the human nervous system.
14. What is a reflex arc? Discuss the passage of a nerve impulse over a reflex arc.
15. Show how the eye and the ear are adapted for their particular sensory functions.
16. Describe the male and female reproductive organs of man.
17. What is the menstrual cycle?
18. Summarize the most important facts about human embryonic development.

Part Three

GENERAL PRINCIPLES

Part Three

GENERAL PRINCIPLES

Chapter XIII

HEREDITY

Heredity is the transmission of traits, physical or mental, from parents to offspring. The scientific study of this transmission is *genetics;* it may follow either statistical or experimental methods.

THE CONTINUITY OF THE GERM PLASM

Some sixty years ago, August Weismann suggested that all hereditary change must originate in the germ plasm, inasmuch as *the germ plasm constitutes the only organic continuity from one generation to the next.* This concept of the continuity of the germ plasm is the basic principle in all studies of biological inheritance.

MENDELISM

Gregor Mendel. Working on garden peas, studying the effects of crossing peas of contrasting characteristics and their descendants, Gregor Mendel discovered in the early 1860's the principles now known as Mendel's Laws. Their true scientific value was not appreciated until 1900, after Mendel's death.

Mendel's Experiments. These involved seven pairs of contrasting characters of the garden pea. Mendel discovered that the progeny of a cross of unlike parents of pure lines were all alike, resembling one parent only. When the flowers of these (the F_1 generation) were permitted to be self-fertilizing, on the other hand, both of the original parental types were present in their progeny. These types were present in numbers approximating a 3 : 1 ratio — three like the F_1 to one like the parental type which did not appear in the F_1 generation. The latter type Mendel called *recessive;* the former, *dominant.* Seeds from plants showing the recessive trait produced plants all having the recessive trait; but seeds from a plant showing the dominant trait but having the recessive trait in its ancestry developed into both types of plants.

Interpretation of Mendel's Experiments. The importance of the gametes was realized by Mendel, who saw that to explain the ratios he obtained he had to assume that a given gamete could contain a determiner for one character but not its opposite. If the determiner for the dominant trait was derived from both parents or *from either one*, the offspring would show the dominant trait; the recessive trait appeared only when the gametes from *both parents* contained its determiner. Each trait appeared as if determined by a single factor in each gamete — the gametes being themselves "pure" for one of the two contrasting characters. This explanation coincided also with Mendel's observation that, regardless of the number of contrasting characters studied at one time, the hereditary behavior of each one was independent of the others.

Mendel's Laws. Aside from the idea of dominance, which is not universally true, Mendel's chief contributions were the concepts of (1) *segregation* and (2) *independent assortment*. A corollary of the former is the concept of the *purity of the gametes*. Independent assortment does not hold true of determiners showing linkage (see below).

Terminology of Mendelian Inheritance. Unit characters may be determined by single *factors* or *determiners*, now called *genes*. Alternative characters are *allelomorphic;* their determiners can not occur in the same gamete. A zygote containing two determiners for the same character is *homozygous;* one containing the genes for alternative characters is *heterozygous*. All organisms that look alike with reference to alternative characters belong to the same *phenotype;* all organisms of the same genetic behavior with reference to alternative characters belong to the same *genotype*. (To illustrate: Heterozygous dominants and homozygous dominants are of the same phenotype but different genotypes.)

Examples of Mendelian Inheritance. While it is not true that all inheritance of unit characters is as simple as was the case for those Mendel studied, yet it is necessary to understand such simple situations in order to comprehend more complex ones.

EXAMPLES FROM THE GARDEN PEA. Three contrasting characters studied by Mendel had to do with length of stem, color of seed, and character of seed coat. Mendel found that the tall stem condition was dominant over dwarf, that yellow seed color was dominant over green, and that a smooth seed coat was dominant over a wrinkled one. The following outlines illustrate the results in these crosses:

(P = parental generation F_1 = first filial generation)

P   Tall × Dwarf
F_1 All Tall

Various combinations failed to modify the principle of dominance:

P   Tall Yellow Smooth × Dwarf Green Wrinkled
F_1 All Tall Yellow Smooth

It is obvious, however, that tall plants from dissimilar parents have really developed from gametes containing the determiners for *both* tall and dwarf. Hence:

(T = gene for tall   t = gene for dwarf
 Y = gene for yellow   y = gene for green
 S = gene for smooth   s = gene for wrinkled
              and G = gametes)

P   TT (homozygous tall) × tt (homozygous dwarf)
G   All T   All t
F_1 All Tt (heterozygous tall)
P   TTYYSS × ttyyss
G   All TYS   All tys
F_1 All TtYySs (heterozygous tall yellow smooth)

(Note: Following the principle of the purity of the gametes, a gamete can not contain two "t's," two "y's," or two "s's"; it will always contain one representative of each group of allelomorphs.)

Mendel found that self-fertilized flowers of heterozygous tall (Tt) plants produced plants both tall and dwarf in approximately a 3 : 1 ratio. The letter method of representation shows how, by chance distribution of genes in gametes and the subsequent chance fertilization of any egg nucleus by any pollen-tube sperm nucleus, this ratio is achieved. In crosses in which one studies two or three pairs of contrasting characters the ratios are different, but all more complicated ratios have definite arithmetical relationship with those found in simple one-factor crosses:

P   Tt × Tt

G $\frac{1}{2}$T, $\frac{1}{2}$t, from each parent

F_1 $\frac{1}{4}$TT $\frac{1}{2}$Tt $\frac{1}{4}$tt

or, the genotypic ratio is:

1 homozygous tall : 2 heterozygous talls : 1 homozygous dwarf; and the phenotypic ratio is 3 tall : 1 dwarf.

(Note: The female gamete represented by T may be fertilized by the male gamete T or t; the chances are equal. The same is true for female gamete t. If one flips two coins simultaneously a great many times, recording results each time, the expected ratio of results is, as here: 25 per cent two heads : 50 per cent one heads, one tails : 25 per cent two tails. See Figure 65.)

P   Tt × tt

G $\frac{1}{2}$T, $\frac{1}{2}$t   All t

F_1 $\frac{1}{2}$Tt $\frac{1}{2}$tt   (or 1Tt : 1tt)

P   TtYy   ×   Ttyy

G $\frac{1}{4}$ each: TY, Ty, tY, ty $\frac{1}{2}$ each: Ty, ty

F_1 1TTYy : 1TTyy : 2TtYy : 2Ttyy : 1ttYy : 1ttyy

(The above is the genotypic ratio; the phenotypic ratio is 3 tall yellow : 3 tall green : 1 dwarf yellow : 1 dwarf green.)

EXAMPLES FROM GUINEA PIGS. Certain contrasting characters in the guinea pig behave in inheritance much as the ones given from the garden pea. Black coat color is dominant over white; in the same way, a rough coat shows dominance over a smooth one; these behave as unit characters.

(B = gene for black   b = gene for white

R = gene for rough   r = gene for smooth)

P   BbRR   ×   bbRr

G $\frac{1}{2}$BR, $\frac{1}{2}$bR $\frac{1}{2}$bR, $\frac{1}{2}$br

F_1 Genotypes: 1BbRR : 1BbRr : 1bbRR : 1bbRr

           Phenotypes: 2 black rough : 2 white rough

Problems in Mendelian Inheritance.

METHODS OF SOLVING MENDELIAN PROBLEMS. The two common methods of solving Mendelian problems are the Punnett-square method and the algebraic method.

The Punnett-square or "Checkerboard" Method (including all pictorial or graphical methods). This method is too unwieldy for problems that can not be solved by rapid inspection. It involves finding

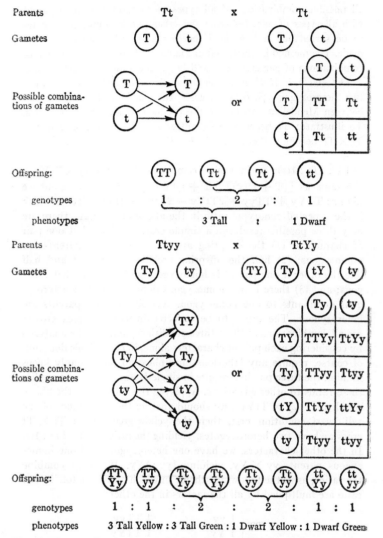

Fig. 65. Diagrams illustrating graphical methods of solving problems in Mendelian inheritance.

all possible combinations of all types of gametes from one parent with all types of gametes from the other parent, duplicate zygotes to be sorted out and grouped together after all combinations are made. The method is illustrated in Figure 65. It illustrates the chance combinations of gametes very well but is too slow for practical use.

The Algebraic Method. Inspection of the results of a cross between two heterozygous parents suggests the fundamental relationship between Mendelian crosses and the products of algebraic quantities. To illustrate: Tt becomes $T + t$ after segregation in the gametes. Tt × Tt becomes, therefore, $(T + t)(T + t)$ or $(T + t)^2$. Just as $(a + b)^2 = a^2 + 2ab + b^2$, so $(T + t)^2 = T^2 + 2Tt + t^2$ (1TT : 2Tt : 1tt); or, in a more complicated cross: Ttyy × TtYy is the same as $[(T + t)(y)] [(T + t)(Y + y)]$. Multiplying out we obtain: TTYy + TTyy + 2TtYy + 2Ttyy + ttYy + ttyy, which is the expected genotypic ratio in the above cross. Now, there are only three possible results in a simple cross involving but one pair of characters: (1) the offspring are all alike if both parents are homozygous; (2) half the offspring are like one parent and half like the other if one parent is homozygous and the other heterozygous; and (3) there is one homozygous dominant to two heterozygous dominants to one homozygous recessive if both parents are heterozygous. The ratios to be expected in more complex crosses are all combinations of these three conditions, and may be analyzed by considering each pair of characters alone, in order. This does not, of course, require any laborious multiplication. One simply keeps in mind the three possible results in single-factor crosses and applies these ratios to other situations. Applying this method to the above problem (Ttyy × TtYy), we should analyze the inheritance of the tall-dwarf condition first, then the yellow-green. In a Tt × Tt cross we have two heterozygotes, yielding the ratio: 1TT : 2Tt : 1tt. In the other characters, we have one heterozygous and one homozygous parent, yy × Yy, yielding 1yy : 1Yy. We then combine the ratios, as in the following scheme in which all the factors in one ratio are multiplied by all the factors in the other:

$$
1\ TT \begin{cases} 1\ yy \\ 1\ Yy \end{cases} \qquad \begin{array}{l} 1\ TTyy \\ 1\ TTYy \end{array}
$$

$$
2\ Tt \begin{cases} 1\ yy \\ 1\ Yy \end{cases} \qquad \begin{array}{l} 2\ Ttyy \\ 2\ TtYy \end{array}
$$

$$
1\ tt \begin{cases} 1\ yy \\ 1\ Yy \end{cases} \qquad \begin{array}{l} 1\ ttyy \\ 1\ ttYy \end{array}
$$

The last column represents the expected genotypic ratio. Any number of characters can be handled similarly, for example:

AabbCCdd   ×   AaBbccDd

1 AA	1 bb	1 Cc	1 dd	1 AAbbCcdd
			1 Dd	1 AAbbCcDd
	1 Bb	1 Cc	1 dd	1 AABbCcdd
			1 Dd	1 AABbCcDd
2 Aa	1 bb	1 Cc	1 dd	2 AabbCcdd
			1 Dd	2 AabbCcDd
	1 Bb	1 Cc	1 dd	2 AaBbCcdd
			1 Dd	2 AaBbCcDd
1aa	1 bb	1 Cc	1 dd	1 aabbCcdd
			1 Dd	1 aabbCcDd
	1 Bb	1 Cc	1 dd	1 aaBbCcdd
			1 Dd	1 aaBbCcDd

The phenotypes, usually fewer in number than genotypes, may be found by this method, simply by combining phenotypic rather than genotypic ratios from single-factor crosses.

SAMPLE PROBLEMS IN MENDELIAN INHERITANCE.

a. *Problem:* What is the expected ratio of genotypes and pheno-types in a cross between a homozygous dwarf yellow plant (pea) and one heterozygous tall and homozygous green?

> *Answer:* Genotypes: 1ttYy : 1TtYy
> Phenotypes: 1 dwarf yellow : 1 tall yellow

b. *Problem:* In a litter of seven guinea pigs, one has black rough hair, three have black smooth hair, two have white rough hair, and one has white smooth hair. The mother has white smooth hair. Describe the father, and give genotypes of both parents and all offspring.

Suggestions for solution: The female parent, showing both re-cessive characters, is, of necessity, a double homozygote. The nearest Mendelian ratio which fits the observation of the litter is 1 : 1 : 1 : 1. This means two 1 : 1 ratios combined; each such results from a heterozygous × homozygous cross. The same type of litter could also result from: Bbrr × bbRr.

Answer: The father had black rough hair, being heterozygous for both characters. The mother is homozygous white and smooth. All black and all rough offspring are heterozygous; all white and all smooth offspring are homozygous.

SEX DETERMINATION

The first clue to the structural basis for Mendelian inheritance came with the discovery that the chromosome constitution of cells differs between the two sexes. Most chromosome pairs are alike in both sexes, but one pair shows consistent differences. In most animals the members of this pair are alike in the female (the two X-chromosomes) whereas in the male only one X-chromosome is present, accompanied by a dissimilar one (the Y-chromosome) or not accompanied at all. The male may be represented by the letters XY (or XO), the female by XX. In segregation, half the gametes of the male contain the X-chromosome, the other half the Y or no homologue of the X; all the gametes of the female contain the X-chromosome. It is really, therefore, a cross of a homozygous with a heterozygous individual, giving the 1 : 1 expected ratio — approximately the observed ratio of the sexes. Other factors may, of course, change the ratio in mature individuals; this is merely the ratio of zygotes at fertilization. To illustrate:

P	XX (female)	×	XY (male)
G	All X		$\frac{1}{2}$X, $\frac{1}{2}$Y
F_1		$\frac{1}{2}$XX (female) : $\frac{1}{2}$XY (male)	

The opposite condition, in which the female is heterozygous, occurs in birds and lepidoptera (moths and butterflies):

P	XY (female)	×	XX (male)
G	$\frac{1}{2}$X, $\frac{1}{2}$Y		All X
F_1		$\frac{1}{2}$XY (female) : $\frac{1}{2}$XX (male)	

In the first type, the gamete from the male determines the sex; in the second type, that from the female. The ratio is not affected. (Various special cases and exceptions occur; i.e., sex-reversal in fishes, amphibians, and birds; and so-called intersexes and gynandromorphs.)

THE GENE THEORY OF HEREDITY

General Statement. It was but a step from the discovery of the chromosome basis of sex determination to the realization that pairs of determiners must exist, similarly, in homologous pairs of chromosomes.

The Gene Theory. The theory which recognizes the deter-miners (*genes*) as localized in the chromosomes is now solidly based on a large number of statistical data — the most significant studies having been carried out by T. H. Morgan and his asso-ciates on the common fruit fly of the genus *Drosophila*. Genes for alternative traits, *alleles*, do not exist in the same gamete because their positions in the chromosomes are identical. There-fore, when the homologous chromosomes are segregated in game-togenesis, the genes for alternative characters are also separated (Fig. 57). The chemical nature of the individual gene (first thought of as a "point" on a chromosome) is now known to be a portion of a DNA molecule (though the orientation of DNA molecules in chromosomes is still unknown). The gene serves as a template in producing a messenger RNA molecule which moves out of the nucleus and, in association with ribosomes and transfer RNA, achieves the synthesis of a particular enzyme. The information required for the synthesis is coded by 3-nucleotide groups, a particular sequence of nucleotides being the code for a particular amino acid in the enzyme synthesis. Thus, the "one gene, one enzyme" theory.

Linkage. It has been further discovered that not all unit characters are independently assorted. Certain traits tend always to accompany certain other traits. All these characters which occur together are said to be linked; their genes apparently occur in the same chromosome pair. As evidence for this, it has been found that the number of linkage groups coincides with the num-ber of chromosome pairs and that one group is typically linked with sex. (In *Drosophila*, there are four linkage groups and four pairs of chromosomes.) In the evening primrose (*Oenothera*) several pairs of chromosomes may occur in a ring or rings, the plants behaving in inheritance as if each ring were a single link-age group.

Crossing Over. During synapsis, in gametogenesis, the chromo-somes of a homologous pair are in intimate contact. It is believed that during this contact allelomorphic genes may be translocated — genes for alternative characters in some way changing places. One explanation given involves the possible twisting of the chromosomes about each other during synapsis. The end result is that certain characters which have occurred together ("linked") may become occasionally separated. One assumes that the farther apart on a chromosome these linked genes occur, the greater is the possibility of crossing over. On that theory, "chromosome maps" have been devised showing the probable position on each chromosome of the genes it is known to bear. The studies of Painter, Bridges, and others on chromosome morphology have yielded a structural as well as theoretical basis for this mapping.

HUMAN HEREDITY

Galton's Laws. Galton enunciated two principles from his statistical study of human inheritance: (1) the *law of ancestral inheritance,* viz., each parent contributes on the average about one-fourth of the inherited traits, each grandparent one-sixteenth, each great-grandparent one sixty-fourth, etc.; (2) the *law of filial regression,* viz., the offspring of unusual parents tend to be more nearly average than their parents.

Mendelian Inheritance. Although human heredity may involve multiple factors, sex-linkage, or other complications, data suggest simple Mendelian inheritance of certain traits. In general, brown eye color is dominant over blue, curly hair over straight, dark hair over light, average intellectual ability over very high or low intellectual ability. Certain abnormalities are inherited as dominants over the normal condition, e.g., excessively short digits, extra digits, hereditary cataract. Others may be recessive to the normal, e.g., albinism, hereditary epilepsy, deaf-mutism. Certain abnormalities appear as sex-linked recessives, appearing in males with a single factor but in females only when there are two, e.g., hemophilia, red-green color blindness.

THE ORIGIN OF VARIATIONS

The structural basis of heredity explains the persistence of traits, but not their modifications. Changes in the genetic constitution of an organism may be due to new combinations, to chromosome mutations, or to gene mutations.

New Combinations. The crossing of two heterozygous individuals may produce new combinations of characters not previously present; the combinations are new, not their individual elements.

Chromosome Mutations. Following synapsis in gametogenesis, the pairs of chromosomes do not always normally separate. In rare cases all or most may go into one germ-cell, leaving none or few in the other. Following fertilization, the chromosome number is abnormal; e.g., it may be triploid if one gamete contained the reduced number but the other was diploid, or it may be tetraploid if both gametes were diploid. Such organisms may show traits entirely different from those of either parent, yet heritable. Similarly, dislocation and translocation of *parts* of chromosomes may result in heritable variations.

Gene Mutations. Traits may disappear or entirely new ones appear in a given line of descent. If these changes are inherited, they may be due to the loss, gain, or modification of genes in particular chromosomes—such changes being due to substitution of one or more different N-bases in the nucleotides involved. These mutations appear spontaneously, but their frequency may be increased by X rays or other forms of high energy radiation, high temperature, and by certain chemicals.

INHERITANCE OF ACQUIRED CHARACTERISTICS

In spite of the obvious adaptation of organisms for their environments, there is no positive evidence for the origin of species through direct action of the environment. The production of heritable changes (mutations) by X rays has involved direct effects on the germ cells. Somatic or body changes are not inherited — apparently because there is no mechanism by which they affect the germ cells.

Review Questions

1. What is meant by the "continuity of the germ plasm"?
2. Describe the experiments of Gregor Mendel and give his results.
3. Define: heredity, segregation, gene, alleles, homozygous, heterozygous, phenotype, genotype.
4. Devise and solve problems illustrating the principles of Mendelian inheritance in garden peas and in guinea pigs.
5. What is the chromosome mechanism of sex determination?
6. Explain the relation between the segregation of genes and the reduction in chromosome number during maturation.
7. What is linkage? Explain its morphological basis.
8. How is the phenomenon of crossing over made use of in the preparation of "chromosome maps"?
9. Name and give the origins of the different types of variations.

Chapter XIV

ORGANIC EVOLUTION

Organic evolution is the progressive development of animals and plants from ancestors of different forms and functions. It is a very slow process, being measured in geological time. The general term *evolution* is applied to any increase in complexity through time — as the evolution of the solar system, the evolution of human society, etc.

EVIDENCE FOR ORGANIC EVOLUTION

Most evidence for organic evolution is indirect, its validity being supported by many different lines of evidence all pointing to the same explanation. This evidence is such that the only scientific justification for much that we observe in nature is organic evolution. One of the best evidences for a common ancestry of organisms, though indirect, is their fundamental similarity. In spite of many adaptive differences, protoplasm and cells and their manifestations of life — metabolism, growth, and reproduction — are essentially the same in all organisms.

Lines of Indirect Evidence.

EVIDENCE FROM PALEONTOLOGY. Remains of previously existing organisms or any indications of their presence are *fossils*. These fossils exist in various types of rock and soil formations. Just as in a lake bottom, the mud on top has been most recently deposited, so in rock strata, the strata on top are more recent than those beneath if they have not been secondarily folded. With this in mind, the geologist is able to construct a chronological series of fossils, associating them with particular periods of geological time. Of course it has been known for a long time that fossils demonstrate the presence of many animals and plants in the past that no longer exist. When the fossils are arranged in a chronological series, faunal and floral changes are found that can only be explained logically by a series of progressive changes, viz., organic evolution. (Table V.)

Table V. Geological Time Scale*

ERA = time GROUP = rocks	PERIOD = time SYSTEMS = rocks	LIFE RECORD (FOSSILS) BOTH ANIMALS AND PLANTS
CENOZOIC Age of mammals and modern flora	QUATERNARY	Periodic glaciation and origin of man (Pleistocene). The transformation of the apelike ancestor into man may have begun in the Pliocene. Culmination of mammals (Miocene). Rise of higher mammals (Oligocene). Vanishing of archaic mammals (Eocene).
	TERTIARY upper lower	
MESOZOIC Age of reptiles	CRETACEOUS	Rise of the archaic mammals in the interval between the Mesozoic and the Tertiary. This ERA is remarkable for the great development of the ammonites which became extinct at the end of the Cretaceous. The molluscs are more highly developed in this ERA than in the preceding one. Culmination and extinction of most reptiles (Cretaceous). Rise of flowering plants (Comanchean); birds and flying reptiles (Jurassic); dinosaurs (Triassic).
	JURASSIC	
	TRIASSIC	
Upper **PALEOZOIC** Age of amphibians and lycopods	PERMIAN	Periodic glaciation and extinction of many Paleozoic groups during and after the Permian. Rise of modern insects, land vertebrates and ammonites (Permian); primitive reptiles and insects (Pennsylvanian); ancient sharks and echinoderms (Mississippian).
	CARBONIFEROUS	
Middle **PALEOZOIC** Age of fishes	DEVONIAN	First known land floras (Devonian) not very different from those of the Carboniferous. Earliest evidence of a terrestrial vertebrate in the form of a single footprint from the Devonian of Pennsylvania. Rise of lungfishes and scorpions (first terrestrial air-breathers) in the Silurian.
	SILURIAN	
Lower **PALEOZOIC** Age of higher (shelly) invertebrates	ORDOVICIAN	Rise of nautiloids, armored fishes, land plants and corals. Also the first evidence of colonial life (Ordovician). First known marine faunas; dominance of trilobites; rise of animals with hard shells or exoskeletons (Cambrian).
	CAMBRIAN	
PROTEROZOIC Primordial life **ARCHEOZOIC** Most ancient life	PRECAMBRIAN	Fossils almost unknown except for a few problematical forms in the Proterozoic. Fossils unknown in the Archeozoic.

NOTE: Geological time scales are constructed to show the oldest periods at the bottom and the youngest periods at the top. *To get the proper order and sequence of events, always read from the bottom to the top.*

* Reprinted by permission from *Geology* by Richard M. Field, copyright, 1951, by Barnes & Noble, Inc.

EVIDENCES FROM COMPARATIVE MORPHOLOGY.

Analogy and Homology. Many rather unlike organisms have organs of similar function. If they are fundamentally unlike except in function, they are said to be *analogous*. Analogous structures indicate no close relationship except in habitat. (Examples: tail fin of lobster and flukes of whale, wings of fly and bird.) Organs fundamentally the same in structure, but perhaps modified for widely different functions, suggest a common plan that can be explained only through common ancestry. Thus, the arm of a man, the wing of a bird, the wing of a bat, the flipper of a seal, and the foreleg of a dog all have the same type of skeleton, Many of the bones correspond directly from one animal to another; all would, if it were not for the evident loss of certain ones. In plants, the scales of an ovulate pine cone correspond with the carpels of a lily, and the scales of the staminate cone are homologous with the stamens of the flower. This fundamental similarity is called *homology*. The criteria of homologies are: (1) similarity in embryonic origin, (2) similarity in structure, (3) similarity in function; the first is of most importance, the last is of least. The presence of homologies, as brought out in studies of comparative morphology, can only be explained logically by a theory of organic evolution. (See Figs. 56 and 66.)

Vestigial Structures. Various organisms possess nonfunctional structures which, in other organisms, have essential functions. The caecum of the rabbit and other animals is homologous with the caecum and vermiform appendix of man. In man the structure is not only of no value but it does more harm than good, whereas in the rabbit it is a very important functional part of the digestive system. In man its presence may best be explained on the grounds that it is a structural vestige, something which functioned in man's ancestry but exists now only as a useless relic. The vestigial muscles at the base of the human ear, the caudal vertebrae (coccyx), and other human structures may be explained only in the same way. In plants, the scalelike leaves on the Indian pipe, a plant which has lost its chlorophyll and become saprophytic, are vestigial, as also are the stamens which in some flowers bear no anthers.

EVIDENCE FROM PHYSIOLOGY. Just as homologous structures exist, homologous functions also occur. It can not be an accident, for example, that chlorophyll — with its remarkable function of

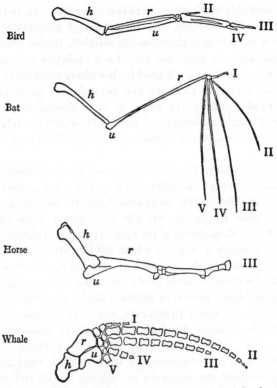

Fig. 66. Homologies of bones of the pectoral limb in the bird and three mammals. Abbreviations: h, humerus, r, radius; u, ulna. Roman numerals refer to the elements of the primitive 5-digit appendage present in each. (Modified from various authors.)

carbohydrate synthesis — is so widely distributed through the plant world. Various types of chemical tests show close similarity between the body fluids of animals, serum precipitation tests on mammals indicating, for example, a much greater chemical kinship between man and apes than between man and swine. Another interesting line of chemical evidence is the remarkable similarity in proportions of constituent salts between vertebrates' blood and sea water. This supports the theory that the ancestors of all vertebrates were inhabitants of the sea.

EVIDENCE FROM EMBRYOLOGY.

General Statement. From the earliest stages of development are found remarkable similarities between organisms. In both plants and animals, for example, the formation of gametes is accompanied by a reduction in chromosome number. Higher plants, even such unlike ones as pine and lily, have embryos so much alike that the same terminology is used in describing their parts. Among animals, the stages of cleavage and blastula and gastrula formation are fundamentally the same in such dissimilar animals as starfish and frog, earthworm and man. The nearer the relationship of adult structures, too, the greater is the similarity in course of development.

The Biogenetic Law. This observation led to the formulation of a theory which, though doubtless largely true, has probably been too widely applied — the *Biogenetic Law.* It may be expressed: *Ontogeny repeats Phylogeny;* or: *The development of the individual recapitulates the development of the race.* Among vertebrates, all embryos pass through a stage in which gill-like structures and their associated blood vessels are present. In fishes, the condition is adult; gills function in some adult amphibia but only in the tadpole stage of higher forms; in reptiles, birds, and mammals these gill structures are never functional, but nevertheless are always present in the embryo. Evolution explains the presence of such an apparently unnecessary stage on the grounds that the embryonic gills of higher vertebrates are embryonic vestigial organs. This suggests that the ancestors of reptiles, birds, and mammals possessed gills. The heart shows similar relationship, the fish heart having one auricle and one ventricle, hearts of amphibians and reptiles having two auricles and one ventricle, and hearts of birds and mammals having two auricles and two ventricles. In embryonic development, birds and mammals pass through *all* these stages, and in the order just given. Among plants illustrations are perhaps less apparent, but they occur: The fern spore germinates into a thalluslike (algalike) plant; the cycads, primitive gymnosperms, have fernlike motile sperm cells.

EVIDENCE FROM TAXONOMY. The principle of homology and the Biogenetic Law are the chief concepts used in classification. The evidences from taxonomy are, then, the evidences from comparative morphology and embryology.

EVIDENCE FROM GEOGRAPHICAL DISTRIBUTION. In groups of islands, the plants and animals of nearby islands are more alike than those of distant islands, whereas all organisms of such an island group show certain affinities with those of the nearest continental land mass. The assumption is that, with isolation due to the appearance of barriers, evolution has proceeded from a common starting type in gradually diverging lines. In conjunction with paleontology, good evidence for evolution may be deduced from the present and past distribution of camels and tapirs. The former are represented today by the true camels of the Old World and by the llama and its relatives in South America. Tapirs occur today only in South and Central America and in Malaya. Fossil camels and tapirs have, however, been found in the intervening territory. The natural assumption is that the forms occurring in the intervening territory have become extinct, leaving only the descendants in the extremes of the range. The existence of a land bridge between present Alaska and Siberia, and a milder climate there at that time than now, are requirements of the theory, but for both conditions there is abundant geological evidence. Maples probably originated in what is now northern Canada or Greenland; they are not now known in their ancestral home but are common in the more temperate northern sections of both Old and New Worlds — a discontinuous distribution. Many illustrations of this particular evidence for evolution are available from both plants and animals.

Lines of Direct Evidence.

EVIDENCE FROM GENETICS. Animal and plant breeders have long been able to develop domestic forms of desired characteristics by selective breeding; students of genetics, similarly, have been able to obtain evidence for evolution through controlled experiments and the study of mutations. Population genetics, study of inheritance within interbreeding populations, supplies abundant evidence for changes of an evolutionary nature. At least one type of genetic experiment (a type of hybridization) has produced artificially a species that presumably arose in nature by the same method.

EVIDENCE FROM OBSERVATION IN NATURE. If large numbers of specimens of one or a few species are collected in a given locality, and the collection is repeated after a long interval of time, one may sometimes detect evolutionary changes which have taken place. Such changes were found by Crampton, studying land snails of the genus *Partula* from Moorea. His extremely large collections were separated by an interval of only fourteen years.

EXAMPLES OF EVOLUTIONARY SERIES

Evolution of the Horse. The most ancient horse known (*Eohippus*) existed in the Eocene. It was about the size of a medium-sized dog, with somewhat the proportions of a modern horse. Its muzzle was shorter than that of a modern horse, however, and its teeth were low-crowned — better adapted for browsing than grazing. The forefeet bore four functional toes and the rudiment of the fifth; the hind feet had four toes — lacking the first digit. The ancestor of *Eohippus*, not yet found, probably had five functional toes on each foot. In subsequent evolution, the number of toes has been progressively reduced through the stage of three on each foot to the modern condition in which only the middle toe is present. (The second and fourth are, however, represented by the "splints.") In the skull, the muzzle has become progressively longer, and the teeth have developed high crowns with ridged surfaces — adapted for grazing. All along, the fossil series, which is very complete, shows gradual increase in size. Horses began their evolution in North America, but completed it in the Old World, becoming extinct on this continent and not returning until introduced by the first Spanish explorers.

Evolution of Man. Human fossils, being fewer than those of the horse and other mammals of longer history, can not be arranged in such a well-ordered series. Certain fossil races, e.g., the Neanderthal and the Cro-Magnon, are known from many skeletons; other races are known, however, from the fragments of one skeleton or a few only. Most fossil races of man are summarized in Table VI and illustrated in Figure 67. In addition to those in Table VI, man-like types of a group called the australopithecines have been found in recent years in considerable numbers in eastern and southern Africa. These may be still more primitive than those in the table, though Early Pleistocene in age. The earliest human type may be represented by *Zinjanthropus*, known from an almost complete skull discovered in east Africa in 1959. Whether man evolved first in Asia or in Africa is, however, still a moot question.

In general, human evolution, probably beginning in the Pleistocene, has involved the following developments:

(1) Increase in brain size — as judged by increase in capacity of brain case.

(2) More erect posture.

(3) Disappearance of prominent supraorbital ridges.

(4) Development of a vertical face.

(5) Formation of a chin.

(6) Shortening of the jaws in an antero-posterior direction.

Table VI. Fossil Races of Man

Name and Locality	Geological Epoch	Nature of Fossils	Brain Volume
Pithecanthropus erectus (Java ape man) Java	Early Pleistocene	Skull fragments from four individuals	870 cc.
Sinanthropus pekinensis (Peking man) Northern China	Early Pleistocene	Fairly complete skeletal material from more than a dozen individuals	1075 cc.
Homo heidelbergensis (Heidelberg man) Germany	Early Pleistocene	One mandible	?
Homo soloensis (Ngandong man) Java	Middle Pleistocene	Skull fragments from eleven individuals	1100 cc.
Homo neanderthalensis (Neanderthal man) Europe, Asia, Africa	Middle Pleistocene	Many skeletons	up to 1600 cc. (equal to modern man)
Homo sapiens (Cro-Magnon man) France, Spain	Late Pleistocene	Several skeletons	up to 1800 cc (equal to modern man)

THEORIES OF THE METHOD OF ORGANIC EVOLUTION

Historically there have been three great evolutionary theories, but these are not mutually exclusive. The views of most modern

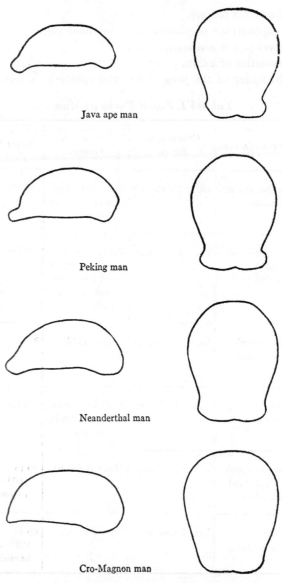

Java ape man

Peking man

Neanderthal man

Cro-Magnon man

Fig. 67. Profiles of the brain case in four fossil species of man. At the left, from the left side; at the right, from the top. The progressive increase in size, heightening of the forehead, and decrease in supraorbital ridges are clearly shown. All drawings to the same scale, from casts. (Compare with data in Table VI.)

biologists combine the second and third of these. There is no experimental evidence for the first theory — Lamarck's.

The Theory of Lamarck — Inheritance of Acquired Characteristics.

(1) Structural variations are acquired as a result of need. (There is no evidence in modern biology for this phase of the theory.)

(2) Use of a structure increases its size; failure to use it results in its atrophy or disappearance. This is the "principle of use and disuse." (In a general way, of course, there is some truth in this phase of the theory.)

(3) These variations (now referred to as "acquired characteristics") are inherited. Thus the progeny have the advantage of the favorable adaptations acquired by their parents. (This phase of Lamarck's theory has no support from modern biology.)

The Theory of Darwin — Natural Selection.

(1) Organisms are prodigal in their production of offspring, far too many being produced to survive.

(2) This prodigal production results in competition or a struggle for existence — actually more of a struggle to escape being destroyed.

(3) Competition leads to natural selection of the most fit through death of those less fit to survive.

(4) The progeny of the organisms most fit to survive inherit the characteristics of their parents — namely those characteristics which have made their parents most fit.

The Theory of De Vries — Mutation. Evolution has not taken place through the accumulation of fortuitous variations; it has been due to the appearance of a series of changes in the germ plasm, *mutations*. These may be very pronounced or minor, but they are not equivalent to individual variations. (De Vries' theory, as first presented, involved major changes only. This is not the modern version, which emphasizes gene mutations.)

Modifications and Corollaries of the Principal Theories.

Isolation. As a factor in the development of new forms, isolation has certainly played a great part. The formation of barriers within the range of a species prevents interbreeding between organisms of different localities; consequently, genetic peculiarities appearing in one region may be so magnified and concentrated that a form becomes distinctly different from its nearest relatives.

AGE AND AREA. According to the concept of Age and Area, organisms having widest geographical ranges are usually the oldest geologically. Hence, within a given genus the species having the widest ranges are probably most like the ancestral type, while those of very limited range are probably of recent origin.

HYBRIDIZATION. Crossbreeding between species may have produced much of the variation in nature — the heterozygotes introducing new combinations.

ORTHOGENESIS. Some students of evolution, particularly paleontologists, observe that fossils forming an evolutionary series indicate progress in a rather definite direction — the unsuccessful forms necessary to the theory of natural selection being absent. This theory that evolution proceeds in definite directions, from the directing tendency or limitations of internal structures, is *orthogenesis.*

Present-day Views of the Method of Evolution. Genetic changes occur spontaneously and relatively frequently. They may be gene mutations or chromosome mutations (see p. 176). These changes are distributed and preserved in a population by several factors. In a given population, if mating is at random, the ratios of all genes to each other tend to remain the same generation after generation (the *Hardy-Weinberg Law*) unless (1) mutation rates of genes differ, (2) natural selection is involved (certain genes being selected for or against), (3) there is differential migration, or (4) genetic drift (variation due to chance) is involved. These four exceptions to the Hardy-Weinberg Law, plus the isolation of populations (implied in 3, above), are the important factors in evolution. Isolation of a population may be brought about by geographical, ecological, or reproductive barriers.

Review Questions

1. What are the evidences for organic evolution?
2. Give the principal tendencies in the evolution of the horse and of man.
3. Analyze the relative merits of the various theories of the methods of organic evolution and their corollaries.
4. What are the relations between genetics and the method of organic evolution?

Chapter XV
TAXONOMY

Taxonomy is the science of animal and plant classification. It has two aspects, the naming of each kind of organism (*nomenclature*) and the grouping of these to show relationships. In order that species may be dealt with accurately each one must have one name and one name only. Classification of organisms is necessary for convenience, of course, its first purpose, but of equal importance now is the effort of the taxonomist to discover and indicate genetic relationships that exist between organisms of different species through evolution. Organisms classified in the same group are believed to be related closely by common descent.

THE CONCEPT OF SPECIES

The working unit of the taxonomist is the species, usually thought of as having a real objective existence. No absolute criterion for recognizing a species as a unit has been found, however. Certain limitations may be suggested: A group of organisms sufficiently alike to have had the same parents belong to the same species; in other words, the extent of difference, morphological or physiological, is within the range of individual variability. Within a species of wide geographical range the variation may be so great that the extremes would not be considered of the same species did they not intergrade with each other. This is another test of species: Members of the same species freely interbreed, while those of different species do not — and therefore do not show intergrades. (Exceptions: some cases of interspecific hybridization.)

THE BINOMIAL SYSTEM OF NOMENCLATURE

Following the *Binomial System of Nomenclature*, the general adoption of which dates from Carolus Linnaeus (18th century), each organism is known by two names. These are: (1) the name of the genus to which it belongs, always written with the initial letter capitalized and (2) the specific name, its initial letter never capitalized. These two names constitute the scientific name. (Examples: scientific name of man, *Homo sapiens;* scientific name of dandelion, *Taraxicum officinale.*) It is customary to print scientific names in italics. The names are in Latin, for two reasons: (1) When the system was adopted, Latin was the international language of scientists and (2) since Latin is a "dead" language, its forms are not subject to change.

CATEGORIES OF CLASSIFICATION

Although the species is the working unit of the biologist, for convenience in treating modifications within a species *subspecies* and *variety* names are sometimes employed. These constitute the third part of a trinominal. (Example: *Turdus migratorius propinquus* is the scientific name of the Western Robin; the eastern form is the one which corresponds to the originally described species; hence, the third or subspecific name is merely a repetition of the second — *Turdus migratorius migratorius.*) With this exception, the *species* is the smallest category in classification. Species form *genera;* a genus is combined with other genera to form a *family;* families form *orders;* orders form *classes;* and classes are combined into *phyla* (animals) or *divisions* (plants). Each succeeding category is more inclusive and larger than the preceding one. Thus a family may contain many genera, and itself be only one of several families in an order. In addition, large families may be divided into *subfamilies*, each containing several genera; or a family may be with other families in a *superfamily*, the order containing more than one of these. Other intermediate steps in classification may be inserted wherever they may clarify the complexities of animal and plant relationships. The criteria of these categories are not established; i.e., a beginner in taxonomy has no way of knowing just how different animals or plants must be from each other to constitute different genera rather than species, or families rather than genera. This puzzles even experts. However, the criteria in a limited part of the Animal or Plant Kingdom tend to be more or less uniform. These are based on the experiences and opinions of individual taxonomists — specialists in particular fields.

EXAMPLES OF CLASSIFICATIONS OF PARTICULAR SPECIES

In the following examples, only major categories are given; there is no significance for the average biologist in the intermediate steps omitted.

Common name.............	American Elm	Red-tailed Hawk
Scientific name (Species)	Ulmus americana Linn.	Buteo borealis (Gmelin)
Kingdom	Plant	Animal
Division — Phylum	Spermatophyta	Chordata
Subdivision — Subphylum...	Angiospermae	Vertebrata
Order	Urticales	Falconiformes
Family..................	Ulmaceae	Accipitriidae
Genus	Ulmus	Buteo
Specific name	americana	borealis

CERTAIN ESSENTIAL RULES OF NOMENCLATURE

Publication. A new species for which a name is being proposed must be described in connection with its name or the latter is not valid.

Avoidance of Duplicate Names. The scientific name of a new species must be such that the organism will not be confused with another. The name must differ from all other species names in the same genus; and there must be no duplicate generic names in the Animal Kingdom or in the Plant Kingdom.

Priority. The first name given a species is the accepted one if it is later described under another name, the later name for the same species being called a *synonym*. The name of the author is ordinarily printed after the scientific name to avoid confusion over synonyms. (The name of Linnaeus is commonly abbreviated Linn., or simply L.; and other, frequently occurring names are also abbreviated.) If subsequent study suggests that a species was placed in the wrong genus, or that the original genus should be subdivided, the genus name is corrected but the original species name is retained; and the original author's name is also retained, but in parentheses.

Review Questions

1. Define and explain the purpose of taxonomy.
2. What is a species; a subspecies?
3. Give the complete classification of one animal and one plant species.
4. By what rules are scientific names kept uniform?

Chapter XVI

ECOLOGICAL AND GEOGRAPHICAL DISTRIBUTION

There are two different points of view in the study of plant and animal distribution, the ecological and the geographical. In ecology, the biologist is concerned with the relations between organisms and their environment. Adaptive relations are the heart of ecology; hence, the ecologist who knows well the environmental relations of a particular organism will know where such an organism can live. In plant and animal geography one studies the actual distribution of organisms in terms of existing land masses and the geological history of land masses. The principal difference between the two points of view lies in the fact that the ecologist is interested in where an organism can live and why while the geographer is interested in where it actually does live and why.

ECOLOGY

Subdivisions of Ecology. Ecology may deal with the relations between one organism and its environment (*autecology*) or the relations of a group of organisms that occur together (*synecology*). By *environment* we mean not only the topographic and climatic factors in the surroundings but other organisms, as well, that have an effect upon the one or ones being considered.

Factors of the Environment. The medium in which an organism lives, the climate, and other organisms associated with it are all factors of its environment.

THE MEDIA IN WHICH ORGANISMS LIVE.

Soil. The chemical composition of the soil is a factor in determining the presence of plants and certain animals (e.g., snails, earthworms). The texture is important in relation to moisture conservation and availability and to the presence of burrowing animals. Angle of slope and exposure to the sun are factors affecting drainage and the absorption of heat from the sun.

Water. This is always present in protoplasm and is essential to life. It is important in preventing rapid temperature changes, as a solvent for many compounds, as a medium for ionization, and because it has high surface tension. Its unusual property of expanding as it cools just before freezing is of paramount importance in insulating water under ice and in aerating the water in the bottom of deep lakes.

Air. The earth's atmosphere consists chiefly of nitrogen (about four-fifths) and oxygen (about one-fifth); a small amount of carbon dioxide is also present. The oxygen is essential to life. But for photosynthesis in green plants, the oxygen would be replaced by carbon dioxide. The nitrogen is not available to most organisms directly, but some soil bacteria are able to "fix" it in nitrates — in which form it is then available to the plants in general. The density of air, and therefore the quantity of its several constituents, decreases with increasing altitude.

Bodies of Other Organisms. Internal parasites must be able to obtain oxygen under extremely unfavorable conditions, and, if they are parasites of the digestive tract, to resist the action of digestive enzymes. They are protected from most enemies; and, in general, they have a more constant environment than do many free-living forms.

CLIMATE. The most important climatic factor is radiation from the sun — which includes heat, visible light, and ultraviolet radiations. Solar radiation, particularly that of longer wave lengths, in heating the soil, in evaporating water, and in causing the air to expand (in conjunction with variable topography and rotation of the earth) produces such climatic variations as winds and rains.

THE BIOTIC ENVIRONMENT. Any living organism that has any effect on another organism, whether of the same species or a different one, is a part of the *biotic* or *living environment* of the latter.

Intraspecific Relations. The relations between individuals of the same species are intraspecific. These include (1) relations required by *reproduction* — the sexual reproduction of dioecious organisms; (2) relations of *assistance*, which include protection and rearing of young and co-operation in a social organization; (3) passive as well as active *competition* for food; and (4) *hostility*, which may take the form of rivalry for territory or mates, elimination of sick and injured, or the devouring of one mate by the other or of young by a parent.

Interspecific Relations. Ecological relations between different species are numerous and complex. They are the key to the existence of different kinds of plants and animals in a single natural community. Such relations include (1) *competition* for food (to a considerable extent this is, in plants, actually competition for space); (2) *prey-predator relations*, the relations between an organism that feeds on others and the organisms fed upon; (3) *host-parasite relations*, the relations between a parasite and its host, the success of which — for the parasite — depends upon the parasite's ability to benefit from the host without doing serious injury to the latter; (4) *symbiosis*, the relations between closely associated organisms that are of benefit to one or both, without injury to either; and (5) *slavery*, the state in which one species is captured by and used to serve another. Symbiosis is sometimes broadly defined to include all close relationships, whether harmful or not, in which case parasitism is considered a form of symbiosis. In other classifications of interspecific relations, symbiosis is narrowly defined to include only relations of benefit to both organisms involved, but this may be more accurately called *mutualism*. A relationship of benefit to one and of no harm to the other may be called *commensalism*. Of course the relations of symbiosis and slavery are less common than the other types indicated.

Special Relations between Plants and Animals. Aside from the relations suggested above certain others should be mentioned. Insects and birds pollinate many flowers, and many animals aid in seed dispersal. Galls are plant structures that result from insect stings. Certain plants capture, kill, and digest animals.

The Major Habitats. These are three in number — the ocean, fresh water, and land.

THE OCEAN. This is the habitat of *marine* organisms.

Characteristics. The ocean is the most constant of all external environments. It is characterized by high salinity of little variability, the range of salt concentration being from about 30 to 37 parts of salt per thousand. The temperature range is also relatively small — about 35 degrees centigrade. There are regular ocean currents that affect the movements of marine organisms and that influence the climate of the sea and adjacent land. The tidal fluctuations are of particular importance to organisms that live along the shore.

Distribution of Marine Organisms. Organisms living in the

intertidal zone (between high and low tides) are adapted to alternate drying and wetting, to periodic feeding, to rapid temperature fluctuations (and more extreme ones than in the ocean proper), and, in many cases, to the impact of waves and a shifting substratum. Those below low tide are subject to fewer variables; the depth at which they live depends chiefly on the distance light penetrates — because that determines the presence of vegetation carrying on photosynthesis. Organisms living between the tide limits and just below low tide are said to be *littoral* in distribution. Floating or drifting *plankton*, and actively swimming *nekton*, constitute the *pelagic* organisms. Bottom organisms occur at depths of even five miles. They withstand enormous pressures. Light is absent at such depths except that from the luminescence of organisms.

FRESH-WATER HABITATS.

Characteristics. The low salinity (therefore low osmotic pressure) of fresh water makes necessary organs for regulating the osmotic pressure of the organisms. Greater fluctuations in temperature and in concentration of gases in solution occur than in the ocean. Other important differences from the ocean are periodic drying up, stagnation, high turbidity, and rapid currents.

Distribution of Fresh-water Organisms. This varies chiefly with the nature of fresh-water bodies. Organisms of rapid brooks and rivers are different from each other and from those of lakes, and these in turn differ from those of swamps and bogs.

LAND OR TERRESTRIAL HABITATS.

Characteristics. Terrestrial habitats experience the greatest fluctuations in climate. Both temperature and moisture vary greatly with seasons, with latitude, with altitude, and with topography. Soil and air temperatures vary enormously, the extremes being more than 120 degrees centigrade apart.

The Distribution of Terrestrial Organisms. Subterranean organisms are least subject to variations in climate. Above ground, organisms may live in direct contact with the soil, e.g., higher plants; or they may live in various strata in the vegetation, e.g., on grasses, in shrubs, in trees. Though some animals are aerial for long periods, they are really terrestrial.

The Community. The most important concept in synecology is the *community*, a group of organisms bound together by various factors. The constituent organisms may be dependent on similar climatic and edaphic conditions, but they are also related through a complex of biotic interrelationships — one of the most important of which is probably the *food chain* or *food cycle.* (Fig. 68.) Com-

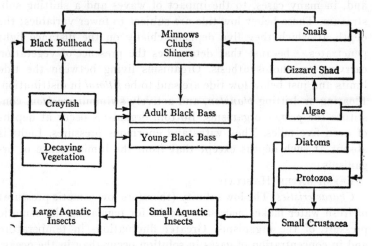

Fig. 68. Diagram illustrating a food chain in a Kansas lake stocked with black bass. Arrows point from prey to predator. (Data from H. H. Hall.) Algae and diatoms are producers; the other organisms form various levels of consumers.

munities of different size (extent) are recognized. Various elaborate terminologies for these have been devised, no one of which is universally accepted by ecologists.

FOOD CHAINS AND TROPHIC LEVELS. A community is dependent upon those organisms in the community that manufacture their own food. These (photosynthetic organisms) are the *producers.* They are fed upon by *primary consumers* (herbivores), and these in turn are eaten by *secondary consumers* (carnivores) — which may occur at several "levels." All levels, from producers to final consumers, constitute *trophic levels.* This succession of levels is a food chain; when we add parasites and organisms of decomposition we have a food cycle.

PYRAMIDS. Producers are usually the smallest and most numerous organisms in a food chain, and the final consumers are the largest and least numerous. This sequence forms a *pyramid of numbers.* Even when the producers are larger and fewer than the herbivores, as in the case of trees fed upon by insects, the total mass decreases in successive trophic levels; this is the *pyramid of biomass.* The basic reason for such pyramids is the dissipation of solar energy as it is transferred through the trophic levels (this phenomenon being called energy flow), the loss of available energy in succeeding steps constituting the *pyramid of energy* in the community.

Ecosystem Concept. It is obvious that community and environment are not independent but together form a complex. The whole system of organisms, in interdependence upon each other and on the non-living environment, constitutes an *ecosystem*.

The Regulation of Population. An organism produces more offspring than can survive. The environment sets the limits on survival. Chapman simplified this relationship in an analogy with Ohm's Law in physics. We may designate this simplification as Chapman's Law. It is: The population of a species at a given time is determined by the ratio of the biotic potential (rate of reproduction) to the environmental resistance, or

$$\text{Population} = \frac{\text{Biotic potential}}{\text{Environmental resistance}}$$

Obviously, as the environmental resistance increases, the population falls; as the resistance decreases, the population increases.

Succession. In each large area of the earth's surface, where conditions tend to repeat themselves year after year, a characteristic group of plants and animals develops. This is referred to as a *climax* community. (Examples: the grasslands of the central states, with their prairie dogs and bison; the evergreen forest of central Canada, with its snowshoe rabbits and moose.) If such a climax community is destroyed in a given area, and that area is then left undisturbed, it will return to the climax condition through a series of changes which constitutes a *succession*. A succession may proceed from a water environment to one of average moisture conditions, a *hydrosere* (Fig. 69), or from a dry environment to one of average moisture conditions, a *xerosere*. These are successions in time. One may observe such successions in space also — e.g., around the shores of a lake which is gradually filling up (Fig. 69) or along the edges of a disintegrating rock mass. In fact, the concept succession has many meanings:

Succession *In Time*   Geological
                        Seasonal (Annual)
                        Daily

Succession   *In Space*   Horizontal — in latitude, or in small areas
                          Vertical — in altitude, or in vegetational
                          strata

Horizontal succession may correspond in space to geological succession in time; altitudinal succession may correspond to latitudinal
succession — higher altitudes being similar to higher latitudes.

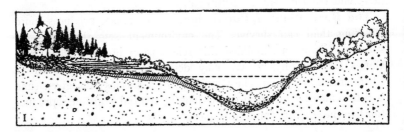

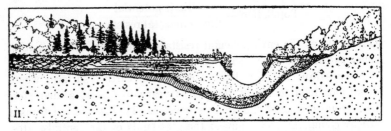

Fig. 69. Stages in a hydrosere succession: evolution of a peat bog. (After Dach-
nowski.) (Reprinted by permission from *Geology* by Richard M. Field, copyright,
1951, by Barnes & Noble, Inc.)

GEOGRAPHICAL DISTRIBUTION

The ecologogist treats organisms from the standpoint of possible
environments; the geographer treats them from the standpoint of
actual environments. The geographer asks why every organism

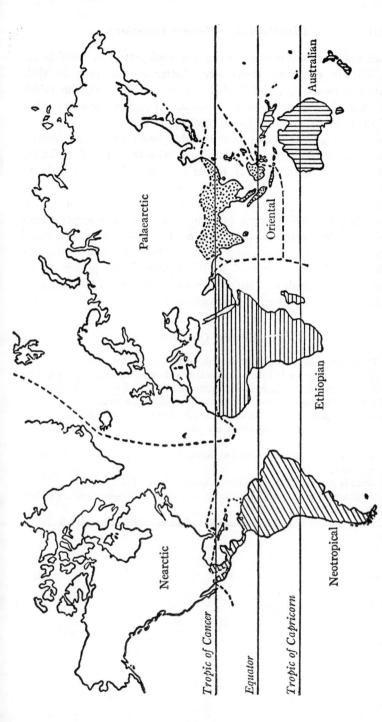

Fig. 70. Zoogeographical regions of the world according to A. R. Wallace. The Nearctic and Palaearctic are combined by many modern authors to constitute the Holarctic.

does not exist every place where the environment is suitable for it. Certain organisms thrive even better outside than in their native homes — e.g., the English sparrow in America, the rabbit in Australia, the mongoose in Jamaica. To explain these anomalies of distribution a knowledge of geology is necessary — changes in the earth's surface, appearance and disappearance of land bridges. All such knowledge must be correlated with the facts of evolution. The presence or absence of topographic and climatic barriers to distribution, and the histories of these barriers, are of extreme importance in any analysis of present-day animal or plant distribution. Various attempts to divide the earth into zoogeographical or phytogeographical provinces, most of which have been based on studies of a limited group of organisms, have been made. One such, the classic attempt of A. R. Wallace, based principally on studies of mammals and birds, is shown in Figure 70. His terms are still the most widely used in zoogeography.

Review Questions

1. Define autecology, ecosystem, pyramid of biomass, trophic level.
2. What are the characteristics of soil, water, and air of most importance in considering them as media in which organisms live?
3. Discuss intra- and interspecific relations between organisms.
4. What important characteristics distinguish the three major habitats?
5. Explain how a food cycle relates the different organisms of a community together.
6. Explain the relations between population, biotic potential, and environmental resistance.
7. What is succession? Name different types of succession.
8. What are the major principles involved in a study of the geographical distribution of plants or animals?
9. Name and locate the zoogeographical regions as suggested by Wallace.

Part Four

RELATIONS OF BIOLOGY TO MANKIND

Chapter XVII

ECONOMIC BIOLOGY

All human activities involving living organisms or their products include phases of economic biology. There is so much of biology in medicine, in agriculture and forestry, and in all phases of the conservation of a natural fauna and flora, that only a few suggestive details are here given.

BIOLOGY IN MEDICINE

The Human Body. Man is an animal. The principles of structure that apply to lower animals apply equally to man. Through a study of the lower animals, and through the study of man as an animal, the underlying principles of human structure and function may best be understood.

Disease. Many organisms live at the expense of others; if they not only derive benefit from but actually do harm to their hosts, they are *pathogenic*. The abnormal conditions in an organism following or accompanying injury by a pathogenic organism is *disease*.

DISEASE-PRODUCING ORGANISMS. Diseases of plants are mostly caused by various fungi — bacteria, smuts, rots; but some insects and some parasitic worms produce symptoms of disease in plants. In animals, diseases are chiefly due to bacteria, protozoa, or parasitic worms. Viruses cause numerous diseases in both plants and animals. Bacteria are the cause of diphtheria, tuberculosis, tetanus, typhoid fever, and many other pathological conditions in man. Protozoa are the cause of malaria (Fig. 9), sleeping sickness, and dysentery (amoebic). (Note: Sleeping sickness is African; American epidemics of the disease called "sleeping sickness" are of encephalitis.) Parasitic worms cause many human diseases, especially in the tropics — those affecting most individuals being hookworms. Hookworms belong to the phylum Nematoda. Many others of the same phylum and Platyhelminthes of the classes

Trematoda (flukes) and Cestoda (tapeworms) cause human ills. (Fig. 38.)

TRANSMISSION OF DISEASE-PRODUCING ORGANISMS. Food or drink contaminated by fecal matter from those infected with intestinal parasites may carry organisms causing typhoid fever, dysentery, or Asiatic cholera. Insufficiently cooked food may contain young stages of flukes, tapeworms, or roundworms. Organisms may gain entrance through wounds — those causing tetanus, for example. Other organisms may enter the respiratory passages in the air. Some organisms are transferred by the bite of insects, ticks or mites; in man, those causing malaria, sleeping sickness, and typhus are carried by insects; Rocky Mountain spotted fever is conveyed by the bite of a tick.

ANTIGEN-ANTIBODY REACTION. In general, organisms are sensitive to foreign proteins in the blood. When such are introduced into the human body, the blood develops some kind of resistance — varying with the nature of the protein. The foreign protein constitutes the *antigen;* the "neutralizing" agent in the blood is the *antibody.* If the foreign protein is soluble in the blood, it is *precipitated;* if it is insoluble (like a microorganism), different individuals are clumped together (*agglutinated*). Following this reaction, *phagocytosis* (the engulfing of the foreign material by white blood corpuscles) is greatly increased. Certain organisms, which may remain in only one part of the body, produce and discharge into the blood powerful poisons called *toxins* (e.g., diphtheria bacteria); an antibody, called under these circumstances an *antitoxin,* is developed, but in many cases too slowly to stay the course of the disease.

IMMUNITY. Some species of animals are immune to certain diseases; animals in general tend to resist later exposures to diseases from which they have recovered. These natural and acquired immunities are both believed due to the presence of appropriate antibodies in the blood; although there is such a thing as cellular immunity, as opposed to immunity due to specific antibodies. Immunity may be established in some cases by the injection of regulated amounts of antigen — e.g., by the injection of dead typhoid bacteria. In one well-known case, immunity against a mild disease, cowpox, confers immunity against a closely related but much more virulent disease, smallpox. Temporary immunity may be conferred by injection of an antibody.

(Note: In rare cases, in man, a violent disturbance may result from the second of a series of injections required in an immunization process. This is called *anaphylaxis*. There are methods by which it may be anticipated and avoided.)

CURE AND PREVENTION OF DISEASE. The trend of modern medicine is in the direction of prevention of disease through the establishment of immunity — *preventive medicine*. Diseases may rarely be cured except by some method based on antigen-antibody reactions. A few drugs are specifically beneficial, the best-known example being quinine in the cure of malaria. Recently, the sulfa drugs have become important. The most effective "drugs," however, are *antibiotics*, substances produced by fungi and bacteria and capable of preventing the growth of many pathogenic organisms. Penicillin and streptomycin are examples.

ORGANISMS OF VALUE TO MAN

Plants.

USES OF PLANTS. Plants serve man as sources of food, drugs, building materials, paper, fuel (wood, coal, and probably natural oil), textiles, rubber, ornament. Fundamentally, plants constitute our only direct method of conserving the energy which we continuously receive from the sun.

DOMESTICATION OF PLANTS. Three chief centers occurred in antiquity: Tropical America (Mexico to Peru), Eastern Mediterranean region (Egypt to the Tigris-Euphrates Valley), and the Orient (China). Many plants were cultivated by man several thousand years ago, e.g., in the Old World: tea, flax, grapes, figs, dates, apples, rice, wheat, sorghum; in the New World: sweet potato, tobacco, maize. Cotton was domesticated independently in the Old and New Worlds. Scientific selection of plants with a view to improving stock began over a century ago; other methods, e.g., hybridization, have developed principally since 1900.

Animals.

USES OF ANIMALS. These include food, sponges, hides and furs, textiles, beasts of burden, protection, hunting. Another function seldom considered is land-building: Large areas of land in the tropics rest on foundations of coral rock, made possible by the action of colonies of coral animals. Figure 71 illustrates the subsidence (Darwin's) theory of the origin of barrier reefs and atolls.

DOMESTICATION OF ANIMALS. Several kinds of animals were domesticated by the late Stone Age. Dogs were probably domesticated first, independently in several regions, and were the only domestic animal common to Old and New Worlds. In America, in addition, were domesticated the llama and alpaca, the guinea pig, and the turkey (the latter probably for ceremonial purposes). Indian

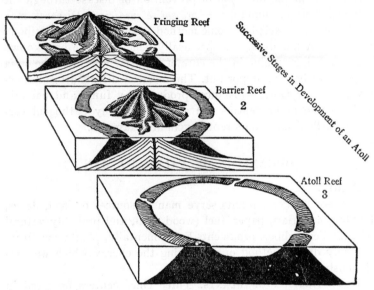

Fig. 71. Origin and evolution of an atoll according to the subsidence theory. (Reprinted by permission from *Geology* by Richard M. Field, copyright, 1951, by Barnes & Noble, Inc.)

horses of America were descendants of those brought over by the first Spaniards. Horses, asses, cattle of several types, pigs, goats, sheep, camels, elephants, reindeer, water buffalo, and cats were all domesticated in the Old World.

FISHERIES. The United States Fish and Wildlife Service, of the Department of the Interior, includes an agency of research and information on all aquatic resources — not those from fish alone. Fish furnish food, oil, fertilizer, and other commercial products. Some crustacea, e.g., lobsters, crabs, shrimps, are important foods. Many mollusks are sources of food, oysters being of chief importance. Pearl buttons formerly came from the shells of fresh-water mussels. Pearls are formed within the shells of bivalve mollusks; these are now successfully cultured in Japan. (Culture pearls are real pearls, not imitations.) Whale oil, once much more important than now, may also be considered a fisheries product — although derived from a mammal. The propagation of fresh-water fishes for game purposes is practiced on a large scale by state agencies.

CONSERVATION OF NATURAL AREAS

In 1872, by Act of Congress, the United States set aside Yellowstone National Park for the enjoyment of the people. Since then a great many areas have been set aside by Congress as National Parks, and the process is still going on; also, by Executive Order, certain areas may be designated as National Monuments and thus be removed from the possibility of exploitation. The national park movement has been taken up and followed in many other countries, also. The National Park Service, under the United States Department of the Interior, undertakes to preserve natural areas for the aesthetic enjoyment of the American people; trees are conserved for their beauty, not their wood; animals are protected for the pleasure which a sight of them may give man, rather than for their furs or for food. Of course areas are also set aside primarily for the preservation of geologic formations.

Other agencies of the United States government are concerned primarily with the continuing and therefore proper use of natural areas — soil for agriculture, forests as a source of lumber, and game for hunting. Agencies which have these particular functions are, respectively, the Soil Conservation Service, the Forest Service, and the Fish and Wildlife Service.

Review Questions

1. What are the principal types of disease-producing organisms in man?
2. How may disease-producing organisms be transferred from one host to another?
3. What are the general facts of antigen-antibody reactions, and in what ways are these reactions involved in immunization?
4. What are the uses of plants and animals?
5. Discuss the geographical sources of the most important domestic plants and animals.
6. What are the purposes of a national park system?

Chapter XVIII

SOCIAL IMPLICATIONS
OF BIOLOGICAL THEORY

To the biologist, sociology may be defined as the ecology of man. The number of biological principles of significance for human society is great, and these are freely incorporated into the body of sociology by students of that field. Such problems as the following involve an application of biology in studies of human society: (1) the origin and evolution of the family and other social units; (2) growth and decline of populations; (3) the roles of heredity and environment in modifying human society; (4) the roles of geographic location and natural resources in determining cultural trends.

BIOLOGICAL UNITS IN HUMAN SOCIETY

The individual is the unit in considering the psychological relations within society; the family is the unit in considering social relations from a genetic viewpoint. The integrative or uniting factor in the family is reproduction; the requirement that individuals of opposite sex associate together is, however, probably less important than that the young, because of their long period of infancy, be cared for by the parents. Although aggregations of lower animals which are primarily not for reproductive purposes do occur, these are more simple than the complex social organizations of man and the social insects. Complex animal societies are based on the reproductive function; other integrative factors, particularly in man, are of course involved, e.g., food, protection, force (as in slavery), education, religion, sentiment.

THE EVOLUTION OF HUMAN SOCIETY —
BIOLOGICAL ASPECTS

The same factors which are involved in the evolution of an individual species are involved in the evolution of a phase of human society. The process of socialization of the individual (produced by the factors of integration) may be considered the genetic unifying factor — the equivalent of heredity in organic evolution. Departures from the previous social type may develop (variations), which modify the nature of the integration. Selection of certain of these departures tends to encourage their development, just as selection encourages the development of a new plant or animal variation.

THE ROLE OF COMPETITION

Competition as a *biological* factor is much less significant for modern than primitive man. There is little of the struggle for existence which characterizes lower forms of life; it is rather a struggle for dominance. The "manly art," for example, is a fad today rather than a necessity. Competition is psychological, sociological, economic — not biological. Furthermore, co-operation is so marked in human society that those who are handicapped are frequently protected, or even pushed beyond their abilities. Through medical progress we have learned to save not only the fit but the unfit as well, a questionable social benefit. Through modern wars, in which death may come to any man, we eliminate many of those who possess the most desirable traits, allowing a larger proportion of the less desirable to survive and produce the next generation. Thus, in two ways, man has modified the course of natural selection by his superior "intelligence": (1) Through medicine, coupled with a sentiment which is desirable for its own sake but unsocial, he preserves those individuals whose descendants are the greatest burdens on the state. (2) Through wars, which he has made impersonal and therefore biologically useless, he reduces the stock which is most capable of reproducing the best qualities of mankind. If wars are "inevitable," then the further improvement of human society is questionable.

HUMAN POPULATION PROBLEMS

World Population. It is theoretically true that mankind is increasing at a greater rate than the food supply (theory of Malthus). This food supply (which it is nonsense to assume can be indefinitely augmented by either more intensive agriculture or chemical discoveries) serves as an environmental limiting factor. (See Population, Chap. XVI.) In other words, the population growth will tend to slow up and eventually will become more or less stabilized, because of the increasing relative resistance offered by the environment.

Rates of Increase in Different Social Strata. At the present time, in most countries, birth rates among people of superior economic and social position average lowest, while those among the middle classes are intermediate. Obviously this condition is not ideal, although we should not assume, necessarily, that those of highest economic and social position are the most desirable members of society. We must first attain the ideal of equal opportunity before our criterion is sound. The ideal condition, according to some biologists, involves elimination of reproduction by the intellectually unfit and maximum rates of increase among those whose attainments are of maximum value to mankind. Such a view provides for the future, but does not consider the present. Society must benefit from her geniuses during their lifetimes, if she is to benefit at all. If the responsibility of a genius lies in rearing a large family, society will gain little by his presence. Probably the ideal balance of reproductive rates (from the standpoint of human society as a whole) would be characterized by maximum rates among the more superior of the middle class. Genius does not come alone from genius; it also comes from the middle class. Of course the chances are much greater in the former case; nevertheless, more distinguished men come from the middle class today than from families in which there is a history of genius, for the simple and obvious reason that the middle class is so much larger.

Migration. Obviously, a long continued emigration reduces the population. If, however, this is largely from the poorer classes it may be indirectly beneficial in increasing the proportion of superior people in the homeland. An influx of such immigrants, particularly if their standard of living is low in comparison with that of their new compatriots, introduces a serious element of economic and social competition within the working classes. This effect is likely to disappear in time, for educational processes in the new land may be the means of developing a desire in the immigrants and their descendants for the higher standard of living.

IMPROVING MANKIND

Heredity and Environment. It is frequently true, although fortunately not always, that the biologist makes a fetish of heredity while the sociologist can think only of environment. Until the two viewpoints are fused, the contribution of neither science can reach its full value; heredity and environment are the two sides of the same coin. Undoubtedly, the hereditary traits are more potent in determining maximum achievement than is the environment; nevertheless, excellent hereditary possibilities may be limited or destroyed by an unfavorable environment. The heredity sets the *potential* limit of achievement, the environment sets the *actual* limit of achievement.

Eugenics. The improvement of mankind by improving his heredity is *eugenics*. The goal may be achieved, theoretically, by selection. We know that all men are not born equal. This difference at birth is the result primarily of differences in heredity. If future generations come from the best representatives of the present generation, then the average of human ability will be raised. The application of eugenics may be either negative — reducing the reproduction of the intellectually unfit; or it may be positive — encouraging the reproduction of the most desirable.

There is no basis in eugenics, however, for race prejudice. Human race differences are morphological; and individual differences within each race are greater than the average differences between races. There is no demonstrable superiority or inferiority of one race with reference to others. Consequently, there is absolutely no biological basis for favoring or discrediting any race.

Euthenics. The improvement of mankind by improving his environment is *euthenics*. This may be thought of as a temporary expedient, since improvement in an individual which is due to his environment is not inherited. However, many individuals of superior heredity are handicapped by unfavorable environment, and an improvement in the latter releases hidden potentialities. Even if heredity may be the more important factor in individual cases, environment is the factor more easily improved. Furthermore, the beneficial effects of an improved environment may be evident within one generation, and some of these benefits will persist.

APPLICATION OF NEGATIVE EUGENICS

The cost of taking care of a large number of unemployables, particularly mental defectives, is already enormous. It will increase as long as the maximum birth-rate occurs among the most inferior people. There are two ways out: (1) spreading birth-control information, at best a questionable solution from this standpoint, for its application requires intelligent volition, something we can not expect from these people; (2) sterilization. The latter might be compulsory in certain cases; its voluntary application should be encouraged wherever children are likely to receive undesirable hereditary traits. The chief criticism against sterilization has been that we do not know enough about human heredity to apply with justice a law requiring it. However, as one sociologist has stated, the same criticism applies to our whole judicial system. The real test lies in the answer to the question: Would the practice of sterilizing those of undesirable heredity benefit human society? It would, unquestionably, for it would gradually reduce the number of socially undesirable, and, by decreasing the number in state-supported institutions and on relief or dole, greatly relieve the taxpayer. It is true, however, that both the inheritance and the permanence of mental disease is questioned by those who should know most about it — the psychiatrists. A distinction should be made, then, between the mentally deficient and the mentally diseased. The former condition is constitutional and hereditary; but we must know much more about the inheritance of "insanity" in its various forms before sterilization can be justly applied to *its* victims.

THE ROLE OF BIOLOGICAL DISCOVERIES IN THE DEVELOPMENT OF SOCIETY

Biological discoveries have contributed to social progress in the following ways: (1) The domestication of plants and animals by primitive man was an essential step in the establishment of more or less sedentary groups. (2) The discoveries of medicine have prolonged life and removed discomforts which formerly handicapped man. (3) Scientific agriculture has, by improving the breeds of domestic plants and animals and by combating their enemies, increased the food supply and therefore the wealth of the world. (4) Biology now proposes that the discoveries in the domain of human biology be applied to the improvement of mankind.

Review Questions

1. In what ways are biological principles applicable to sociology?
2. Draw an analogy between social and organic evolution.
3. How has man modified the course of natural selection?
4. Discuss the relative roles of eugenics and euthenics in the improvement of mankind.
5. In what ways have biological discoveries aided human social evolution?

Chapter XIX

THE HISTORY OF BIOLOGY

The beginnings of biology are lost in antiquity. Man began as a hunter, undoubtedly, and his occupation forced him into a knowledge of nature. The thoroughness of his knowledge is reflected in the cave paintings and sculptures left by the Cro-Magnon race. Domestication of plants and animals was followed by a still more intimate acquaintance with nature. Crude medical practice involved a certain amount of human anatomical knowledge, just as use of animals for food gave primitive man a certain superficial familiarity with their structures. Scientific biology began with the dawn of civilization.

CHRONOLOGICAL SUMMARY, BY PERIODS

Biology in the Ancient Historic World.

BIOLOGY IN ANCIENT BABYLON, EGYPT, ISRAEL, AND THE FAR EAST. In Babylon, the priesthood knew something of anatomy (particularly of sacrificial animals) and medicine, the latter sadly involved in astrology, however. The medicine of ancient Egypt was more practical, being based chiefly on knowledge of the human body. The ancient Jews contributed to our modern conceptions of hygiene through their laws. In the Far East, the knowledge of nature and medicine never got far beyond the primitive stage; the peoples were concerned with other problems.

BIOLOGY IN ANCIENT GREECE. Scientific medicine was founded by Hippocrates (*cir.* 460–377 B.C.); his method was empirical. The ethics associated with the profession date from him or earlier. Aristotle (384–322 B.C.) was the first great organizer of biological knowledge, the "Father of Biology." Theophrastus (*cir.* 380–287 B.C.), his successor, was the "Father of Botany." Greek tradition continued in the Museum of Alexandria until about 30 B.C., but under Roman rule steadily declined.

BIOLOGY UNDER THE ROMAN EMPIRE. A work for plant identification appeared in the first century A.D. (by Dioscorides), and the first botanical drawings appeared. Some progress was made in anatomy and physiology, particularly by Galen (A.D. 130–200), the greatest physiologist of antiquity.

Biology in the Middle Ages.

THE DARK AGES IN EUROPE. From about the time of the death of Galen until the thirteenth century works of Greeks and Romans were recopied, both text and drawings, with no recourse to sources in nature. They progressively acquired more and more errors.

THE ARABIAN EMPIRE. During the Dark Ages in Europe, the Arabs not only preserved the finest of ancient Greek science but added some contributions of their own.

THE THIRTEENTH-CENTURY REVIVAL. Beginning somewhat earlier, but reaching a climax in the thirteenth century, Europeans began to translate into Latin the scientific works available to them in Arabic. In this way Aristotle's works reappeared.

Biology during the Renaissance. The thirteenth-century revival expanded into the Renaissance. Art became more natural-istic and involved a thorough study of subjects (e.g., by Leonardo da Vinci, 1452–1519). In 1530 appeared the first of a series of *printed* and illustrated works on plants (herbals). In 1543 Vesalius' great work on human anatomy was published, and natural his-tories of animals appeared in the same century. In 1629 Harvey's work on the circulation of the blood was printed.

Biology in the Seventeenth and Eighteenth Centuries. The attitude of scientific men began to change — they looked to nature herself for information. The period of geographic explora-tion expanded their vision; the invention of the microscope inten-sified it. The first scientific societies and journals were founded. Detailed studies on the anatomy of small organisms and parts of larger ones were pursued, and cells were discovered and named (Hooke, Malpighi, Grew, Swammerdam, Leeuwenhoek). Schemes of plant and animal classification were devised, following the stimulus of explorations (Jung, Ray, Linnaeus).

Nineteenth-century Biology.

MORPHOLOGY. Anatomy became not only more detailed, but comparative. Cuvier (1769–1832) founded comparative anatomy; he studied extinct as well as modern vertebrates. Lamarck (1744–1829), his contemporary, best known today for his theory of evol-ution, was a thorough student of plants and animals. Bichat (1771–1802) made a classification of human tissues. The cell theory was propounded in about 1810 (Chap. III). The doctrine that protoplasm is a universal characteristic of life was accepted within another thirty years. Hofmeister (1824–1877) demonstrated the fundamental similarities between higher and lower plants. Studies on mitosis, the history of germ cells, fertilization, and embryology characterized the last of the century.

PHYSIOLOGY. At the beginning of the century, the discoveries of the identity of combustion and respiration and of the formation of oxygen by green plants (Lavoisier and Priestley) gave an impulse to the application of chemical knowledge to organisms. The first organic compound to be synthesized, urea, was prepared by Wöhler and was followed rapidly by many others. Liebig (1802–1873) applied chemistry to living phenomena, especially in plants. Claude Bernard (1813–1878) was the great chemical physiologist of the century. The germ theory of disease was developed, and biological control of disease begun (Pasteur, Koch, Lister). Johannes Müller (1801–1858), extremely versatile, applied comparative anatomy, chemistry, and physics in physiology. Ludwig (1816–1895) also approached physiology from the standpoint of physics; he invented some of the most widely-used laboratory apparatus of today.

EVOLUTION. Lamarck's doctrine of use and disuse, with inheritance of acquired characteristics, came at the beginning of the century. It was opposed by Cuvier, whose influence was great, with the result that it found little favor. Evolution was not widely accepted until after 1859, in which year was published *The Origin of Species*, by Charles Darwin (1809–1882). August Weismann (1834–1914) brought out, toward the close of the century, the importance of the germ plasm and the noninheritance of acquired characteristics.

GENETICS. The experiments of Gregor Mendel (1822–1884), performed in the 1860's, were not appreciated until 1900. Statistical methods were applied by Francis Galton (1822–1911) to studies of human inheritance.

Twentieth-century Biology. The present century has been characterized by a more intensive application of experimental methods. The application of physical chemistry in biology has become prominent; other aspects have attained considerable recognition — e.g., ecology. But the twentieth century has been the period of greatest advance in genetics and cell physiology. The mutation theory was proposed in 1901 by Hugo de Vries and marked achievements have come in the study of the mechanism of heredity, particularly by T. H. Morgan and his associates. In recent decades, biochemists have clarified many details of cellular metabolism, and electron microscopists have described the minute structure of cells.

BRIEF BIOGRAPHIES OF GREAT BIOLOGISTS

Aristotle (384–322 B.C.). The Father of Biology. He was tutor of Alexander the Great and founder of the Lyceum at Athens. Aristotle organized the knowledge of his period. His chief contributions were on the natural history, anatomy, and reproduction of animals and on the nature of life.

Theophrastus (*cir.* 380–287 B.C.). The Father of Botany. Theophrastus was the successor of Aristotle in the Lyceum — not a thinker of equal rank, however. He left us the most extensive treatises on plants of the ancient world.

Andreas Vesalius (A.D. 1514–1564). Vesalius was a Belgian, who became professor of anatomy at Padua, Italy. In 1543 he published the first scientific treatise on human anatomy, beautifully illustrated.

William Harvey (1578–1667). English physician, educated at Padua, Italy. Harvey published the first accurate account of the course of the blood in the human body (1628); his embryological studies emphasized the origin of both viviparous and oviparous forms from the egg.

Carolus Linnaeus — Carl von Linné (1707–1778). Swedish botanist and zoologist. He established on a firm basis the binomial system of nomenclature — in the 1750's.

Charles Darwin (1809–1882). He was naturalist of the *Beagle* on a trip around the world, 1831–36. On his return he established a notebook on the change of species. *The Origin of Species* was published in 1859 — in its effect on human thought the most significant book of the century. Darwin published many other works, not all of which were in the field of evolution.

Wilhelm Hofmeister (1824–1877). German botanist, self-educated. He was the first to describe fertilization and embryo-formation in higher plants. He demonstrated the wide occurrence of the alternation of generations in plants; and he pointed out the fundamental relationships of all plants.

Gregor Mendel (1822–1884). Monk, and later abbot, of a monastery in Austria. His most important contribution was the discovery of the laws of inheritance which we now call Mendel's Laws. (See Chap. XIII.)

Louis Pasteur (1822–1895). French chemist and bacteriologist. Simultaneously with Robert Koch, a German, Pasteur demonstrated the bacterial origin of disease. He developed a method of attenuating (weakening) a disease-producing organism so that it could be used in developing immunity. He established inoculation against rabies or hydrophobia. In his memory there now exist many Pasteur Institutes throughout the world.

August Weismann (1834–1914). German zoologist. Weismann proposed the theory of the continuity of the germ plasm. He made the first important scientific denial of the inheritance of acquired characteristics.

Hugo de Vries (1848–1935). Dutch botanist. His early experiments formed a basis for the theory of electrolytic dissociation. He was founder of the *Mutation Theory* of evolution.

Theobald Smith (1859–1934). American parasitologist and immunologist. Among many other discoveries in medicine, he was first to demonstrate experimentally the transmission of a disease-producing organism by an arthropod (Texas cattle fever transmitted by a tick, demonstrated in 1889).

Thomas Hunt Morgan (1866–1945). American zoologist, Nobel Prize winner. His experiments with *Drosophila*, coupled with those of his students and associates, were the basis for the gene theory of heredity.

Hans Krebs (b. 1900). British biochemist, Nobel Prize winner. Discoverer of important steps in the process of cell respiration.

Review Questions

1. Trace the progress of biology from prehistoric times to the present.
2. What have been the major trends in a biological research since the Renaissance?
3. Give the essential contributions of a representative number of great biologists, including Aristotle, Vesalius, Harvey, Linnaeus, Darwin, and Mendel.

Chapter XX

PHILOSOPHY AND BIOLOGY

Ostensibly or otherwise, a biologist believes in the independent existence of a world of objects which he, through his sense organs, perceives. Objects in that world which exhibit a certain group of properties (life) are his province. Given the same instruments, all normal human beings are able to find the same properties in an external object. This uniformity of perception by different individuals means to the biologist that the objects exist apart from the minds that perceive them. Consequently, a biologist does not believe that mind is the only reality. Modern scientists have been handicapped by the view of Descartes that knowledge of one's self is prior to other knowledge. As a matter of fact, we do not know in full the relations between body and mind. The validity of knowledge, however, is not dependent on our understanding of how we know.

LIFE

No simple criterion makes it possible to distinguish between living and nonliving matter. The complexity of life and its essentially mysterious nature make it a subject for conjecture.

Mechanism and Vitalism. In general, there are two antithetic approaches to life. The *mechanist* considers a living organism a machine, whose parts and their interactions obey the same physical and chemical laws which we know in the nonliving world. The *vitalist* believes that the ordinary physical and chemical laws are insufficient to explain life — that the condition of being alive is due to some other factor about which we know nothing, but whose existence we must assume. The former viewpoint has, of course, been the fruitful one in scientific research. That does not prove that life is a mechanism, however, but it does suggest that the practical or methodological approach involves an assumption that the known laws of chemistry and physics do explain living matter. Hence, modern biologists are mechanists in experimental approach, regardless of their fundamental convictions.

The Organismic Hypothesis. Certain biologists, and more particularly psychologists, have suggested that the activity or behavior of an organism is not the sum of the actions or functions of its separate parts, but that, as a dynamic whole, it transcends in behavior these separate parts. In other words, the whole is not functionally the sum of its parts. Such a view is the *organismic hypothesis.* According to the opposite hypotheses, the *atomistic,* the behavior of the organism is merely the sum of its separate functions. Followers of either hypothesis may be mechanistic in their general interpretation of life.

Origin of Life. Since the biologist has been unable to demonstrate the spontaneous origin of living matter, he has been inclined to ignore theories of the origin of life as outside his field. His working hypothesis of mechanism, however, implies that living matter has in some way been derived from nonliving. And there is now experimental evidence that complex organic compounds are formed spontaneously from the inorganic compounds that were present in the primitive earth's atmosphere. From these it is possible to postulate formation of the first compounds that behaved with the properties of living matter. Henderson, some years ago, emphasized the reciprocal relationship between environment and organism, believing that the fitness of the cosmos for life suggests that both inorganic and organic evolution are essentially one, and that the universe is *biocentric,* viz., that its central and most fundamental fact is life, not nonliving matter.

Evolution. Various biologists and philosophers have suggested the presence of a directing or controlling force, external or internal, in evolution. Modern theories of evolution find this view irrelevant and unnecessary, however; it is now only of historical interest.

SCIENCE AND RELIGION

Many unfortunate controversies between defenders of organized religion and scientists have arisen during the course of history. They have been, however, in final analysis, based on superficials — either of faith or of knowledge. The two provinces represent different viewpoints, but not opposite ones. Most controversy has been over the matter of organic evolution, particularly as applied to man. Opponents of the evolutionary doctrine, none of whom is a trained biologist, have in common one viewpoint which is not consistent with the discoveries of biology. (It is in fact inconsistent with true religion.) That viewpoint is a belief in the literal inspiration of the Bible and in the strict truth of every word in the particular translation they follow. Of course such a view is inconsistent with the findings of biology, but it is equally inconsistent with discoveries in other fields as well. Unfortunately, the religious fanatic can almost never be convinced by what to the scientist is evidence; he puts his faith in religious dicta and denies the evidence of his own senses. That is the crux of the controversy, a matter of fundamental difference in viewpoint — a difference which involves the nature of reality itself. That there is no inconsistency between true religion and a belief in evolution is abundantly demonstrated by the great number of biologists and other evolutionists who are active in the support of religious institutions. In fact, the biologist, as others, realizes that no force equals religion as a means of drawing out from man the best qualities which he possesses.

Review Questions

1. Distinguish between the mechanistic and vitalistic theories of living matter.
2. What is a biocentric theory of the universe?
3. Discuss the evolution-religion controversy.

APPENDICES

Appendix A
REFERENCES

Books to which students are referred for supplementary reading material are here classified in four groups, these groups corresponding to the four Parts of this Outline. References that are most general in scope are included among those in the list for Part II. No textbooks of General Biology are included; cross references to these are provided in the Tabulated Bibliography and Quick Reference Table.

Part I: Life in Its Simplest Form

Borek, Ernest. *The Code of Life.* Columbia University, 1966.
DeRobertis, E. D. P., Nowinski, W. W., and Saez, F. A. *Cell Biology.* Saunders, 1965.
Downes, H. R. *The Chemistry of Living Cells.* Harper Bros., 1962.
Frobisher, Martin. *Fundamentals of Microbiology.* Saunders, 1957.
Giese, A. C. *Cell Physiology.* Saunders, 1962.
Kennedy, Donald (compiler). *The Living Cell: Readings from Scientific American.* Freeman, 1965.
McElroy, W. D. *Cellular Physiology and Biochemistry.* Prentice-Hall, 1961.
Porter, K. R., and Bonneville, M. A. *Introduction to the Fine Structure of Cells and Tissues.* Lea & Febiger, 1963.
Stern, Herbert, and Nanney, D. L. *The Biology of Cells.* Wiley, 1965.
Thimann, K. V. *The Life of Bacteria.* Macmillan, 1963.
Wilson, E. B. *The Cell in Development and Heredity.* Macmillan, 1928.

Part II: Multicellular Organisms

Arey, L. B. *Developmental Anatomy.* Saunders, 1965.
Barth, L. G. *Embryology.* Dryden, 1953.
Best, C. H., and Taylor, N. B. *The Physiological Basis of Medical Practice.* Williams and Wilkins, 1966.
Bloom, W., and Fawcett, D. W. *A Textbook of Histology.* Saunders, 1962.
Bonner, James, and Galston, A. W. *Principles of Plant Physiology.* Freeman, 1952.

Buchsbaum, R. M. *Animals without Backbones*. University of Chicago, 1948.

Carlson, A. J., and Johnson, Victor. *The Machinery of the Body*. University of Chicago, 1962.

Chandler, A. C., and Reed, C. P. *Introduction to Parasitology*. Wiley, 1961.

Corner, G. W. *The Hormones in Human Reproduction*. Princeton University, 1947.

————. *Ourselves Unborn*. Yale University, 1944.

Eames, A. J., and MacDaniels, L. H. *An Introduction to Plant Anatomy*. McGraw-Hill, 1947.

Elliott, A. M. *Zoology*. Appleton-Century-Crofts, 1963.

Emerson, F. W. *Basic Botany*. Blakiston, 1954.

Frohse, Franz; Brödel, Max; and Schlossberg, Leon. *Atlas of Human Anatomy*. Barnes and Noble, 1957.

Fuller, H. J., and Tippo, Oswald. *College Botany*. Holt, 1954.

Goss, C. M. *Gray's Anatomy of the Human Body*. Lea & Febiger, 1959.

Guthrie, M. J., and Anderson, J. M. *General Zoology*. Wiley, 1957.

Haupt, A. W. *Plant Morphology*. McGraw-Hill, 1953.

Hegner, R. W., and Stiles, K. A. *College Zoology*. Macmillan, 1957.

Holmes, S. J. *The Biology of the Frog*. Macmillan, 1927.

Huettner, A. F. *Fundamentals of Comparative Embryology of the Vertebrates*. Macmillan, 1949.

Huxley, T. H. *The Crayfish: An Introduction to the Study of Zoology*. Appleton-Century, 1880.

Hyman, L. H. *The Invertebrata*. McGraw-Hill, 1940–1959. 5 vols. (I: *Protozoa through Ctenophora;* II: *Platyhelminthes and Rhynchocoela;* III: *Acanthocephala, Aschelminthes, and Entoprocta;* IV: *Echinodermata;* V: *Smaller Coelomate Groups*.)

Jacques, H. E. *How to Know the Insects*. Wm. C. Brown Co., 1947.

————. *Plant Families — How to Know Them*. Wm. C. Brown Co., 1948.

Kimber, D. C., *et al*. *Textbook of Anatomy and Physiology*. Macmillan, 1966.

Meyer, B. S., and Anderson, D. B. *Plant Physiology*. Van Nostrand, 1952.

Orr, R. T. *Vertebrate Biology*. Saunders, 1961.

Parker, T. J., and Haswell, W. A. *A Text-book of Zoology*. 2 vols. Macmillan (London), 1949.

Patten, B. M. *Human Embryology*. Blakiston, 1953.

Pennak, R. W. *Fresh-water Invertebrates of the United States*. Ronald, 1953.

Prosser, C. L. (ed.). *Comparative Animal Physiology*. Saunders, 1961.

Romer, A. S. *The Vertebrate Body*. Saunders, 1962.

Ross, H. H. *A Textbook of Entomology.* Wiley, 1965.

Scheer, B. T. *Animal Physiology.* Wiley, 1963.

Schmidt-Nielsen, K. *Animal Physiology.* Prentice-Hall, 1960.

Smith, G. M. *Cryptogamic Botany.* Vol. 1: *Algae and Fungi.* Vol. 2: *Bryophytes and Pteridophytes.* McGraw-Hill, 1938.

Steen, E. B., and Montagu, A. *Anatomy and Physiology.* (2 vols.) Barnes and Noble, 1959.

Storer, T. I., and Usinger, R. L. *General Zoology.* McGraw-Hill, 1965.

Swain, R. B. *The Insect Guide.* Doubleday, 1948.

Telfer, William, and Kennedy, Donald. *The Biology of Organisms.* Wiley, 1965.

Part III: General Principles

Allee, W. C., *et al. Principles of Animal Ecology.* Saunders, 1949.

Anderson, Edgar. *Plants, Man and Life.* Little, Brown, 1952.

Arnold, C. A. *An Introduction to Paleobotany.* McGraw-Hill, 1947.

Bates, Marston. *The Forest and the Sea.* Random House, 1960.

Blum, H. F. *Time's Arrow and Evolution.* Princeton University, 1955.

Cain, S. A. *Foundations of Plant Geography.* Harpers, 1944.

Carson, Rachel L. *The Sea Around Us.* Oxford University, 1951.

Darlington, P. J., Jr. *Zoogeography.* Wiley, 1957.

Daubenmire, R. F. *Plants and Environment.* Wiley, 1959.

Dobzhansky, T. G. *Genetics and the Origin of Species.* Columbia University, 1951.

Dodson, E. O. *Evolution: Process and Product.* Reinhold, 1960.

Herskowitz, I. H. *Genetics.* Little, Brown, 1965.

Hesse, R., Allee, W. A., and Schmidt, K. P. *Ecological Animal Geography.* Wiley, 1951.

Hough, J. N. *Scientific Terminology.* Rinehart, 1953.

Huxley, Julian. *Evolution, the Modern Synthesis.* Harpers, 1942.

Kendeigh, S. C. *Animal Ecology.* Prentice-Hall, 1961.

MacArthur, Robert, and Connell, Joseph. *The Biology of Populations.* Wiley, 1966.

Mayr, Ernst, Linsley, E. G., and Usinger, R. L. *Methods and Principles of Systematic Zoology.* McGraw-Hill, 1953.

———. *Animal Species and Evolution.* Harvard University, 1963.

Moore, John A. (ed.). *Ideas in Modern Biology.* Natural History Press, 1965.

Odum, E. P. *Fundamentals of Ecology.* Saunders, 1959.

Oosting, H. J. *The Study of Plant Communities.* Freeman, 1956.

Orr, R. T. *Vertebrate Biology.* Saunders, 1961.

Ross, H. H. *A Synthesis of Evolutionary Theory.* Prentice-Hall, 1962.

Simpson, G. G. *The Major Features of Evolution.* Columbia University, 1953.

———. *Principles of Animal Taxonomy.* Columbia University, 1961.

Sinnott, E. W., Dunn, L. C., and Dobzhansky, T. G. *Principles of Genetics.* McGraw-Hill, 1958.

Snyder, L. H., and David, P. R. *Principles of Heredity.* Heath, 1957.

Srb, A. M., *et al. General Genetics.* Freeman, 1965.

Stebbins, G. L. *Processes of Organic Evolution.* Prentice-Hall, 1966.

Stern, Curt. *Principles of Human Genetics.* Freeman, 1960.

Wallace, Bruce, and Srb, A. M. *Adaptation.* Prentice-Hall, 1961.

Winchester, A. M. *Heredity.* Barnes and Noble, 1961.

Woods, R. S. *The Naturalist's Lexicon.* Abbey Garden Press, 1944; and *Addenda,* 1947.

Part IV: Human Relations of Biology

Bates, Marston. *Man in Nature.* Prentice-Hall, 1961.

Beckner, Morton. *The Biological Way of Thought.* Columbia University, 1959.

Dobzhansky, T. *Evolution, Genetics, and Man.* Wiley, 1963.

Dunn, L. C., and Dobzhansky, T. G. *Heredity, Race and Society.* Mentor, 1952.

Grobstein, Clifford. *The Strategy of Life.* Freeman, 1964.

Hall, T. S. *A Source Book in Animal Biology.* McGraw-Hill, 1951.

Henderson, L. J. *The Fitness of the Environment.* Peter Smith, 1959.

Huxley, Julian. *Man in the Modern World.* Mentor, 1948.

Locy, W. A. *The Growth of Biology.* Holt, 1925.

Montagu, M. F. A. *Man's Most Dangerous Myth; The Fallacy of Race.* Harpers, 1952.

Osborn, Frederick. *Preface to Eugenics.* Harpers, 1951.

Robbins, W. W., and Ramaley, Francis. *Plants Useful to Man.* Blakiston, 1933.

Singer, Charles. *A History of Biology.* Schuman, 1950.

Sinnott, E. W. *Cell and Psyche.* University of North Carolina, 1950.

Vogt, William. *Road to Survival.* William Sloane Associates, 1948.

Wing, Leonard W. *Practice of Wildlife Conservation.* Wiley, 1951.

Woodger, J. H. *Biological Principles.* Routledge and Kegan Paul (London), 1948.

Appendix B

AN ABRIDGED CLASSIFICATION
OF PLANTS AND ANIMALS

PLANT KINGDOM:
Division 1. Thallophyta. Algae and fungi.
  Subdivision 1. Algae.
    CLASS 1. Cyanophyceae. Blue-green algae (e.g., *Oscillatoria*).
    CLASS 2. Chlorophyceae. Green algae (e.g., *Spirogyra*).
    CLASS 3. Phaeophyceae. Brown algae (e.g., *Laminaria*, *Fucus*).
    CLASS 4. Rhodophyceae. Red algae.
  Subdivision 2. Fungi.
    CLASS 1. Schizomycetes. Bacteria.
    CLASS 2. Myxomycetes. Slime molds. (Sometimes considered animals of the Phylum Protozoa.)
    CLASS 3. Phycomycetes. Algalike fungi (e.g., bread mold).
    CLASS 4. Ascomycetes. Sac fungi, including yeasts.
    CLASS 5. Basidiomycetes. Club fungi (e.g., mushrooms).
Division 2. Bryophyta. Mosses and liverworts.
    CLASS 1. Hepaticae. Liverworts.
    CLASS 2. Musci. Mosses.
Division 3. Pteridophyta. Ferns and fern allies.
    CLASS 1. Lycopodineae. Club mosses.
    CLASS 2. Equisetineae. Horsetails or scouring rushes.
    CLASS 3. Filicineae. Ferns.
Division 4. Spermatophyta. Seed plants.
    CLASS 1. Gymnospermae. Conifers and related plants.
    CLASS 2. Angiospermae. Flowering plants.
      SUBCLASS 1. Dicotyledoneae. (Examples: buttercup, bean, dandelion, oak, elm.)
      SUBCLASS 2. Monocotyledoneae. (Examples: grasses, sedges, tulip, palms.)

This classification is being replaced in some botany texts by the following classification in which the algae and fungi are in a series of only distantly related Phyla and the Pteridophyta and Spermatophyta are combined to form the Phylum Tracheophyta.

Subkingdom. Thallophyta. Plants not forming embryos.

Phylum 1. Cyanophyta. Blue-green algae.
Phylum 2. Euglenophyta. Euglenoids.
Phylum 3. Chlorophyta. Green algae.
Phylum 4. Chrysophyta. Yellow-green algae, golden brown algae, diatoms.
Phylum 5. Pyrrophyta. Cryptomonads, dinoflagellates.
Phylum 6. Phaeophyta. Brown algae.
Phylum 7. Rhodophyta. Red algae.
Phylum 8. Schizomycophyta. Bacteria.
Phylum 9. Myxomycophyta. Slime molds.
Phylum 10. Eumycophyta. True fungi.

Subkingdom. Embryophyta. Plants forming embryos.

Phylum 11. Bryophyta or Atracheata. Plants lacking vascular tissues.
    CLASS 1. Musci. Mosses.
    CLASS 2. Hepaticae. Liverworts.
    CLASS 3. Anthoceratae. Hornworts.
Phylum 12. Tracheophyta or Tracheata. Plants with vascular tissues.
    SUBPHYLUM 1. Psilopsida. Psilopsids.
    SUBPHYLUM 2. Lycopsida. Club mosses.
    SUBPHYLUM 3. Sphenopsida. Horsetails and relatives.
    SUBPHYLUM 4. Pteropsida. Ferns and seed plants.
        CLASS 1. Filicineae. Ferns.
        CLASS 2. Gymnospermae. Cone-bearing plants and relatives.
        CLASS 3. Angiospermae. True flowering plants.
            SUBCLASS 1. Dicotyledoneae.
            SUBCLASS 2. Monocotyledoneae.

ANIMAL KINGDOM

Phylum 1. Protozoa. Unicellular animals.
    CLASS 1. Mastigophora. Flagellate protozoa (e.g., *Euglena*).
    CLASS 2. Sarcodina. Amoeboid protozoa (e.g., *Amoeba*).
    CLASS 3. Sporozoa. Spore-producing protozoa (e.g., *Plasmodium*).
    CLASS 4. Infusoria. Ciliate protozoa (e.g., *Paramecium*).
Phylum 2. Porifera. Sponges.
Phylum 3. Coelenterata.
    CLASS 1. Hydrozoa. Hydroids (e.g., *Hydra*, *Obelia*).
    CLASS 2. Scyphozoa. Jellyfishes.
    CLASS 3. Anthozoa. Corals and sea anemones.
Phylum 4. Ctenophora. Comb jellies or sea walnuts.
Phylum 5. Platyhelminthes. Flatworms.
    CLASS 1. Turbellaria. *Planaria* and related animals.
    CLASS 2. Trematoda. Flukes.
    CLASS 3. Cestoda. Tapeworms.

Phylum 6.   Nemertea. Nemertine worms.
Phylum 7.   Nematoda. Roundworms.
Phylum 8.   Rotatoria. Rotifers.
Phylum 9.   Nematomorpha. Horsehair worms.
Phylum 10.   Bryozoa. Moss animals.
Phylum 11.   Brachiopoda. Lamp shells.
Phylum 12.   Echinodermata.
  CLASS 1.   Asteroidea. Starfishes.
  CLASS 2.   Ophiuroidea. Brittle stars, serpent stars.
  CLASS 3.   Echinoidea. Sea urchins, sand dollars.
  CLASS 4.   Holothuroidea. Sea cucumbers, sea slugs.
  CLASS 5.   Crinoidea. Crinoids (sea lilies).
Phylum 13.   Mollusca. Mollusks.
  CLASS 1.   Pelecypoda. Clams, mussels, oysters.
  CLASS 2.   Amphineura. Chitons.
  CLASS 3.   Gastropoda. Snails, slugs.
  CLASS 4.   Scaphopoda. Tooth shells.
  CLASS 5.   Cephalopoda. Squids, octopus, nautilus.
Phylum 14.   Annelida. Segmented worms.
  CLASS 1.   Chaetopoda. Earthworms, clamworms.
  CLASS 2.   Hirudinea. Leeches.
Phylum 15.   Onychophora. *Peripatus.*
Phylum 16.   Arthropoda.
  CLASS 1.   Crustacea. Crayfish, crabs, barnacles, water fleas.
  CLASS 2.   Diplopoda. Millipedes.
  CLASS 3.   Chilopoda. Centipedes.
  CLASS 4.   Insecta. Insects: bees, grasshoppers, beetles, flies, etc.
  CLASS 5.   Arachnida. Ticks, spiders, scorpions, horseshoe crab.
Phylum 17.   Chordata.
 Subphylum 1.   Hemichorda. *Dolichoglossus.*
 Subphylum 2.   Urochorda. Tunicates: sea squirts, sea pork.
 Subphylum 3.   Cephalochorda. *Amphioxus.*
 Subphylum 4.   Vertebrata. Vertebrates.
  CLASS 1.   Agnatha. Lampreys, hagfishes.
  CLASS 2.   Chondrichthyes. Sharks, rays.
  CLASS 3.   Osteichthyes. Bony fishes: perch, trout, catfish, eel.
  CLASS 4.   Amphibia. Salamanders, frogs, toads.
  CLASS 5.   Reptilia. Turtles, snakes, lizards, alligators.
  CLASS 6.   Aves. Birds: ostrich, chicken, sparrow, robin.
  CLASS 7.   Mammalia. Mammals: opossum, squirrel, rat, bat, whale, horse, man.

Appendix C
GLOSSARY

The definitions given are brief. It is intended that they suggest the ordinary significance of each term as used in biology, rather than the various usages. Less common terms which are explained where they occur in the Outline have been omitted.

Abdomen: the major body division posterior to head and thorax.

Age and area: the theory which holds that the oldest types of plants and animals occupy the widest geographic areas.

Allelomorph: one of two or more alternative genes.

Alternation of generations: alternation of gametophytic and sporophytic generations in plants.

Analogy: superficial similarity — due only to similarity in function. (See *homology*.)

Anatomy: the study of visible structure, or gross structure.

Androecium: the stamens collectively.

Anterior: toward the forward end.

Anther: the pollen sacs of the stamen.

Antheridium: a plant organ in which male gametes are formed.

Antibody: something produced in the body to combat the injurious effect of a foreign substance (antigen).

Antigen: a foreign protein which causes the production of an antibody in the organism.

Anus: outlet of digestive tract.

Archegonium: a plant organ in which female gametes are formed.

Asexual reproduction: reproduction by one individual, independent of others.

Assimilation: the manufacture of reserve food or protoplasm.

Atrium: a chamber of the heart in which blood is received.

Auricle = atrium.

Autecology: the ecology of an individual organism or species.

Autotrophic: a type of nutrition in which the organism manufactures its own food.

Biogenetic law: the statement that the development of the individual repeats the development of the race.

Biology: the science of life.

Biotic potential: an expression of the rate of reproduction of an organism.

Blastula: an early stage of the embryo which consists essentially of a hollow ball of cells.

Botany: the science of plant life.

Calyx: the outer whorl of a complete flower; the sepals collectively.

Cambium: meristem tissue responsible for secondary thickening in stem or root.

Capillary: a small thin-walled blood vessel connecting an artery with a vein or (in portal systems) a vein with a vein.

Carpel: a megasporophyll of a flowering plant.

Cell: the unit of structure and function in organisms.

Central body: a structure, present in cells of animals and lower plants, from which radiate the spindle fibers during mitosis.

Cephalothorax: the head and thorax combined in one structure.

Chlorophyll: the pigment of green plants involved in photosynthesis.

Chloroplast: a plastid containing chlorophyll.

Chromatid: one of the two strands constituting a chromosome prior to its division.

Chromatin: a nuclear constituent staining readily with basic dyes; the material of chromosomes.

Chromosome: a structure formed from chromatin which appears in cells during mitosis; the bearer of hereditary determiners.

Cleavage stages: cell division characteristic of early stages of the embryo.

Coelom: body cavity — a space, in which the viscera lie, lined with mesoderm.

Colony: a group of organisms of the same species living together.

Community: a group of organisms related together by environment requirements.

Corolla: next to outer whorl of complete flower; the petals collectively.

Corpuscle: a blood cell.

Cotyledon: an embryo leaf.

Cranium: that portion of the skull which surrounds the brain.

Cytology: the study of cells.

Cytoplasm: the protoplasm of the cytosome.

Cytosome: that part of the cell outside the nucleus.

Digestion: preparation of food for absorption and assimilation — by hydrolysis.

Dioecious: condition in which male and female flowers occur on different plants; condition in animals in which the male and female gametes are produced in different individuals.

Diploid: the chromosome number in which the chromosomes are represented by homologous pairs; twice the haploid number.

Distal: away from the point of attachment or place of reference.

Dominant: the one of two alternative characters which is evident in a heterozygous individual. (See *recessive*.)

Dorsal: toward the back.

Ecology: the study of relations between organism and environment.

Ectoderm: outer layer of cells of early embryo.

Egestion: the discharge of unabsorbed food from an animal.

Egg cell: a female gamete.

Embryo: an early stage in the development of an organism.

Embryogeny: the process of development of the embryo.

Embryology: the study of development.

Embryo sac: female gametophyte of higher plants.

Endocrine gland: a gland of internal secretion (ductless gland); a gland which produces a hormone.

Endoderm: innermost layer of cells in the gastrula stage of the embryo.

Endoskeleton: internal supporting structure.

Enzyme: a catalyst characteristic of living organisms.

Epidermis: a layer of cells covering an external surface.

Epithelium: a layer of cells covering a surface or lining a cavity (animals).

Evolution: the process of racial development.

Excretion: the discharge of waste materials formed in metabolism.

Exoskeleton: external supporting structure.

Fertilization: the union of two gametes to form a zygote.

Food cycle: a group of organisms related together through food requirements.

Gamete: a mature germ cell or "marrying cell"; sperm cell or egg.

Gametogenesis: the process of gamete formation; maturation.

Gametophyte: gamete-bearing generation in plants.

Ganglion: a concentration of nerve cells.

Gastrovascular cavity: a combined digestive and circulatory cavity.

Gastrula: an early stage of the embryo which consists essentially of an invaginated blastula.

Gene: an hereditary determiner — located in a chromosome.

Genetics: the science of heredity.

Genotype: the fundamental hereditary (genetic) constitution of an organism. (See *phenotype*.)

Germ layer: one of the three embryonic cell layers of multicellular animals.

Germ plasm: the gametes and the cells from which they are formed, considered as a unit.

Glycogen: a complex carbohydrate, a polysaccharide; "animal starch."

Gonad: a gamete-producing organ in animals; testis or ovary.

Growth: increase in size.

Gynoecium: the carpels collectively.

Haemocoel: a body cavity that functions as a part of the blood-vascular system.

Haploid: the chromosome number in which only one set of chromosomes is present; half the diploid number.

Heredity: transmission of characters from parent to offspring.

Hermaphroditism: the condition in which gonads of both sexes occur in the same individual.

Heterozygous: said of an individual which has unlike or alternative genes (allelomorphs) for the character being considered. (See *homozygous.*)

Histology: the study of tissues.

Holozoic: type of nutrition in which solid food is ingested.

Homology: fundamental similarity — based primarily on development and structure. (See *analogy.*)

Homozygous: said of an individual which has duplicate genes for the character being considered. (See *heterozygous.*)

Hormone: a chemical regulator; a substance which serves in the chemical co-ordination of the body.

Hyphae: filaments characteristic of the fungi.

Immunity: resistance to disease.

Irritability: the capacity to respond to a stimulus.

Linkage: the condition in which characters are inherited together because of the presence of their genes in the same chromosome.

Mantle: the membrane lining the respiratory cavity of mollusks.

Maturation: the process of gamete formation; gametogenesis.

Mechanistic: the theory of life which holds that life can be explained by laws known from the nonliving world.

Megagametophyte: female gametophyte (embryo sac).

Megaspore: the larger of the two types of spores in heterosporous plants — forms the female gametophyte; ovule.

Megasporophyll: an organ producing megaspores — in a strobilus, a scale; in a flower, a carpel.

Meiosis: cell division in which the chromosome number is reduced from diploid to haploid; it involves two successive cell divisions.

Mendelism: the principles of heredity discovered by Gregor Mendel — in particular, segregation and independent assortment.

Meristem: plant tissue consisting of actively growing and dividing cells.

Mesoderm: the layer of cells which forms between ectoderm and endo-derm in animal embryos.

Metabolism: the chemical processes characteristic of protoplasm.

Metagenesis: alternation of sexual and asexual methods of reproduction.

Metamerism: segmental arrangement of organs or organ systems.

Metamorphosis: pronounced change in form during the course of development.

Microgametophyte: male gametophyte, pollen tube.

Micron: unit of length, $\frac{1}{1000}$ millimeter.

Microspore: pollen grain; the smaller of the two types of spores in heterosporous plants — forms the male gametophyte.

Microsporophyll: an organ producing microspores (pollen grains) — in a strobilus, a scale; in a flower, an anther.

Mitosis: cell division in which the nuclear constituents are divided equationally; indirect cell division.

Monoecious: condition in which male and female flowers are separate but borne on the same plant.

Morphology: the study of structure.

Mutation: an inherited change due to a modification of the germ plasm.

Mycelium: the hyphae of a fungus, considered together.

Natural selection: the process leading to the survival of the best adapted (most fit) in the competition in nature.

Nephridium: an organ of secretion; a kidney unit.

Nucleus: a definite controlling body within a cell, containing chromatin and surrounded by a membrane.

Nutrient: an inorganic constituent essential for plant growth.

Ocellus: a simple eye.

Oögenesis: the process of maturation of egg cells.

Organ: a group of cells or tissues functioning as a unit.

Orthogenesis: evolution in definite lines, due to a directing influence.

Ostium: an opening.

Ovary: in plants, the swollen portion of the pistil, in which the ovules develop; in animals, the female gonad, producing eggs.

Oviduct: the tube by which the eggs leave the body of the female animal.

Ovule: the structure in seed plants that develops into the seed; it is borne on a megasporophyll.

Ovum: an egg; a female gamete.

Parasite: an organism that lives at the expense of another.

Parenchyma: plant tissue consisting of rounded, thin-walled cells.

Parthenogenesis: reproduction by development from an unfertilized egg.

Pathogenic: disease producing.

Pectoral appendage: one of the anterior pair of paired appendages in vertebrates.

Pelvic appendage: one of the posterior pair of paired appendages in vertebrates.

Perianth: the calyx and corolla collectively.

Pericardium: a cavity surrounding the heart; also, the membrane covering the heart and lining the pericardial cavity.

Pericycle: a region in stem or root enclosing the vascular tissues of the plant.

Peristalsis: rhythmic muscular contractions which pass along a tubular organ.

Petal: one of the units of the corolla.

Phenotype: the appearance of an organism without regard to its hereditary constitution. (See *genotype*.)

Phloem: vascular tissue involved chiefly in a transfer of food materials within the plant.

Photosynthesis: synthesis with energy from light; specifically, the synthesis of carbohydrates by green plants in the presence of sunlight.

Phylum: a major group of animals (or plants).

Physiology: the study of function.

Pistil: a structural unit of the gynoecium — formed of one carpel or several, united.

Plastid: a specialized cytoplasmic body.

Pleural cavity: the cavity in which the lungs of mammals lie.

Pollen grain = microspore.

Pollen tube = microgametophyte or male gametophyte.

Posterior: toward the hinder end.

Priority: the principle by which the first scientific name given an organism is considered the valid one.

Protoplasm: the physico-chemical system which constitutes living matter.

Proximal: near point of attachment or place of reference.

Recessive: the one of two alternative characters which is not evident in a heterozygous individual. (See *dominant*.)

Reproduction: the maintenance of a species from generation to generation.

Respiration: oxidation of food (botanists); the taking in of oxygen and giving off of carbon dioxide, and all steps involved in this process (zoologists).

Saprophytic: type of nutrition in which the organism absorbs food through its walls.

Sclerenchyma: strengthening tissues (plants).

Sepal: one of the units of the calyx.

Sexual reproduction: reproduction involving two individuals of opposite sex.

Skull: the skeleton of the head in vertebrates.

Sorus: a group of sporangia.

Species: a group of similar organisms, the basic unit in classification; a group of interbreeding (or potentially interbreeding) individuals isolated reproductively from other such groups.

Spermatogenesis: the process of maturation of sperm cells.

Spermatozoon: a male gamete (animals); sperm cell.

Sperm cell: a male gamete.

Sporangium: a spore-producing structure.

Spore: a cell capable of developing independently into a new individual.

Sporophyll: scalelike structure bearing sporangia.

Sporophyte: spore-bearing generation in plants.

Stamen: the pollen-producing organ of the flower.

Stele: the vascular column of root or stem, including as its outer portion the pericycle.

Stomata: openings in the leaf epidermis.

Strobilus: a structure of the general form of a cone, consisting of sporophylls attached to an axis; a cone.

Succession: a natural sequence of changes in type of community.

Synecology: the ecology of community relations.

Taxonomy: the science of plant and animal classification.

Testis: the male gonad, producing spermatozoa.

Thallus: a plant body undifferentiated into root, stem, and leaves.

Thorax: the major division of the animal body next posterior to the head.

Tissue: a group of cells having the same function and structure.

Tracheae: air tubes.

Transpiration: controlled evaporation from leaves.

Tropism: growth movement in response to directional stimulus.

Turgor: the state of rigidity characteristic of plant cells.

Uterus: a swollen region which may be present at the posterior end of the oviduct, in which the embryos are retained in viviparous animals until birth.

Vacuole: a relatively large globule of liquid suspended in the cytoplasm.

Vascular tissue: general term applied to tissues which form the conducting channels in plants — xylem and phloem.

Vegetative: pertaining to nonreproductive functions.

Ventral: toward the lower side, away from the back.

Ventricle: a chamber of the heart from which blood leaves the heart.

Vitalistic: the theory of life which holds that its explanation requires the postulation of a force not known in the inorganic world.

Xylem: vascular tissue involved chiefly in conducting sap upward in a plant.

Zoology: the science of animal life.
Zygote: a fertilized egg.

Appendix D

SAMPLE FINAL EXAMINATION

Two types of examination questions are readily distinguishable, those of essay-type — requiring an organized discussion as an answer — and objective questions — requiring factual answers in words or phrases only.

Examples of essay-type questions that might be included in final examinations have already been given at the ends of the chapters in this Outline. Facts are necessary in answers to such questions, of course, but these can not be presented merely as facts; the answers must be organized discussions. A good essay-type answer involves ability in exposition as well as an understanding of facts and principles. The best insurance for a good answer, therefore, is a little time spent in planning the answer before beginning to write.

Answers to an objective examination require thorough understanding of vocabulary. Vocabulary is the key to any objective method of testing scientific knowledge. A full understanding of the technical language does depend, however, upon knowledge of both facts and principles. Hence, both types of examination questions test for facts. In objective examinations much more material can be covered in a given length of time than in those of essay-type. This is one reason objective examinations are widely used. Another reason is that papers may be graded more "objectively," therefore more justly, when large numbers of students are being examined at one time.

The following sample final examination does not necessarily correspond in length or content to an average final examination. It is designed primarily to suggest the various kinds of objective tests in common use in biology and contains a sample of each with the exception of one — an unlabeled drawing from a laboratory exercise, to which the student is expected to add the appropriate labels.

Multiple Choice. In each of the following sentences two or three alternative words or phrases are included in parentheses, but only one of these words or phrases may be used correctly. Underline the expression which will make each sentence correct.

1. A group of organisms bound together by environmental factors constitutes (an environment, a community, a succession).
2. An organism that manufactures its own food is (autotrophic, heterotrophic, saprophytic).
3. Oxidation taking place in the absence of oxygen is (reducing, aerobic, anaerobic).

4. (Trypsin, Lipase, Amylase) acts in the digestion of protein.

5. The human ovum after ovulation first enters the (ovary, Fallopian tube, uterus).

6. Cytoplasmic granules that are centers of enzyme activity are (chromatids, vacuoles, mitochondria).

7. Meiosis invariably involves (one division, two divisions) of the cell.

8. Darwin's theory of evolution is known as the theory of (mutations, acquired characteristics, natural selection).

9. The ocean as a habitat for organisms differs from land and fresh water in its greater (stability, variability).

10. Photosynthesis begins with a reaction that can occur in (darkness, light, the absence of water).

11. Amylase digests (cellulose, sugar, starch).

12. Calcium balance is regulated by the (parathyroid glands, thyroid gland, islets of Langerhans).

13. Bowman's capsule functions by (secretion, filtration, evaporation).

14. There are (two, three, four) separate cavities of the human coelom.

15. The cavity of the vitreous humor is (behind, in front of) the lens of the eye.

Matching. Each of the characteristics or conditions listed in the first column is appropriate to one (and one only) of the phyla in column two. Place the number of the characteristic in front of the name of the phylum to which it applies:

1. Stinging cells	_____ Bryophyta
2. Hyphae	_____ Coelenterata
3. Without definite nuclei	_____ Annelida
4. Sporophyte parasitic on green gametophyte	_____ Eumycophyta
5. Pharyngeal gill slits	_____ Chordata
6. Xylem present	_____ Arthropoda
7. Tube feet	_____ Cyanophyta
8. Metameric coelom	_____ Chlorophyta
9. Thallus plants that store starch	_____ Tracheophyta
10. Chitinous exoskeleton	_____ Echinodermata

Completion. In the following paragraphs certain essential terms have been omitted, their places being taken by numbers in parentheses. In the spaces provided, insert the appropriate terms.

The science dealing with all living things is called (1) _____, that subdivision dealing with plants being (2) _____ and that dealing with animals being (3) _____. Either of these may be subdivided into (4) _____, the study of function, and (5) _____, the study of structure.

(*The following statements apply to man.*)

The location of a muscle is given by naming the place of attachment of each end, the end moving more during contraction being the (6) _____ and the end moving less being the (7) _____. In the biceps muscle these two ends are attached respectively to the (8) _____ and the (9) _____. The action of the biceps is (10) _____ of the arm at the (11) _____, illustrating a (12) _____ class lever. The opposing action is accomplished by the (13) _____ muscle, operating as a (14) _____ class lever, the end with greater movement being attached to the (15) _____.

Oxygen, necessary in the recovery phase of muscular contraction, is carried to the muscles in loose combination with (16) _____, a pigment contained in blood cells called (17) _____. The waste products of cellular oxidation are (18) _____ and (19) _____. These are carried in the blood to the heart, where they empty into the (20) _____ atrium, thence passing into the (21) _____. From the latter chamber blood flows to the lungs through the (22) _____. In the lungs the blood flows through microscopic vessels called (23) _____, which lie in the walls of the air sacs or (24) _____. Movement of gases between the cavities of the air sacs and the blood takes place by (25) _____.

Completion of a Table. In the following table of parts of a typical flower, the four whorls of structures in a complete flower are numbered from outside in, the outer whorl being Whorl 1. Complete the table.

	Collective name	Name of individual part
Whorl 1		
Whorl 2		
Whorl 3		
Whorl 4		

True-False. Place a plus sign (+) in front of each true statement, a minus sign (−) in front of each false one. Remember that if any part of a statement is false the whole statement must be considered false.

1. _____ Protoplasm is a definite chemical compound.
2. _____ Protoplasm contains at least one chemical element found only in living matter.
3. _____ A single cell may be as much as an inch in diameter.
4. _____ A cell wall is a typical constituent of a plant cell.
5. _____ The presence of turgor explains the flabbiness of animal cells.
6. _____ The cell membrane is freely permeable to all substances in solution.
7. _____ In asexual reproduction the progeny are derived from a single parent.
8. _____ A fruit is the ripened ovule.

9. ____ Yeasts carry on autotrophic nutrition.

10. ____ *Paramecium* reproduces by both sexual and asexual methods.

11. ____ Malaria is caused by a protozoan.

12. ____ In classification, orders are combined to form families and families to form genera.

13. ____ Basidia are borne on the gills of mushrooms.

14. ____ Cells in the leaves of a moss plant are diploid.

15. ____ The fern sporophyte contains vascular tissue.

16. ____ In flowering plants, the egg nucleus is but one of several haploid nuclei in the female gametophyte.

17. ____ Tropisms in plants are the result of differential rates of growth.

18. ____ Cell division occurs in all parts of higher plants.

19. ____ Monocots have more seed leaves than dicots.

20. ____ The excretory system of the earthworm is metameric.

21. ____ Complete metamorphosis of insects is development in which the hatched young are quite similar to the adults.

22. ____ The appendages of a crayfish are modified from a biramous type.

23. ____ All Chordata have a dorsal, tubular nerve cord.

24. ____ One difference between the Heteroptera and the Coleoptera is in the type of mouth parts.

25. ____ The segments of a typical insect leg are: coxa, trochanter, femur, tibia, tarsus.

Arrangement in Sequence. Trace the blood through the path it must follow by the *shortest route* in each of the following cases, naming all heart chambers, arteries, veins, and capillary systems in order.

a. In the frog, lung capillaries to mesonephric capillaries:

1. lung capillaries   6.
2.   7.
3.   8.
4.   9. mesonephric (renal) capillaries
5.

b. In man, inferior vena cava to common iliac artery:

1. inferior vena cava   6.
2.   7.
3.   8.
4.   9.
5.   10. common iliac artery

Lists:

1. List and characterize the major types of compounds in protoplasm.

2. Name in order the four phases of mitosis.

3. Name the twelve cranial nerves of higher vertebrates and give their distributions.

4. List four developments that took place in human evolution.
5. Give the complete classification of one species of plant or animal, including six categories.
6. Name and locate the six Zoogeographic Regions according to Wallace.
   Genetic Problems:
a. In guinea pigs black or pigmented hair (P) is dominant over white (p), the unpigmented condition; and rough hair (R) is dominant over smooth (r). A female with smooth white hair has a litter of five young, two of these black with rough hair and the other three white with smooth hair. Give genotypes of both parents and the five young:

   Parents: Male: Female:
   Progeny: 2:
                   3:

b. Four-o'clock plants with pink flowers are the heterozygous progeny of homozygous red (RR) and homozygous white (rr) parents. Give the expected phenotypic and genotypic ratios of progeny in the following crosses:

   b¹   Pink   X   White
   b²   Pink   X   Red
   b³   Pink   X   Pink

ANSWERS

Multiple Choice: 1. a community. 2. autotrophic. 3. anaerobic. 4. trypsin. 5. Fallopian tube. 6. mitochondria. 7. two divisions. 8. natural selection. 9. stability. 10. light. 11. starch. 12. parathyroid glands. 13. filtration. 14. four. 15. behind.

Matching: 1. Coelenterata. 2. Eumycophyta. 3. Cyanophyta. 4. Bryophyta. 5. Chordata. 6. Tracheophyta. 7. Echinodermata. 8. Annelida. 9. Chlorophyta. 10. Arthropoda.

Completion: 1. biology. 2. botany. 3. zoology. 4. physiology. 5. morphology. 6. insertion. 7. origin. 8. radius. 9. scapula. 10. flexing. 11. elbow. 12. third. 13. triceps. 14. first. 15. ulna. 16. hemoglobin. 17. erythrocytes. 18-19. carbon dioxide and water. 20. right. 21. right ventricle. 22. pulmonary arteries. 23. capillaries. 24. alveoli. 25. diffusion.

Table:

Whorl 1:	calyx	sepal
Whorl 2:	corolla	petal
Whorl 3:	androecium	stamen
Whorl 4:	gynoecium	carpel

True-False:

True: Nos. 3, 4, 7, 10, 11, 13, 15, 16, 17, 20, 22, 23, 24, 25.

False: Nos. 1, 2, 5, 6, 8, 9, 12, 14, 18, 19, 21.

Arrangement in Sequence:

a. 2. pulmonary veins. 3. left atrium. 4. ventricle. 5. conus arteriosus. 6. systemic arch. 7. dorsal aorta. 8. renal arteries.

b. 2. right atrium. 3. right ventricle. 4. pulmonary arteries. 5. lung capillaries. 6. pulmonary veins. 7. left atrium. 8. left ventricle. 9. aorta.

Lists:

1. See Chapter II.
2. See Chapter III.
3. See Chapter IX, especially Table II and page 159.
4. See Chapter XIV.
5. See Chapter XV.
6. See Chapter XVI, especially Figure 70.

Genetic Problems:

a. Parents: Male: PpRr   Female: pprr
   Progeny: 2: PpRr
             3: pprr
b. b^1 Progeny: 1 pink (Rr): 1 white (rr)
   b^2 Progeny: 1 pink (Rr): 1 red (RR)
   b^3 Progeny: 1 red (RR): 2 pink (Rr): 1 white (rr)

INDEX

INDEX